Y0-BYK-358

Play, Exploration and Territory in Mammals

SYMPOSIA OF THE ZOOLOGICAL SOCIETY OF LONDON
NUMBER 18

Play, Exploration and Territory in Mammals

(*The Proceedings of a symposium held at The Zoological Society of London on 19 and 20 November* 1965)

Edited by

P. A. JEWELL

Wellcome Institute of Comparative Physiology
The Zoological Society of London, London, England

and

CAROLINE LOIZOS

Department of Psychology, University College, London, and
The Zoological Society of London, London, England

Published for the
ZOOLOGICAL SOCIETY OF LONDON
BY
ACADEMIC PRESS
1966

ACADEMIC PRESS INC. (LONDON) LTD
Berkeley Square House
Berkeley Square
London, W.1

U.S. Edition published by

ACADEMIC PRESS INC.
111 Fifth Avenue
New York, New York 10003

Library of Congress Catalog Card Number: 66–27816

PRINTED IN GREAT BRITAIN BY
J. W. ARROWSMITH LTD., BRISTOL

CONTRIBUTORS

BROWN, L. E., *Department of Zoology, Imperial College, London, England* (p. 111)

CROOK, JOHN HURRELL, *Department of Psychology, University of Bristol, England* (p. 237)

GRUBB, P., *Wellcome Institute of Comparative Physiology, The Zoological Society of London, London, England* (p. 179)

HALLIDAY, M. S., *Laboratory of Experimental Psychology, University of Sussex, Brighton, Sussex, England* (p. 45)

HUTT, CORINNE, *Park Hospital for Children, Oxford, England* (p. 61)

JEWELL, P. A., *Wellcome Institute of Comparative Physiology, The Zoological Society of London, London, England* (pp. 85 and 179)*

KLEIMAN, DEVRA, *The Zoological Society of London, London, England* (p. 167)

LOCKIE, J. D., *Department of Forestry and Natural Resources, University of Edinburgh, Scotland* (p. 143)

LOIZOS, CAROLINE, *University College, London, and The Zoological Society of London, London, England* (p. 1)

LOWE, V. P. W., *The Nature Conservancy, Speyside Research Station, Aviemore, Inverness-shire, Scotland* (p. 211)

POOLE, T. B. *Department of Zoology, University College of Wales, Aberystwyth, Wales* (p. 23)

RYSZKOWSKI, LECH, *Polska Akademia Nauk, Zaklad Ekologii, Warsaw, Poland* (p. 259)

SCHENKEL, RUDOLF, *Department of Zoology, University of Basel, Switzerland* (p. 11)

SIMMONS, K. E. L., *Department of Psychology, University of Bristol, England* (p. 83)

TAYLOR, JAN C., *Ministry of Agriculture, Fisheries and Food, Infestation Control Laboratory, Tangley Place, Worplesdon, Guildford, Surrey, England* (p. 229)

* Present address: Department of Zoology and Comparative Anatomy, University College, London, England.

ORGANIZERS AND CHAIRMEN

ORGANIZERS

D. J. MORRIS *and* CAROLINE LOIZOS *on behalf of The Zoological Society of London*

M. G. HARDY *and* P. A. JEWELL *on behalf of the Mammal Society*

PEGGY ELLIS *on behalf of the Association for the Study of Animal Behaviour*

CHAIRMEN OF THE SESSIONS

H. KALMUS, *Galton Laboratory, University College, London, England*

H. N. SOUTHERN, *Bureau of Animal Population, Botanic Garden, Oxford, England*

L. HARRISON MATTHEWS, *The Zoological Society of London, London, England*

J. M. CULLEN, *Department of Zoology, University of Oxford, England*

FOREWORD

The fact that mammals may occupy a territory, or confine themselves to a home range, has been recognized for a long time. Intensive study of the phenomenon is, however, a recent development, perhaps stimulated by the recognition that this behaviour is one of the ways in which animals regulate their own abundance. But completed field studies are far too few to enable us to understand the great diversity of ways in which animals use the space available to them. A strong new impetus has been given to this work by the current concentration of effort in field studies of primates. Such studies are of vital importance to an understanding of social and family organization among these animals; and there is the added incentive that this kind of new knowledge might ultimately lead to a better understanding of the biology of our own species.

Other orders of mammals, however, have not had the same attention and the most conspicuous species remain the least studied. Almost nothing, for example, is known of the ranging behaviour of the elephant, rhinoceros or buffalo, and only now is information being gathered on a species as spectacular in its migrations as the wildebeeste of East Africa. Similarly the great carnivores, like the lion and hyena, are just beginning to receive due attention from zoologists. If studies of the kind that are presented in this symposium are extended to a wider assemblage of mammals we shall be enriched by a much deeper understanding of the origins and adaptive significance of mammalian behaviour. A shadow hangs over this prospect, however, for already the time is limited in which adequate studies of any large species in the wild can be made. Some species are perilously near extinction and others will soon exist nowhere except within the confines of national parks and zoos. Home ranges and territories may then be largely those imposed by man.

Both play and exploratory behaviour are topics that to a large extent tend to have been ignored, or even avoided, by researchers in animal behaviour, perhaps because of their diverse and complex nature. This symposium represents an attempt to narrow and clarify the areas of investigation and to consider them in relation to the ways in which animals orient themselves to the environment. Exploration occupies a natural position in a symposium dealing with territory, since it is an essential part of the complex of territorial behaviour. Through exploration and investigation the animal establishes and maintains familiarity with the area that is its home. Many types of behaviour are grouped under this general heading, including at least one easily recognizable form of play. Although exploratory play may have other functions, an animal engaging in it will inevitably gain information about the properties of whom or with what it is playing.

So far only this type of play has been subjected specifically to experimental investigation. However, play with conspecifics, or social play, has long been recognized to be of equal importance in the development of those species which play. Field workers, particularly those studying the primates, have often expressed the conviction that social play is important in establishing and maintaining the social hierarchy (an individual's social territory in fact). Laboratory studies on the mother–infant relationship in rhesus monkeys have given added weight to this impression, since play with the peer-group appears to be crucial for full adult social development.

It is clear that some kinds of behaviour will only be expressed, and can only be understood, in free-ranging wild populations; these are behaviour patterns of profound importance to our understanding of evolutionary processes. Other aspects of behaviour, however, may be studied profitably in the laboratory, and the results of the two approaches can be combined to build up a total and accurate picture of animal behaviour. We hope that this symposium includes enough of both kinds of approach to the study of play, exploration and territory to stimulate and encourage new observation and research on all these related topics.

P. A. Jewell
Caroline Loizos

July 1966

CONTENTS

Exploration and Fear in the Rat

M. S. HALLIDAY

Exploration and Play in Children

CORINNE HUTT

Anting and the Problem of Self-stimulation

K. E. L. SIMMONS

The Concept of Home Range in Mammals

P. A. JEWELL

Home Range and Movement of Small Mammals

L. E. BROWN

Territory in Small Carnivores

J. D. LOCKIE

Scent Marking in the Canidae

DEVRA KLEIMAN

Social Grouping and Home Range in Feral Soay Sheep

P. GRUBB and P. A. JEWELL

Observation on the Dispersal of Red Deer on Rhum

V. P. W. LOWE

Home Range and Agonistic Behaviour in the Grey Squirrel

JAN C. TAYLOR

Gelada Baboon Herd Structure and Movement A Comparative Report

JOHN HURRELL CROOK

The Space Organization of Nutria *(Myocastor coypus)*

LECH RYSZKOWSKI

Symp. zool. Soc. Lond. (1966) No. 18, 1–9.

PLAY IN MAMMALS

CAROLINE LOIZOS

University College, London, and The Zoological Society of London, London, England

SYNOPSIS

Problems faced in studying animal play are discussed, and some generally held views examined. Play in animals has generally been thought to be without function. This attitude has possibly arisen from a false analogy with the use of the word as it applies to human behaviour, where play is opposed to work. Animals do not work and therefore cannot be said to play, at any rate in the human sense of the word. It is suggested that it might be a more fruitful approach to start with the assumption that animal play does have survival value, in view of the time and energy spent in play by, in particular, the carnivores and the primates. Much behaviour has been classified as play simply because it was imperfectly understood: the category needs definition. Some play patterns are possibly remnants of phylogenetically ancient behaviour that have become freed through a change in the environment from their original adaptive functions.

Some of the motivating conditions necessary for the occurrence of play are discussed, including the apparent need for the animal to be free of conflicting physiological and environmental pressures. Play invitations are mentioned, and the fact that priority is given to the play signal over other conflicting and equally strong signals.

Current theories of the causation and function of play are treated briefly. Observers have tended to regard as play all behaviour performed while the young animal's primary needs were being taken care of by its adult conspecifics; but although young animals may be playing, they may equally well be performing at maximum efficiency for their particular level of development. Behaviour must not be called play simply because it appears inefficient. Practice is generally regarded to be the primary function of play, but it has yet to be shown that animals prevented from playing are less efficient as adults than those that play. This is not to deny that practice is certainly one of the incidental benefits of play, but it is not necessary to play in order to practice. The same objection is offered to the other main theory of the function of play: that is, that it provides the animal with vital information about the environment. It clearly does, but so does everything the animal engages in; it certainly is not necessary to play in order to gain information about the environment, since the animal may simply explore.

Theories of the causation of play have stated that it arises from the overflowing of surplus energy; that it is its own motivation in that it is "fun", "is enjoyed purely for its own sake", is "self-rewarding activity." The surplus energy hypothesis is shown to be an insufficient explanation for play, and the self-rewarding hypotheses are not considered to be explanations at all.

The actual behaviour that is called play is then looked at, and a comparison made of the motor patterns occurring in play with the same motor patterns occurring in their originally motivated contexts. Differences between the two are shown to consist of the economy with which the pattern is performed, or the efficiency in terms of its function in its original context. Lack of economy arises in several ways, amongst them exaggeration, repetition, reordering of the sequence, and breaking up of the sequence by insertion of apparently unrelated activities.

Since many of these characteristics are also shared by ritualized behaviour, the similarity between the two is discussed. Current research is concerned with precise distinction between them.

The main problem in studying animal play has resulted from a basic misconception in the approach, arising purely from our use of the word *play*. Play is an exclusively human concept used of activity that is other than, or even opposed to work. By analogy the word has come to be applied to behaviour in animals which cannot be seen to have any immediate biological end, any obvious survival value. Bierens de Haan's (1945) statement that "animal play is useless" is fairly typical of this attitude. The implication is simply that animal play cannot be serious, since if it were, if it had a function, it would not be play.

But for animals, of course, it is different. Since they do not work, at any rate in our sense of the word, they cannot really be said to play—in our sense of the word. The problem is not solved by thinking of an alternative word for play. The fact that even an untrained observer may be quite accurate in determining when an animal is playing suggests that somewhere in the complex of behaviour called play there is a fundamental similarity with the same kind of activity in human beings. What this similarity might consist of will be suggested later.

It is probably more useful to change the direction of approach. Instead of saying that human play appears to be without survival value and that therefore the same must be true of animal play, let us assume that animal play *has* survival value and that it has possibly become divorced from its original function, or functions, by the time it occurs in human beings—at any rate adult human beings. I think it would be rash to assume that it does not have survival value in animals, is not in this sense serious, since amongst other things the amount of time and energy spent in play by, for instance, the carnivores or the primates, would surely put these animals at a disadvantage if their play were totally without function.

Of course there are examples of animal behaviour that have been regarded as play simply because they were imperfectly understood. Beach (1945) quotes an instance in which various fishes had been observed to leap over free-floating objects in the water, such as sticks and reeds. This was considered to have no practical value and was therefore called play, until Breder (1932) suggested that what the fish were doing was using the sticks to scrape encrustations of ectoparasites from their undersides. It would be interesting to speculate on what might happen to this behaviour were the species to rid itself permanently of these particular parasites. It is quite possible that the habit of leaping over floating objects in the water would remain, and ethologists in the next century would certainly be tempted to call it play once more. Tembrock (1960) has pointed out that in the Arctic fox (*Alopex lagopus*) certain behaviour which now appears only in playful contexts probably originally had specific adaptive value in a particular earlier environment; when freed of the necessity to perform this particular function, perhaps through a change in the environment, such behaviour could be incorporated freely into the repertoire of play patterns. Thus it is likely that some play consists of the vestiges of phylogenetically very old behaviour; in some cases it may be no more than a trace, but in others complete sequences may have become "fossilized" and preserved whole. One cannot do more than make informed guesses about the origins of some play patterns. On the other hand, there are probably many more instances of what we now think of as play that will turn out to have quite specific and other functions, since the concept has, certainly until very recently, always been used as the wastepaper basket of imperfectly understood animal behaviour.

For the moment it might be useful to approach play in a roundabout way, in terms of some of the conditions necessary for its occurrence, and some of the features which invariably accompany it. There are motivating conditions which are necessary for the occurrence of play, though as they consist almost entirely of the absence of other conflicting sources of motivation, they cannot be said in any way to be sufficient. As far as can be told, play only occurs when the animal is free of environmental pressures such as heat, cold, wet and the presence of predators; and free of physiological pressures such as the need for food, drink, sleep or a sexual partner. Thus play is often most characteristic of young animals, whose needs are taken care of by their parents, and of animals in captivity for whom the same functions are served by their guardians. Again, however, this is only part of the story, since there is some evidence from observation of zoo animals (Morris, 1964) that there exists a positive need to engage in certain types of play. Play probably does not occur solely as the result of the absence of conflicting drives.

Play also appears to be voluntary, in that as far as one can tell an animal cannot be made to play by means of specific kinds of deprivation or reinforcement. Schiller (1957) reported that ". . . with no incentive the chimpanzee displayed a higher variety of handling objects than under the pressure of a lure which they attempted to obtain." In his case, the attempt to direct play by reinforcing the animals for this behaviour resulted in its inhibition.

However, those animals which do play may be encouraged to play by the presentation of suitable stimuli in a suitable manner. Moreover, they may be *invited* to play by a conspecific, or even a member of another species, as for example often happens with humans and domestic animals. A mother cat lying on her side and twitching the tip of her tail on which her kittens will pounce might well be an example of such a play invitation. This kind of invitation—what Altmann (1962) called metacommunication, or a signal about the quality of the communication which is to follow—may be seen in many mammals. Cats and dogs both have preliminary play movements, play intention movements in fact, which consist of a half-crouch with forelegs extended stiffly combined with wide-open eyes and ears pricked forward. Brownlee (1954) has described this phenomenon in domestic cattle. It occurs most noticeably in chimpanzees and other primates, but at that level on the phylogenetic scale the signal area has been reduced to the face, and a special facial expression indicating a playful mood is sometimes used as a kind of shorthand for the full motor play invitation. Similarly with humans: if one is punched quite hard by somebody with a broad grin on his face one will at least hesitate before interpreting it as an aggressive act. The interesting thing in this situation is that given the choice of two conflicting signals to attend to, the one that is always given priority is the one announcing that this is play, even though the punch may have been hard enough to hurt. Play signals seem to be very powerful and unambiguous. One can observe young chimpanzees putting up with treatment from each other that is rough enough to cause pain, provided it has been made clear at the outset that they are playing.

Current theories of the causation and function of play will now be treated briefly, before its actual motor characteristics are discussed. The most generally accepted theory of the function of play is to consider it as practice for adult activity (Pycraft, 1912; Mitchell, 1912; Groos, 1898). The main problem with this approach is that no clear distinction has been drawn between playful and serious behaviour in the young of any particular species. During the infancy and adolescence of many mammals it is possible to see immature forms of behaviour patterns which will appear in their complete form and appropriate context in adult life. In the young animal this kind of behaviour does not appear to serve the same biological ends that it does in maturity, and consequently observers have tended to regard as play all behaviour performed while the young animal's primary needs were being taken care of by its adult conspecifics. Now often these immature forms of adult behaviour are performed in a characteristically playful manner (what that might mean will be discussed later). But equally often such behaviour is performed with the greatest possible degree of efficiency for whatever level of development the animal is at *at that point*. Thus, a kitten can and often does chase bits of paper and string and so on in a playful manner; but it may equally well deal with them in a way that would have meant instant death to a mouse. In the same way, a fight between young chimpanzees may be quite as seriously intended as one between two adults, but the effects are obviously less drastic. It is a mistake, therefore, to regard as play all chase behaviour by a kitten, either because it is a kitten or because the pursued object is inedible; and the same principle holds for all young animals.

Nevertheless it is a widely held view that the animal that plays—or practises—will become more expert, and thereby have a selective advantage over the animal that does not (Groos, 1898). None of this is to deny that practice or rehearsal of many forms of behaviour is likely to improve the efficiency with which they are performed in adult life. But it has yet to be shown that it is the *playful* execution of these particular patterns in infancy or childhood that is crucial to their later perfection, as opposed to their *serious* execution at whatever level of maturity at which the animal is then operating. Quite simply, it is not necessary to play in order to practise: there is no reason why the animal should not just practise. Certainly social interactions involving play within the peer group in rhesus monkeys have been shown by Harlow (1962) to be crucial for the full development of adult social behaviour. But the precise role of each of play's component parts—vision, smell, sound, physical contact, movement and any combination of these factors—has yet to be isolated and defined.

As well as this, to regard play as practice for adult function does not account for the fact that adults as well as infants play in most mammalian species in which play occurs at all. They may certainly play less, but they still play. The fact that they play does not of course prevent the same behaviour in infants from serving as preparation of some kind; but as an explanation of function this must be enlarged to account for the persistence of, for example, play-wrestling in the adult cat.

The same objection is offered to the other major theory of the function of play; that it provides the animal with a constant stream of vital information about every feature of the environment with which it comes into contact. Again, it is simply not necessary to play in order to learn about the environment. The animal could explore as in fact some mammals that do not appear to play certainly do; for example, the rat. Of course it is inevitable that during play an animal will be gaining additional knowledge about what or who it is playing with but if this is the major function of play one must wonder why the animal does not use a more economical way of getting hold of this information.

The earliest attempt to account for the causation of play, especially as seen in the young, suggested that it represented the release or overflowing of abundant energy which had no other immediate outlet.

A modern parallel to this theory is that of "vacuum" activity, which occurs when a particular response has not been released for some time, and eventually occurs in the apparently total absence of any specific releasing stimulus. However, there are clear motoric differences between playful and vacuum activity, which led Lorenz (1956) to propose a distinction between them.

Tolman suggested that under certain conditions men and lower animals have a need to redress a state of physiological imbalance produced by the presence of abundant energy by achieving a complementary state of mild fatigue. Beach (1945), however, considered this to be simply a "variation . . . in modern dress" of the surplus energy hypothesis. He points out that interpretation of the energy expended in a particular action as surplus simply depends on whether you consider the behaviour under observation to be playfully, or otherwise motivated. In any case, as Groos (1898) pointed out, young animals can be seen to lie panting and exhausted after a bout of play and suddenly resume the game with apparently equal vigour. Although play is most likely to occur when the animal is not exhausted, so also is non-playful activity. So again, although energy may be a necessary condition for play, it has not been shown to be sufficient.

Play has sometimes been accounted for by stating that it is "fun" (Bierens de Haan, 1952), "expresses a joy of living" (Pycraft, 1912), "is enjoyed purely for its own sake" (Tinkelpaugh, 1942), or, more recently, is "self-rewarding activity" (Morris, 1962). Bolwig (1963) describes the motivating condition for play as one of joy and goes on to describe joy as a condition which motivates increased activity. "Postures of aggression and retreat never become complete, and non-aggressive movements are frequently exaggerated. In other words, joy is a condition which induces play actions." All these statements may at the moment be the most useful shorthand way we have of describing the apparent affect accompanying certain motor patterns; but their use as an explanation of that same behaviour is unjustified and not at all useful.

However, before causation and function can be discussed to any great effect, it is necessary to consider the actual behaviour that is going to be classed as play. One of its immediately noticeable characteristics is that it is behaviour that adopts for its purposes patterns that appear in other contexts where they achieve immediate and obvious ends. When these patterns appear in play they seem to be divorced from their original motivation and are qualitatively distinct from the same patterns appearing in their originally motivated contexts. Lorenz (1956) points out that although in play fighting movements occur which are only seen at the peak of intensity in a serious fight, the next moment the animal demonstrates that such specific motivation is lacking by switching to behaviour seen in defensive or grooming, or other unrelated situations. Thus a *reordering* of the original sequence is one way in which play differs from the source of its motor patterns. All the other ways in which it differs are of economy, or degree; and it is here that we come back to a statement made earlier, about the fundamental similarity to the observer between human and animal play. This similarity lies in the exaggerated and uneconomical quality of the motor patterns involved. Regardless of its motivation or its end-product, this is what all playful activity has in common; and it is possible that it is all that it has in common, since causation and function could vary from species to species. Beach puts this more strongly: ". . . no single hypothesis can be formulated to explain all forms of play in every animal species".

These are some of the ways in which motor patterns may be altered and elaborated upon when transferred to a playful context.

1. The sequence may be *reordered*.
2. The individual movements making up the sequence may become *exaggerated*.
3. Certain movements within the sequence may be *repeated* more than they would usually be.
4. The sequence may be broken off altogether by the introduction of irrelevant activities, and resumed later. This could be called *fragmentation*.
5. Movements may be both *exaggerated and repeated*.
6. Individual movements within the sequence may never be completed, and this incomplete element may be repeated many times. This applies equally to both the beginning of a movement (the *intention element*) and to its ending (the *completion element*).

In every case, during play, the performance of the movements from which the play is derived is uneconomical, and therefore would be inefficient in terms of the original motivating context. It might, of course, be possible to consider that it is the exaggerated movements of play that are refined and economized, and used in chasing, wrestling, biting, jumping, chewing and so on, instead of the reverse process. However, since the patterns of aggression and defence occur in the phylogenetic scale long before unequivocal play behaviour makes its appearance, it seems fair to assume that the "original" context—in this case at any rate—is that of aggression. Aggression is also of course more basic to survival. The same is true of most other motor patterns that are employed in play: investigation of objects occurs both phylogenetically and ontogenetically before play with objects. Thus play patterns owe their origin to behaviour that appeared earlier phylogenetically and for purposes other than play. It follows that just as patterns of fight, flight, sexual and eating behaviour and so on are species-specific, so will the play behaviour making use of these same patterns be species-specific.

One final point remains to be made. It is clear that the motor differences between a pattern used in play and the same pattern occurring in its original context are not exclusive to play. Ritualized behaviour shares many of the characteristics described as typical of play; and social play clearly contains a strong element of ritualization. Morris (1956a) quotes the following examples of some of the ways in which basic patterns can be modified—or ritualized—to form signals: (a) threshold lowering; (b) development of rhythmic repetition; (c) differential exaggeration of components; (d) omission of components; (e) change in sequence of components; (f) changes in component co-ordination; (g) increases or decrease in speed of performance; (h) change in vigour of movements.

Although Morris (1956b) has shown that the sequence of events in a highly ritualized piece of behaviour such as the stickleback's courtship dance is not nearly as rigid as it was once considered to be, it is suggested that the most likely area in which the precise differences between play and other forms of ritualized behaviour will be isolated is that of relative rigidity in the ordering of the sequence. It may be that play has no formalized sequence of events, such that action A will always be followed by actions B, C or D. In play, depending upon the feedback from the object or the social partner, A may be followed with equal likelihood by B or by Z; anyway by a far greater range of responses than are seen in other forms of ritualized behaviour. In short, it is suggested that in play the number of combinations or permutations of the available motor patterns is greater than in almost any other form of behaviour.

Research on play at the London Zoo is now concerned with precise analysis and comparison of the motor patterns involved with the same motor patterns occurring in their originally motivated contexts. It is hoped that this may help to answer the above questions, and to disentangle the essential qualities that make much play instantly recognizable to professional and casual observers alike.

Acknowledgements

I am very grateful to many people at the London Zoo for helpful discussions on the subject of play; and in particular to D. J. Morris and G. H. Manley.

I am also grateful to P. B. Medawar for his critical reading of the manuscript; and to J. M. Cullen for valuable suggestions made while chairing the meeting at which the paper was read.

I should also like to thank the Medical Research Council who supported this work with a grant for Research Training.

References

Altmann, S. A. (1962). Social behavior of anthropoid primates: analysis of recent concepts. *In* "Roots of Behavior" (E. L. Bliss, ed.), pp. 277–286. Harper & Bros., New York.

Beach, A. F. (1945). Current concepts of play in animals. *Am. Nat.* **79**, 523–541.

Bierens de Haan. (1952). The play of a young solitary chimpanzee. *Behaviour* **4**, 144–156.

Bolwig, N. (1963). Facial expression in primates. *Behaviour* **22**, 167–192.

Breder, C. M. (1932). On the habits and development of certain Atlantic Synentognathi. *Pap. Tortugas Lab.* **28** (1), 1–35.

Brownlee, A. (1954). Play in domestic cattle in Britain: an analysis of its nature. *Br. vet. J.* **110**, 46–68.

Groos, K. (1898). "The Play of Animals." Chapman and Hall, London.

Harlow, H. H. and Harlow, M. K. (1962). Social deprivation in monkeys. *Sci. Am.* **207**, 136–146.

Lorenz, K. Z. (1956). Plays and vacuum activity in animals. *In* "Symposium. L'Instinct dans le comportement des animaux et de l'homme," pp. 633–645. Masson, Paris.

Mitchell, P. C. (1912). "The Childhood of Animals". Frederick A. Stokes, New York.

Morris, D. (1956a). "Typical intensity" and its relation to the problem of ritualization. *Behaviour* **11**, 1–12.

Morris, D. (1956b). The function and causation of courtship ceremonies in animals (with special reference to fish). *In* "Symposium. L'Instinct dans le comportement des animaux et de l'homme," pp. 261–286. Masson, Paris.

Morris, D. (1962). "The Biology of Art", pp. 144. Methuen, London.

Morris, D. (1964). The response of animals to a restricted environment. *Symp. zool. Soc. Lond.* No. 13, 99–118.

Pycraft, W. P. (1912). "The Infancy of Animals." Hutchinson, London.

Schiller, P. H. (1957). Innate motor action as a basis of learning manipulative patterns in the chimpanzee. *In* "Instinctive Behaviour" (C. H. Schiller, ed.), pp. 264–287. International Universities Press, New York.

Tembrock, G. (1960). Spielverhalten und vergleichende Ethologie. Beobachtungen zum Spiel von *Alopex lagopus*. *Z. Saugetierk.* **25**, 1–14.

Tinkelpaugh, O. L. (1942). *In* "Comparative Psychology", 2nd. ed. (F. A. Moss, ed.). Prentice-Hall, New York.

Symp. zool. Soc. Lond. (1966) No. 18, 11–22.

PLAY, EXPLORATION AND TERRITORIALITY IN THE WILD LION

RUDOLF SCHENKEL

Department of Zoology, University of Basel, Switzerland

SYNOPSIS

Prides of wild lions were observed in the Nairobi National Park from December 1962 to April 1965, with an interval of 3 months. The main objects of observation were the development of cubs from the first weeks of life on, their play and exploratory behaviour and their integration into the pride. In this connexion the structure of a pride and the phenomenon of territoriality in the lion were also studied. This paper gives an outline of the results with emphasis on play, exploration and territoriality.

INTRODUCTION

The lion as a cat shows very pronounced *play activity*, especially in childhood.

In the wild a fully grown lion spends its life in a home range of considerable area—approximately 10–20 sq. miles. During its youth it has to become acquainted with this area and with the possibilities it offers for meeting its needs. *Tradition* within the special group the lion belongs to may play an important role in becoming acquainted with the area and—perhaps even more important—*exploration*.

Lions live in a home range and belong to a social group. The intimacy that exists within the group is a well-known fact for observers both in the zoo and in the wild. But are lions friendly towards strangers within their home range, or are they intolerant towards them in a certain area; are they, in fact, *territorial*?

There is no doubt that the lion is a suitable subject with which to study play and exploratory behaviour as well as the problem of territoriality. It is the aim of this paper to show the development of play and exploration, and their role in the young lion, and to demonstrate the existence of territorial behaviour in the adult lion on the basis of observations in Nairobi National Park.

AREA AND OBJECT OF OBSERVATION

The studies were carried out in Nairobi National Park, Kenya, during the whole of 1963 and from April 1964 to April 1965. This park, close to the city of Nairobi, is nearly 50 sq. miles in size. It is bounded by fence to the west (Magadi road) and to the north-east (Mombasa road). To the south it borders on the Masai Game Reserve, a large area, where game is protected. About twenty to thirty lions live in or visit the park area. These lions form prides, each of which live in a more or less defined home range (Fig. 1). The main object of study was the

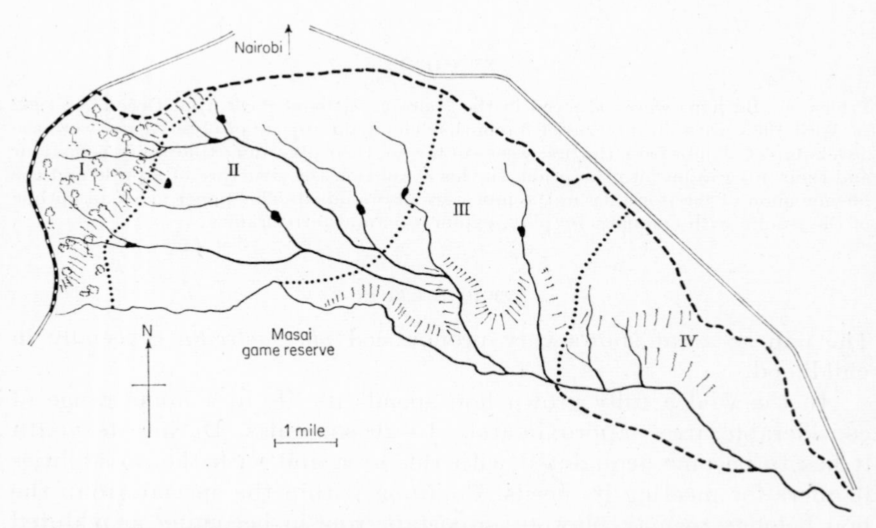

Fig. 1. Map of Nairobi National Park. Home range of the different lion prides: I, Forest pride; II, Central pride; III, Eastern pride; IV, Athi Basin pride.

central pride, which consisted in 1963 of two adult males, a very old female without cubs and two other females, each of which had three cubs. One litter had been born late in July, and the other in November of 1962. During the two years of this study five litters of lions were observed (Table I). Four of them (A_1, B_1, A_2 and B_2) belonged to the central pride and one was the joint litter of the two forest lionesses. Three of the litters, namely B_1, A_2 and B_2, were observed from the first moment they could be detected, and two of them, A_1 and B_1, over a period of more than $1\frac{1}{2}$ years.

BIRTH AND PERIOD OF ISOLATION

In every case the lionesses gave birth in isolation and at first kept the litter hidden in dense thicket or, in one case, in a rock shelter.

Parturition itself was never observed, but the enlarged teats of the mother made it evident that it had happened. The litters were not seen for the first 6–7 weeks after parturition. Each lioness, A and B, was observed to meet the pride quite often as early as a few days after having given birth, but there was no contact between the pride and the newborn cubs for the first 2 months. During a considerable part of the day the cubs were left alone while the mother was either hunting, or had joined the pride for a rest or at a kill.

TABLE I

Litters observed

Mother	A	B	2 lionesses
Pride	Central	Central	Forest
First litter	A_1	B_1	C_1
No. of cubs	3	3	5
Born	Late July 1962	November 1962	Approx. January 1964
Mating	January 1964	January 1963 (shortly after parturition) July 1964	—
Second litter	A_2	B_2	—
No. of cubs	3	3	—
Born	Early May 1964	November 1964	—

When the cubs were about 6–7 weeks old it was possible to detect and observe them by carefully following their mother on her way to the rendezvous. In the absence of the mother the cubs' behaviour was completely cryptic; they were not found venturing on their own, indulging in play or exploration.

This changed the moment that the mother joined the litter. She called the cubs with a soft roar, which stimulated them to run towards her in a clumsy gallop. A greeting ceremony followed, in which the cubs jumped up to their mother's head and forelegs. They rubbed their heads against her muzzle, forelegs and chest, while the mother licked them and often continued to lick them when lying in a grassy hollow between bushes. Quite often greeting was followed by nursing, lasting a few minutes. Then, while the mother had her rest, the cubs engaged in a number of characteristic activities. The following scenes were observed most frequently.

(1) After a posture indicating readiness, one cub rushed at another or at its mother, flung its body over the partner, pawed it and perhaps used its mouth to seize and then lick the partner's cheek or ear or neck while lying in a relaxed body contact. The intention posture was often taken up by the partner who would then in turn perform the rush; alternatively he would stand his ground expecting the other. In most cases, while lying in close contact or perhaps whilst rolling over each other, both partners used their paws and mouths as mentioned before.

(2) A cub suddenly paid attention to a stick, a little shrub or a piece of grass. It pawed the object, perhaps rolling on the ground, stretching out its forepaws to reach the object. Very often another cub joined the scene.

(3) Sometimes even the mother took part in a restrained manner: she moved her tail repeatedly, thus stimulating a cub to play with it. Alternatively she knocked a cub over very gently with a paw or a push of her nose, and while it pawed and struggled with all four legs, she licked it with repeated strokes of her tongue.

(4) From time to time a cub ventured a few yards from its mother and examined the surroundings—especially strange apparitions like the Landrover of the observer—with concentrated attention showing an ambivalent attitude between curiosity and shyness. In a situation of this type, a cub would often be joined by another one.

It would be very interesting to discuss the many aspects of this kind of activity, but it is impossible in this short paper. A few remarks may point out some of its characteristics.

All this activity occurs in an undisturbed area and in an atmosphere of intimacy and security, in which the resting and completely relaxed mother is the centre and guarantee. Apparently this activity is *play*. On the other hand, when the young lions come into contact with something unknown, and are at the same time both attracted and frightened, but reassured by the presence of the mother, it is typical *early exploratory behaviour*.

Most of the play activity is not only the result of a basically *social situation*, but it is *social activity* proper, in which two or more individuals are involved. In this atmosphere of intimacy and security play activity is *infective*; even the mother is sometimes stimulated to join in.

The play activity itself expresses tenderness and fondness. Pawing, seizing with jaws, licking and the apparently pleasing body contact show the same fondness as the suckling scene. But the play scenes have still another, a prospective quality: they sometimes contain features vaguely resembling those of stalking and sudden attack of prey; of facing, attacking and fighting another member of the species; of escape and pursuit. In the context of early play these features are not only vague, but are not yet individually developed or "worked out," and do not yet belong to separate functional units.

LIFE WITHIN THE INTIMACY OF THE PRIDE

Introduction to the pride

When the cubs reach the age of about 10 weeks they are introduced to the pride. I have never witnessed this scene in an East African park, but have observed it several times in the zoo.

This introduction has, in the wild, a marked consequence on the pride as a whole. It appears much more harmonious than when it is without young cubs; all the social relations seem to be impregnated with tenderness and fondness and there is practically no room for social conflict and tension. All the adult members are tolerant, if not amiable towards the cubs. Even the males occasionally mother them. The attitude of different adult individuals to the cubs may, however, have a personal note. In the central pride each mother preferred her own cubs to those of her sister. The old lioness often refused the obtrusive caresses of the cubs with a growl. The two forest lionesses, on the other hand, showed the same love and devotion to all five cubs.

Between the children of the two forest lionesses, as well as between the cubs of A_1 and B_1 and A_2 and B_2, a very close friendship arose which was never seriously disturbed during the whole period of observation.

Instruction and exploration

In the central pride, after the cubs had been introduced, both mothers and their cubs were often found together in the morning. The old lioness joined them quite often, but the two males did so only sometimes. However, each litter was still alone for hours while the mothers went hunting. The cubs at first continued to hide whenever they were left alone. Only gradually did their self-reliance prevail over their shyness. At 5 months they often left the cover of the thicket in the morning to wait in the open for their mother, daring at this point to play timidly. But play and exploration still only flourished in the presence of the mother. When mother came "home", enthusiastic greetings occurred immediately, followed by wild play and exploration in the surroundings. The cubs, usually operating together, pushed through bush, shrub and grass, explored rocky river beds, got acquainted with the water and so on.

Until the cubs were 2 months old the hide of the litter had not been shifted very much, but from about 3 months on, the hiding and rendezvous place of mother and children was changed regularly every 4–6 days. In this way the cubs were given the opportunity to explore one after the other the traditional hiding places within the home range and to get acquainted with the main tracks and many other features of the habitat.

Soon after the cubs had been introduced to the pride, the mother brought them to the communal kills. If she had caught a small animal, she normally carried it to the rendezvous place. At a common kill the cubs were not only tolerated by the fully grown members of the pride, but the mother obviously stimulated them to come to the prey and to feed on it. She could often be seen to settle down beside it, and then by licking, biting, pulling and gnawing she induced her cubs to join her in a kind of friendly competition.

As already mentioned, the self-assurance of the cubs increased steadily. When after a nightly meal the adult members of the pride were lying lazily in the open, the 4-month-old cubs were observed to start on their own for a shade and hiding place.

One rainy morning in June 1963 a strange lioness approached the pride and was immediately chased by all the adult lions. The two litters A_1 and B_1 now left the place on their own and made for the gallery forest about 600 yd away, playing and frolicking on the way.

Differentiation of play scenes

At this stage the play scenes appeared much more differentiated than in the first few months; most frequently observed were:

(1) *Locomotory and contact play with obstacles*: e.g. the cubs climb the trunk of a tree and try to reach the first branches; they balance along the trunk of a fallen tree; they try to reach a twig of a tree with the forepaw by rising into an upright position and by jumping vertically; they play with water, pawing it, splashing it, running with the movement of the stream.

(2) *Partner-play with clearly developed scenes and roles*: e.g. stalking, getting ready for the sudden attack, then attack, sometimes followed by chasing if the partner showed play-flight; sham fighting over a sham prey, a piece of wood or an object introduced into the park by a human; play-fight or sparring with attack and defence at close quarters, often with a kind of wrestling.

Not only the scenes as a whole, but many elementary behaviour patterns had by now a well-developed shape: the clumsy pawing movements had developed into slaps or blows which were quite soft and friendly but often had a definite aim; by now, the attack after stalking was clearly aimed at the jump onto the partner's back, upon which the latter rolled onto his back and used his paws in play-defence; precise play-bites applied to the neck and throat region of the partner were now a usual element of play-wrestling.

It is most likely that the play scenes develop with growing strength, co-ordination and experience, but on the other hand the play scenes contribute to develop and shape the elementary behaviour patterns and their co-ordination.

The mother contributes to the play activity of her cubs over at least the first year. Two observations may demonstrate this fact. After a greeting scene in the early morning a mother was observed to wrestle with a cub. In another case, when guiding the group to shade after a meal, a mother stimulated one youngster to stalk, attack and chase her in play by jerking her tail upwards and by reacting with play-flight to the attack.

Play hunting and hunting exercises

From the age of approximately 5 months on the cubs were observed to develop active responses to other animal species—and to cars. They closely followed a slowly rolling car at its side aiming at the wheels with the eyes and sometimes with a pawing movement. Apparently wildebeeste were even more tempting because they reacted with flight when the cubs started an open clumsy chase. But it was only at 10–12 months that the cubs, stimulated by their mother, developed an activity which we are entitled to call hunting exercise. Two observations may be mentioned.

(1) At dawn the two mothers approached the six cubs, A_1 and B_1, and were immediately greeted by them. After a little play all the lions settled down on a minute elevation in the otherwise flat terrain, covered sparsely with gall acacias, and watched the surroundings. When two wildebeeste bulls passed the group at a distance of 50–60 yd, one of the mothers rose immediately followed by the other one. Both stepped forward in a stalking gait with a distance of about 15 yd between them, in order to approach the bulls transversely from behind. Without hesitation the young lions joined in, forming an irregular front line and taking advantage of the acacias as cover. As the bulls walked at fair speed, the lions did not get much closer and one after the other including the mothers gave up. Only two young lions continued to stalk until they had to cross a nearly completely bare flat. Here the wildebeeste bulls detected them and ran away in an easy gallop.

(2) Late one evening the old lioness, the two mothers and the six

cubs (A_1 and B_1) lay in the open near the edge of a little gallery forest, surveying the scene. When two warthogs approached slowly from a distance of about 200 yd, all the lions rose to stalk them, some using the sloping border of a track for cover, the others a collapsed warthog or hyena burrow. Mother A approached the warthogs and then waited behind a small mound for them to come closer. One of her children, a female, was advancing behind her, carefully stalking. When the warthogs became suspicious, the young lioness still continued to stalk and was detected by the warthogs at less than 15 yd. Both ran away immediately.

It is justifiable to ask whether these two and many similar scenes were not cases of unsuccessful hunting rather than a kind of exercise or training. However, for several months following these episodes, when the adult females went on a hunting excursion, they walked off decidedly, while the youngsters did not even try to follow. It seems therefore, that on the occasions when the lionesses allowed them to take part or even stimulated them to do so, they did not really intend to hunt.

At about 20 months of age the cubs were often observed to hunt on their own in the morning; for example, a young female entered a warthog burrow and started to dig with her forepaws. On another occasion, a sub-adult male and female together tried to dig out a warthog. In yet another case the youngsters, resting on a ridge, detected warthogs some 50 yd away. One young lioness stalked them, while the other youngsters watched the scene with great interest. Not only warthogs, but also wildebeeste and zebras were stalked frequently.

In every case observed, with one exception, the young lions had no success. But it was precisely the one successful instance which showed that juvenile hunting activity still has an important play component. A young male lion was moving through the grass and came upon a newborn gazelle, which did not react to danger with flight, but remained motionless on the spot. The young lion grabbed it by the neck and shook it. He then joined the other youngsters, the prey in his jaws, and with jerking tail invited them to chase him.

It seems that as long as a mother is hunting for the sub-adult lions, their own hunting activity is not motivated by hunger, but is therefore to some extent *play activity*.

CHANGES IN THE SOCIAL STRUCTURE OF THE PRIDE

When in January 1964 mother A mated again, mother B hunted for all six youngsters (A_1 were then about 18 months old, B_1 about 14 months old). After the mating period A joined them again, but during the next months she appeared less and less attached to her cubs and, from the end of March, B did all the hunting.

Over the same period the social structure of the pride had changed slowly but radically: the old lioness and both adult males showed an increasing lack of tolerance towards the youngsters, and even between the adult members of the pride the general intimacy decreased and personal relations with different components of friendship and tension appeared. From April 1964 on, the youngsters were no longer tolerated when the old lioness was with the two males. But the old lioness joined the youngsters when the two males were on an excursion. This was the case one day in May 1964 when all six cubs together threatened the old lioness, knocked her over and threatened her again until she remained lying completely crouched and no longer showed any aggressive reactions. But when later on she was again with the two males, she took part in chasing the youngsters whenever they were near.

Apparently when the mother is involved in a new reproductive cycle the abandoned sub-adult lions have a hard time: they have to acquire their own food. When they manage to make a kill, they risk being robbed of it by the older generation and being chased away. Whenever the old lions are in the vicinity the teenagers have to give way or even flee. This leads us to the next problem: territoriality.

TERRITORIALITY

Former observations and opinions

Whilst adult members of a lion pride are within their home range, intolerance is not only a particular reaction toward sub-adult members of their own pride, but also forms the normal reaction towards strange lions. Strangely enough, the fact of territorial intolerance or territoriality of the adult lion has not been studied, if at all recognized, by any one of the many lion hunters or experts with the exception of Adamson (1964). Yet a considerable number of observers have reported fights between lions—males as well as females—and some have even witnessed the killing of a lion by others. But the basic fact of *territoriality of a lion pride* has not been understood. Instead we find explanations or suggestions of the following type (for references, see Guggisberg, 1960).

(1) Observation: a strong male has killed a younger one.
Explanation: fight over a female (Guggisberg, pp. 145–146).

(2) Observation: several females were successively killed by a group of males.
Explanation: conflict in the course of mating contact, abnormal disposition (Guggisberg, p. 146).

(3) Observation: a female was killed by a male at a prey.
Explanation: the possession of the prey led to a fight (Guggisberg, p. 147, quoting C. J. Anderson).

(4) Observation: juvenile lions found dead at a kill.
Explanation: they were killed by the fully grown members of the pride over greed for food (Guggisberg, p. 152).

(5) Observation: a female was killed by other lionesses.
No explanation (Guggisberg, quoting J. Stevenson-Hamilton, p. 140).

(6) Observation: a fully grown male lion "hunts" a juvenile lion and then eats it.
Explanation: abnormal, cannibal disposition (Guggisberg, p. 147).

On the other hand, during the last few years the theory has been put forward that lions do not kill lions at all (Grzimek, 1959). Since Lorenz (1943) has stated that in general vertebrates with dangerous weapons are strongly innately inhibited from killing weaker members of their own species, several authors have repeated this statement with regard to the lion.

Territoriality of the lions in Nairobi National Park

During 1961 and 1962, two lionesses and a sub-adult lion were killed by the two adult males of the central pride (reported by Chief Game Warden, S. Ellis, Nairobi National Park). The park authorities and their advisers were convinced that the stronger of the two males was "abnormal" and that castration was the appropriate remedy for his abnormality, a remedy which had the added advantage of saving the imposing animal as an attraction for park visitors. The castration was performed, but the expectations proved futile: the male, after having lost his beautiful mane within 4 months as a result of the successful castration, together with the other adult male killed two more lionesses in 1963. One of these I detected at dawn, soon after it had been killed, with the two males and the old lioness of the central pride nearby. In the other case I witnessed the killing itself.

Furthermore, I have observed three more instances of serious attack by one or both males of the central pride with, in two of these cases, the participation of the females. In every case mentioned the individuals attacked were foreign lionesses and all the attacks occurred in areas which were frequently visited by the central pride. These areas undoubtedly were parts of the home range of the pride; moreover, the fact of intolerance towards strangers within these areas justifies their being defined as parts of the *territory* of the central pride.

Evidently a territory is not strictly avoided by strangers. Several times trespassers were observed in the territory of the central pride, but when the latter happened to stay a few miles away, no conflict arose. However, these intruders did not show the air of self-reliance and carelessness which a lion displays in his own territory. The maned lion of the eastern pride, whom I found one day at the border of the central territory, returned home under cover when he heard the central males roar from about a distance of 1 mile. On another occasion two strange lionesses with a half-grown male had killed a warthog in the central territory, but only after having carefully scrutinized the surroundings for several minutes did they dare to start the meal.

Intruders appear more careless in the late morning. When it is hot, no lion tends to be active, so an intruder hardly risks being attacked by resident lions at this time of the day.

Territorial display

For a species with as marked a territorial intolerance as the lion, behaviour patterns which inform transient animals that an area is already occupied by a member or a group of the species must have selective value.

The lion is equipped with several types of display which reveal his presence in an area.

(1) *Roaring*, which is often a choric display by the whole pride.

(2) *Scent marking* with urine, mainly by the male, in two patterns: sniffing at a bush, rubbing the head at it and finally squirting urine upwards into the branches; squirting urine downwards, while squatting in a crouched position and rubbing the hind feet in it, a behaviour pattern which results in scent marking the track.

(3) The open, unconcerned manner of moving in their own territory and the "proud" posture in looking around. Both these patterns make it easy to detect a lion whenever he is not stalking or resting in the shade.

It should be mentioned here that roaring, scent marking, and the open, unconcerned way of moving do not only have territorial functions, but this question cannot be discussed within the scope of this short paper.

The difference between territory and home range

It was stated several times in this paper that the two males of the central pride of Nairobi National Park left the females when on excursions of their own. Sometimes they were not seen within the park for days. The Game Warden, who visited the neighbouring parts of the Masai Game Reserve occasionally happened to find them there. Sometimes they also left their usual home range, but not the park area. They were observed to visit the forest area and, less frequently, to trespass into the eastern sector. There is no evidence that in these areas surrounding the central home range the two lions ever attacked another member of the species. On the contrary, the uncastrated male was seen to mate with the forest lionesses and to withdraw from the eastern sector, when he met the resident lion.

Apparently territoriality and aggressive behaviour in lions is restricted to the normal range of the pride they belong to. Further observations showed that the following factors are effective in enhancing aggressiveness: cubs, belonging to the pride, in the vicinity; more adult members of the pride taking part in the aggression; the comparative inferiority of the intruder in fighting.

This may support the concept that a territorial system is a dynamic system. Territoriality is not a stable, independent factor, but the fluctuating result of a multitude of factors. This is as true for the lion as it is for other vertebrates.

Acknowledgements

The preparation of this publication was supported by a grant of the Freie Akademische Stiftung, Basel.

The author would like to thank Mrs. Teda Sears for valuable information.

References

Adamson, G. A. G. (1964). Observations on lions in Serengeti National Park, Tanganyika. *E. Afr. Wildl. J.* **2**, 160–161.

Grzimek, B. (1959). Warum "benehmen sich Löwen besser als Menschen"? *Weltwoche*, 28 August, No. 1346, p. 7.

Guggisberg, C. A. W. (1960). "Simba." Hallwag, Berne.

Lorenz, K. (1943). Die angeborenen Formen möglicher Erfahrung. *Z. Tierpsychol.* **5**, 235–409.

Symp. zool. Soc. Lond. (1966) No. 18, 23–44.

AGGRESSIVE PLAY IN POLECATS

T. B. POOLE

Department of Zoology, University College of Wales, Aberystwyth, Wales

SYNOPSIS

The patterns of aggressive behaviour in the polecat first appear during the animal's lifetime in the context of play. This paper is an attempt to compare aggressive play with genuine adult aggression.

Four of the behaviour patterns found in aggression are absent from aggressive play. These four patterns are all directly concerned with the biological goal of aggression which is intimidation of the opponent. Aggressive play therefore differs in its goal from genuine aggression.

Evidence was obtained which showed that polecats of different strengths and sizes play amicably together and that the strength of the attack by the more powerful opponent is related to the strength of retaliation of the weaker one. Aggressive play is therefore make-believe aggression.

The development of aggressive play in the polecat was studied and it was found that each behaviour pattern emerged in a completed form and resembled that of the adult. It was therefore concluded that experience did not play an important role in the development of aggressive patterns of behaviour.

Finally, the effects of some environmental factors on aggressive play were studied. It was found that a situation which elicited behaviour directed towards a goal of immediate importance to the animal's survival, inhibited play. Make-believe must obviously take second place to serious activity. Like true aggression, aggressive play was stimulated by the presence of a polecat which was a stranger. If the stranger refused to play, the playful animal would none-the-less continue to follow it around and attempt to stimulate it by teasing. Teasing appears to act as a powerful stimulus to play. The presence of new objects in an environment or, after initial exploration, an entirely new environment, both stimulate aggressive play.

Nearly all the play shown by young polecats takes the form of aggressive play which is simple and stereotyped in pattern. None-the-less young polecats play a great deal so that it must occupy an important role in their lives. General theories of play were considered in relation to polecat play as it was felt that this was justified on the grounds that the theories must apply to all animals to be valid. Three views were rejected; polecat play lends no support to the hypothesis that play is practice for adult life nor does it accord with the idea that play is motivated by a non-specific urge to activity or results from the possession of excess energy.

In conclusion aggressive play in polecats shows the following attributes. It is goal-less in that it is not directed towards the normal aim of aggression. It does not appear to have any substitute goal other than the stimulation of further aggressive play, it is make-believe and played acording to rules. Aggressive play consists of adult patterns of behaviour which are stereotyped and unmodified by experience; it is inhibited by stimuli in the environment which lead to goal-directed behaviour. Aggressive play appears to give pleasure to the animal for it is sought after and may be directed towards an unresponsive animal or object.

INTRODUCTION

This work forms part of a study of aggressive behaviour in the European polecat (*Putorius putorius putorius* Linn.) and the ferret (*Putorius putorius furo* Linn.). After studying adult aggression it was decided to make an investigation of how aggressive behaviour develops in the young polecat. The patterns of behaviour found in aggression first appear in the context of play; this paper aims to make a comparison between aggressive play and true aggression.

Aggressive play will be defined as play which employs patterns of behaviour usually found in the context of adult aggression. This kind of play predominates in the young polecat and other forms of play occur only sporadically. Although general activity play (*Rennspiele* of Rensch and Dücker, 1959) and predatory play have been observed in polecats, the former occurs mainly in isolated animals, whilst the latter is ill-defined and difficult to distinguish from aggressive play on the one hand and true predation on the other.

After describing aggressive play in the young polecat a comparison will be made between the patterns of aggressive behaviour which occur in polecat play and those which occur in the adult as aggression; this will be followed by an account of the order in which these patterns develop, and finally some of the factors which stimulate or inhibit aggressive play will be described and compared with their effect on adult aggression.

SOURCES OF DATA

Studies were made on a tame polecat and laboratory-bred ferrets and polecat–ferret hybrids. A male polecat was kept for two years as a pet and, although caged most of the time, it was allowed considerable freedom and had the run of the house and garden for regular periods daily. This gave opportunities to study a polecat under relatively free conditions and records were made of the behaviour of the animal.

The second source of information came from observations on groups of polecat × ferret hybrids and ferrets separated from the mother at the age when their eyes opened and reared under laboratory conditions. Attempts to breed wild polecats under these conditions have, however, so far proved unsuccessful. Polecats and ferrets readily interbreed (see Pitt, 1921) and have been bred by the author to the F_3 generation. No differences in the patterns of aggressive behaviour have been observed between polecats and ferrets or in polecat × ferret hybrids so that they will all be referred to subsequently in this paper as polecats.

Play is at a maximum in young polecats between the ages of 6 and 14 weeks, though it appears to a lesser extent in animals as young as 4 weeks and occurs occasionally in adults.

Play was observed amongst litters in their cages and also in an arena 16 m^2 under conditions comparable to those under which genuine aggression had been studied.

RESULTS

Description of aggressive play

Aggressive play in the young polecat is initiated by an attacker which jumps on to the back of its opponent and bites it on the back of the neck (see Fig. 1A). The opponent rolls over on to its back and makes a

FIG. 1A. Neck-biting and mounting.

series of snapping bites at the muzzle and neck of its attacker, at the same time pushing it away with its paws (see Fig. 2A). In response to this, the attacker either stands above its opponent and snaps its jaws in a playful attempt to bite its neck or alternatively rolls on to its back and the two animals exchange their roles of aggressor and defender. If the animals become very excited, the aggressor shakes its opponent vigorously by the neck and may drag it around the arena by the scruff of its neck (Fig. 1B). Sometimes both animals lie side by side

FIG. 1B. Dragging. The paler animal is dragging the dark one.

FIG. 1C. Sustained neck bite. Both animals are gripping their opponent's neck.

on their backs, snapping their jaws at one another and waving their legs in the air. Occasionally polecats direct bites at one another's limbs and tails but this is not a common pattern in aggressive play.

Fig. 1D. Sideways attack. The animal on the right is the aggressor and is moving towards the top left-hand corner of the picture.

If one animal is in a playful mood whilst the other is not, the playful animal teases its victim in an attempt to incite it to join in the play. Teasing takes several forms. A polecat may mount the other animal whilst holding its neck with the teeth until the opponent is incited to roll over and playfully retaliate or it may dance up to the other polecat, finally jumping on it, or it may chase it around, frequently biting it in the pelvic region (see Fig. 2C).

A polecat which does not wish to indulge in play or has already had enough, threatens its opponent by hissing and baring the teeth; this results in the attacker desisting. If one of the animals is smaller or weaker than its opponent which is being too rough, it cries plaintively until it is released. Playful aggression is frequently accompanied in the older animals by vocalization which takes the form of an excited clucking.

The above patterns constitute, together with chasing and flight, the most frequent patterns of aggressive play. One other pattern, however, occurs commonly when one animal is in a tunnel and is approached by a playful attacker; the animal in the tunnel directs snapping bites in the direction of its opponent, simultaneously rolling on to its back, stretching its neck out and snapping its jaws.

A comparison between the aggressive behaviour of the adult and aggressive play in the young polecat

Patterns of behaviour found in aggressive play and aggression

Table I shows the patterns of behaviour commonly found in aggression in the adult animal and those which occur in aggressive play. Four patterns of behaviour, absent from aggressive play, are found in adult aggression.

TABLE I

Comparison between aggression and aggressive play in polecats

	Aggression (adults)	Aggressive play (young)	Age when first observed
Attacking behaviour			
Neck-biting	+	+	4 weeks
Mounting	+	+	6 weeks
Shaking	+	+	8 weeks
Dragging	+	+	8 weeks
Chasing	+	+	8 weeks
Sustained neck-biting	+	−	Adult
Sideways attack	+	−	Adult
Defensive behaviour			
Rolling on back	+	+	4 weeks
Playbiting	+	+	6 weeks
Flight	+	+	8 weeks
Defensive threat	+	−	Adult
Vocalizations			
Hissing	+	+	5 weeks
Screaming	+	−	Adult

During true aggression the polecat bites the neck of its opponent and holds on (see Fig. 1C). This results in retaliation on the part of the opponent in a similar attempt to bite its adversary's neck. During the fierce and vigorous fighting of adult male polecats in the breeding season the sustained neck-bite plays a major role; it is generally true in most of the higher animals that continued gripping and holding of any part of the anatomy produces fear and retaliation on the part of the victim of this kind of attack.

FIG. 2A. Rolling over and playbiting.

FIG. 2B. Defensive threat. The animal on the left is the aggressor; its opponent adopts defensive threat.

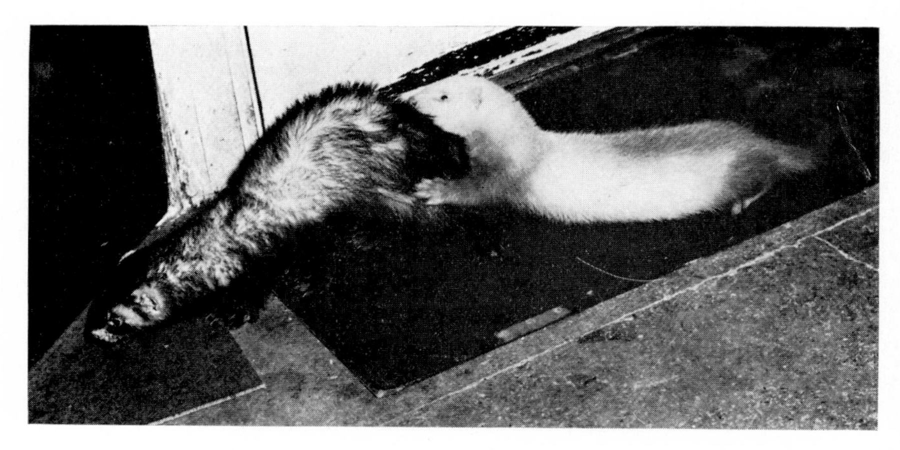

FIG. 2C. Teasing. The young polecat, the paler animal, is following the adult around the arena making playful attacks upon it.

Sideways attack (see Fig. 1D) is a form of behaviour directed by a highly aggressively motivated polecat towards a defensive or frightened opponent, the effect being to initiate or prolong a fight with an unwilling partner. This further terrorizes the opponent who adopts an attitude which has been called defensive threat, in which it stands with arched back and raised head facing its aggressor with bared teeth and hissing or screaming (see Fig. 2B). Screaming, which is the vocalization produced by a frightened polecat, is absent from aggressive play in the young polecat.

Effect of superior strength and agility on aggressive play and aggression

Experiments were carried out in which young animals were confronted with adults or with other young polecats of different ages to compare the behaviour of animals of different strengths and vigour in the context of play.

If the younger litter were under 6 weeks old, they grouped together and followed any larger polecat, whether young, adult, male or female, but they did not play. If the older litter were more than 6 weeks old, they tried to play with the smaller ones, gripping them by the neck and mounting them and sometimes carrying them to a corner and chewing them gently.

When the younger litter were older than 6 weeks they joined in aggressive play with the older litter. The latter were usually the aggressors, being more often on top in the contest. The younger litter played a more passive and defensive role. The reason for this seems to be the greater agility of the older animals. In some cases where the younger litter were larger or more active than normal for their age they proved to be the equals of older animals. This was not therefore the result of experience but of superior physique. Whatever the age gap between litters the older animals did not inflict pain on the younger ones or terrorize them; if the younger ones tired of the game they cried or hissed, and the older ones released them.

If there was some considerable age gap between litters, each group usually ended by playing with members of the same age group in preference to those of a different age. If the age gap was smaller or the younger animals were unusually active, all played together indiscriminately.

At 14–18 weeks males and females of the same litter play together even though males of this age usually weigh one and a half times as much as the females; the females frequently adopt the aggressive role but the males do not hurt their female opponents.

In contrast to the situation in young polecats, in adult aggression the animal which possesses the greater strength and vigour is the victor and terrorizes its opponent. The smaller or weaker opponent either takes to flight or displays defensive threat. If the attacker continues the assault the weaker animal screams and attempts to break away at the first opportunity.

Development of aggressive play in polecats

The patterns of aggressive play which develop earliest are neck-biting and its response of rolling over on to the back. These patterns can be demonstrated amongst young in the nest at 4 weeks old which is a week before the eyes open (see Table I). If the young are awoken and activated by stroking with the fingers, holding their muzzles gently and rolling them over on to their backs, they become excited and play with one another. Play takes the form of neck-biting, rolling over in response to an attack and indiscriminate biting of the opponent's body and appendages. Neck-biting differs from indiscriminate biting in that it is quite precisely aimed at the back of the neck of the opponent in spite of the fact that the attacker is blind at this stage. Neck-biting does not develop out of indiscriminate biting as both patterns appear simultaneously.

At 6 weeks the polecats' eyes are open and their behaviour can be studied either by stimulating them in the nest by turning them over and holding their muzzles gently or by placing them in an arena where after exploration they usually remain in a corner and play. They are now more active and mounting and its response of play-biting develop.

Like neck-biting and rolling over these patterns appear in a completed form and are not gradually acquired through trial and error or random movements.

By the age of 8 weeks polecats are very active creatures. Dancing, dragging, shaking, jaw snapping and chasing all appear. At the age of $9\frac{1}{2}$ weeks the dancing has become extended to jumping upon an opponent as a form of teasing and by $14\frac{1}{2}$ weeks play has become very active and rough. Animals which are unwilling to play either cry or hiss at their opponent. Although crying and hissing develop much earlier in the polecat's life (crying in the first few days of life and hissing by the age of 5 weeks), they do not occur in play until this later stage. It seems probable that their appearance in play is related to the increased roughness of the play.

Observations on aggressive play show that it consists almost entirely of instinctive patterns of behaviour which develop in sequence; the basic patterns of the neck bite and rolling over appear even before the eyes are open. The patterns of aggressive play emerge one by one in a completed form and at their first appearance resemble the adult behaviour pattern, so that they do not appear to be modified by experience as the animal grows older. This is also suggested by observations on a pet polecat, which suggested that play in the polecat contains very little inventiveness so that learned patterns of behaviour play a very small part.

A comparison of the factors which influence aggressive play and aggression

Factors which stimulate aggressive play in polecats

As in true aggression the most powerful stimulus which induces play aggression is the presence of another polecat. Isolated polecats play aggressively with inanimate objects in their cages; these are generally ignored if another polecat is introduced and can be induced to play.

The presence of a polecat which is a stranger elicits play from a group of polecats which had not previously been playing, in the same way that the presence of a stranger elicits aggression in a group of adult polecats.

Aggressive play is also induced by placing the animals in a strange situation or putting some new object in a familiar environment. The new situation or object is carefully investigated by the polecat but subsequently the animals indulge in aggressive play directed towards one another.

Teasing also acts as a stimulus to aggressive play; an animal which is not playing is frequently incited to do so by provocative attacks from other polecats. This can be illustrated by one example. If an adult and a young polecat are placed together in the arena the young one teases the adult by playful attacks. This frequently elicits aggressive play from the adult, though adults themselves do not normally show this kind of behaviour towards a stranger.

Factors which inhibit aggressive play in polecats

In young polecats three environmental situations predictably inhibit play; these are a fear-inducing stimulus, the presence of prey or the animal finding itself in an unfamiliar environment. The behavioural responses which are substituted for play differ in the three situations.

In the case of a fear-inducing stimulus the animal adopts a defensive posture and takes flight or hides. Where prey is present the polecat immediately chases it and if it is capable of doing so, kills the prey. A polecat finding itself in an unfamiliar environment immediately changes to exploratory behaviour.

In a situation where a young polecat has been given time to explore the arena before a second polecat is introduced, the first arrival attempts to play aggressively with the intruder which ignores it and explores its surroundings. In a similar situation adult polecats behave in a comparable manner. The first arrival in an arena always has the initial aggressive advantage over its opponent, which invariably directs its behaviour towards exploration.

DISCUSSION

This work is concerned mainly with the relationship between true aggression and aggressive play. Aggressive play has already been defined as "play which employs the patterns of behaviour usually found in the adult context of aggression". The author considers adult aggression to be any activity which is directed towards the discomfiture of another individual. In the polecat this takes the form of well-defined stereotyped behaviour patterns.

The comparison between the patterns of behaviour which occur in genuine aggression and those which are found in aggressive play shows that four patterns are absent from play which occur in genuine aggression. Two of these patterns "sustained neck-biting" and "sideways attack" are active attempts to terrorize or discomfit the opponent whilst defensive threat and screaming are found in a vanquished polecat which has been terrorized by its adversary. These four patterns therefore are all related to intimidation of the opponent which is the biological goal of aggression. Their absence from aggressive play therefore suggests that the goal of aggression is absent from aggressive play.

The difference in aim of aggression and aggressive play is further supported by the evidence obtained from experiments in which young polecats of different ages and young polecats and adults were placed together. This shows that the strength of attack is inhibited when young polecats play with younger polecats or when young male polecats play with the much smaller females; for although they play vigorously they do not inflict pain on the younger animals or terrorize them. When a young polecat of 10 weeks or more is confronted with a strange adult in the arena, it makes playful or teasing attacks on the intruder. This usually results in the adult playing with the young one, and although the adult is larger and far more powerful it does not hurt the younger animal which ignores the threatening hisses which the other makes. The adult may also make a short-lived but genuine attack upon the young one, but even in these circumstances the attack must be to some extent inhibited for it seldom acts as a lasting deterrent to the playful attacks of the younger animal. Play between man and polecat also shows that inhibition of biting occurs. Playing with the original captive male polecat in his cage, it was found that his bites were gentle but that the more roughly one played with him, the harder the bites became. If the game became too rough he became genuinely aggressive and would inflict a painful bite. The biting of a playful animal was shown to be inhibited when, after playing with it for some time gently, using one hand, it was offered the other, smeared with blood and holding a small piece of meat. The polecat seized the meat and the hand and the bite delivered was far more powerful than anything it was inflicting during play.

It can be concluded from this, therefore, that in contrast with genuine aggression, play is adapted to the strength of the opponent and avoids both pain and fear-producing situations. The strength of the opponent is judged on the basis of the vigour of its attack. If the attack of a human opponent is too vigorous, inhibition of biting disappears and genuine aggression results. Between polecats this does not occur, since if one finds the play too rough, it cries or threatens and is at once released.

It can therefore be concluded from this evidence that aggressive play is "make-believe aggression". In real aggression the stronger and more vigorous contestant is the victor who terrorizes its opponent, whereas in play-aggression the stronger and more vigorous contestant adapts its strength to that of its opponent.

Observations on the development of play patterns in the young polecat show that when they first emerge they resemble those of the adult. There is no gradual perfection of patterns over a period of time. The basic patterns of attack and defence develop before any of the others but most of the patterns seem to appear when the polecat possesses the agility and co-ordination necessary to carry them out. Between the ages of 8 and 14 weeks polecats of different ages play together as equals if the age gap is compensated for, either by slow development of agility in the older litter, or more rapid development in the younger. The size and agility of the animals depends on the number in the litter from which they come; members of litters of two or three are often larger and more agile than those from litters of seven or eight.

The most important environmental factor which induces aggressive play in polecats is the presence of another polecat, especially a stranger. This situation has the same effect on adult polecats in that a stranger elicits aggressive behaviour. Inadequate environmental stimuli may induce aggressive play in isolated young polecats which spend much of their time playing aggressively with, for example, their plastic feeding bowls. This seems to indicate a need for play in the young animal, and this is normally evident when polecats seek playful contests with others by teasing a stronger adult or an unwilling litter mate.

Certain factors have been shown to inhibit play and the three situations described, fear, prey or a strange environment, share in common the fact that they all elicit behaviour which is orientated towards a goal which bears a direct relevance to the survival of the animal. The biological goals in these situations are avoidance of danger, capture of food and familiarization with a potentially hostile environment. These are of real and immediate importance to the young animal, whereas play is concerned only with make-believe situations.

From these studies the following conclusions about aggressive play in polecats can be drawn.

1. Aggressive play is goal-less in that it is not directed towards the normal aim of aggression. It does not appear to have any substitute goal other than the stimulation of further aggressive play.
2. Aggressive play is make-believe aggression, for the contest is played according to the rule that the vigour of the attack is related to the vigour of retaliation by the opponent.
3. Aggressive play consists of adult patterns of behaviour which are stereotyped and unmodified by experience.
4. Aggressive play is inhibited by stimuli in the environment which lead to goal-directed behaviour.

5. Aggressive play appears to give pleasure to the animal; it i actively sought after and may be directed towards an unresponsiv animal or object (e.g. plastic dish).

The study of play in a single animal does not qualify one to produc a general theory of play. None-the-less the author believes that th conclusions reached from a study of polecat play must be applicable t play in general and that the simple and stereotyped type of play found i polecats may help to throw some light on the biological goal of play.

As play in polecats is almost entirely confined to aggressive play it is justifiable to examine some general theories of play which do no accord with the findings of this work and to reject their universa application to play on this account.

Groos (1898) described the biological value of play as practice, bu this is not true of polecat play for the patterns involved are stereotype and unmodified by experience and the outcome of true aggression i polecats is determined by the size and vigour of the animal and no by practice or strategy. Nor does aggressive play provide usefu opportunities for incidental learning or the acquisition of skills. Th biological goal of aggressive play cannot therefore be practice.

Meyer-Holzapfel (1956) favours a non-specific activity drive as th motivation for play. She suggests that when the animal is not con cerned with a serious activity, providing the special readiness for pla occurs, the animal will then indulge in playful activity.

However, the way in which play is sought after by the young pole cats suggests that a more specific drive to play exists. Meyer-Holzapfel' views do not explain why the "special readiness" for play declines i adult polecats kept in the same conditions as the young.

Many authors believe that play arises from surplus energy, but lik Beach (1945) the author rejects this hypothesis for under conditions o captivity the adult polecats are kept under similar conditions to th young with no demands upon them to hunt for food or avoid enemies One would therefore expect them to have equal amounts of surplu energy yet play occurs rarely in the adults but regularly in the young

Finally, so far as the polecat is concerned, play may be defined a activity which is not orientated towards a goal which is directly con cerned with the survival of the individual. Play consists to a larg extent of adult patterns of behaviour which are normally used t promote the survival of the individual but which appear in play ou of their true context. An essential feature of play is that it appears t give satisfaction to the animal by mere repetition and can be indulge in by either a solitary animal or several animals concertedly.

References

Beach, F. A. (1945). Current concepts of play in animals. *Am. Nat.* **79**, 523–541.

Groos, K. (1898). "The Play of Animals". Chapman and Hall, New York.

Meyer-Holzapfel, M. (1956). Über die Bereitschaft zu Spiel und Instinkthandlungen. *Z. Tierpsychol.* **13**, 442–462.

Pitt, F. (1921). Notes on the genetic behaviour of certain characters in the polecat, ferret and in polecat–ferret hybrids. *J. Genet.* **11**, 99–115.

Rensch, B. and Dücker, G. (1959). Die Spiele von Mungo und Ichneumon. *Behaviour* **14**, 185–213.

Appendix

Details of experiments on aggressive play

Date of expt.	Litter	Heredity	Age (weeks)	No. of animals in expt.	Film record	Neck-biting	Mounting	Shaking	Dragging	Chasing	Sustained neck-biting	Sideways attack	Rolling over	Playbiting	Flight	Defensive threat	Hissing	Screaming	Crying	Dancing	
1964																					
19 vii	1	F	7	4	—	+	+						+	+							Play
	1	F	7	2	—																Followed ♀ in a clump
	♀	F	Adult	1		+															♀ gently bit necks of young
27 vii	1	F	8	4	—	+	+						+	+						+	Play
	1	F	8	2	—	+	+		+												Playful aggressors
	2	F	$4\frac{1}{2}$	3																	Inactive
5 viii	1	F	$9\frac{1}{2}$	2	—	+	+	+	+	+											Playful aggressors
	2	F	6	3									+								Defensive reaction only
	1	F	$9\frac{1}{2}$	2	—	+	+			+											Tease adult
	♂	F_1	Adult	1		+	+						+	+							Adult joins play
	1	F	$9\frac{1}{2}$	2	—	+	+			+											Teased ♀
	♀	F	Adult	1																	No response
6 viii	1	F	$9\frac{1}{2}$	2	—	+	+			+											Teased ♀
	♂	F_1	Adult	1													+				Ignored or threatened young
	1	F	$9\frac{1}{2}$	2	—	+	+		+	+			+	+					+		Teased ♂
	♂	F	Adult	1		+	+		+	+						+	+				Replied with genuine aggression
	♂	F	Adult	1	—	+	+		+												Gentle play (same ♂ as above)
	2	F	6	3		+	+			+											Followed ♂ attempted to play

Date of expt.	Litter	Heredity	Age (weeks)	No. of animals in expt.	Film record	Neck-biting	Mounting	Shaking	Dragging	Chasing	Sustained neck-biting	Sideways attack	Rolling over	Playbiting	Flight	Defensive threat	Hissing	Screaming	Crying	Dancing	
11 viii	1	F	10½	4	—	+	+						+	+					+		Active play
	1	F	10½	2	—	+	+														Attempted play
	2	F	7	3						+											Attempted to follow litter 1
	2	F	7	3																	No play
	3	F_2	5	2																	No play
18 viii	1	F	11	2	—	+	+		+											+	Playful attacks
	2	F	8	3									+	+							Played defensively or ignored older animals
	1	F	11	2	—	+	+		+												Playful attacks but too rough for all to join in play together
	3	F_2	6	2									+								
	2	F	8	3	—	+	+														Teased younger animals
	3	F_2	6	2																	Ignored older animals
18 ix	1	F	13½	2	—	+	+			+			+	+						+	Played together
	♂	F_1	Adult	1		+	+			+			+	+							
	1	F	13½	2	—	+	+		+	+										+	Litter 1 playful aggressors 2 defensive 2 ♂ larger, however, and attacked small ♀
	2	F	10	3		♂	♂			♂			+	+							
	2	F	10	3	—	+	+		+	+											Litter 2 playful aggressors 3 defensive 3 ♀ was dragged but not 3 ♂ which is larger
	3	F_2	8	2									+	+							
	1	F	13½	2	—	+	+													+	Tried to play
	3	F_2	8	2																	Ignored older animals

Date of expt.	Litter	Heredity	Age (weeks)	No. of animals in expt.	Film record	Neck-biting	Mounting	Shaking	Dragging	Chasing	Sustained neck-biting	Sideways attack	Rolling over	Playbiting	Flight	Defensive threat	Hissing	Screaming	Crying	Dancing	
10 ix	1	F	15	2	—	+	+													+	Aggressors in play
	♂	F_1	Adult	1		+	+						+	+						+	Joined in but also explored arena
	1	F	15	4	—	+	+			+			+	+					+	+	Rough but amicable play
	1	F	15	2	—	+	+														Litter 1 usually on top but amicable
	2	F	11	3	—	+	+						+	+							play
	1	F	15	2	—	+	+		+												1 carried 5 to a corner and chewed
	5	F	6	3						+									+		No play. 5 followed 1 around
	1	F	15	2	—																
	2	F	11	3																	Played amicably together
	3	F_2	$9\frac{1}{2}$	3																	No detailed record
	4	F_2	6	5	—	+															One of 5 placed in cage of 4
	5	F	6	1									+								5 explored. Playful attack from 4
	5	F	6	3	—	+															One of 4 placed in cage with 5
	4	F_2	6	1									+								Playful attack from 5. 4 explored
22 ix	1	F	$16\frac{1}{2}$	4	—	+	+	+	+	+			+	+	+		+		+	+	Very rough + active play
	1	F	$16\frac{1}{2}$	2	—	+	+		+												1 rough play with 4 which ignored
	4	F_2	8	5																	and explored
	1	F	$16\frac{1}{2}$	2	—	+	+		+												1 rough play with 5 which ignored
	5	F	8	3																	and explored
	1	F	$16\frac{1}{2}$	2	—	+	+			+			+	+	+					+	Played equally together
	3	F_2	11	1♀		+	+			+			+	+	+					+	
	1	F	$16\frac{1}{2}$	2	—	+	+			+			+	+	+						Played equally together
	♀	F_1	Adult	1		+	+			+			+	+	+						

Date of expt.	Litter	Heredity	Age (weeks)	No. of animals in expt.	Film record	Neck-biting	Mounting	Shaking	Dragging	Chasing	Sustained neck-biting	Sideways attack	Rolling over	Playbiting	Flight	Defensive threat	Hissing	Screaming	Crying	Dancing	
29 ix	1	F	17½	2	—	+	+			+										+	Young teased adult
	♂	F_1	Adult	1		+	+						+	+	+					+	Adult played defensively, then true aggression
	1	F	17½	2	—	+	+		+												1 carried 5 to corner and chewed their necks
	5	F	9	3									+								
	5	F	9	3	—	+															One placed in cage of strangers which bit its neck
	4	F_2	9	1		+											+				
	4	F_2	9	5	—	+															4 explored, brief but genuine aggression shown by F_2
	5	F	9	1																	One placed in cage of others explored. Others bit neck
1965 23 vii	1	P	11	4	—	+	+						+	+						+	Played
	1	P	11	4		+	+						+	+							Attempted to play
	2	F	5½	6	—					+									+		Followed, cried, did not play, tried to climb on 1
	2	F	5½	6	—														+		Clump together
	♀	F	Adult	1		+			+	+											Mother retrieves them 2 days after separation from her
	2	F	5½	6	—					+									+		Cried, clumped together, followed adult
	♀	F	Adult	1																	Not mother
	2	F	5½	6	—																Investigated one another and clumped together. No play
	3	F_3	5	5																	

Date of expt.	Litter	Heredity	Age (weeks)	No. of animals in expt.	Film record	Neck-biting	Mounting	Shaking	Dragging	Chasing	Sustained neck-biting	Sideways attack	Rolling over	Playbiting	Flight	Defensive threat	Hissing	Screaming	Crying	Dancing	
24 vii	2	F	$5\frac{1}{2}$	6	—														+		Mother retrieved both litters irrespective. No play
	3	F_3	5	5															+		
	♀	F	Adult	1		+			+	+											
3 viii	1	P	13	6	3	+	+	+	+	+			+	+	+					+	Play
	1	P	13	1	3	+	+		+				+	+						+	Teasing + play
	♂	P	Adult	1		+	+	+	+												Aggressor in play
	2	F	7	1	—																Followed adult in clump
	♂	P	Adult	1																	No play
4 viii	1	P	13	1♂	—																No play
	2	F	7	6																	Clumped and followed adult
	1	P	13	4	4	+	+	+	+	+			+	+	+					+	Play
	3	F_3	$6\frac{1}{2}$	5	4																Clumped together and followed adult
	♀	F	Adult	1	—																
	3	F_3	$6\frac{1}{2}$	5	4																Clumped together and followed adult, ignored young. No play
	♀	F	Adult	1																	
	3	F_3	$6\frac{1}{2}$	5	4																Clumped together and followed adult
	♀	F_2	Adult	1		+			+												Adult (mother) retrieved young
	3	F_3	$6\frac{1}{2}$	5	—																Clumped together and followed adult, ignored young
	♀	F_2	Adult	1																	
	1	P	13	1	4	+	+	+	+	+											Attacking play
	4	F_3	6	2						+			+	+							Defensive play

Date of expt.	Litter	Heredity	Age (weeks)	No. of animals in expt.	Film record	Neck-biting	Mounting	Shaking	Dragging	Chasing	Sustained neck-biting	Sideways attack	Rolling over	Playbiting	Flight	Defensive threat	Hissing	Screaming	Crying	Dancing	
11 viii	2	F	8	6	5		+						+	+							Played defensively
	♂	F	Adult	1	—	+	+	+					+							+	Played aggressively
19 viii	1	P	15	6	7	+	+			+			+	+	+					+	Very active play
	1	P	15	6		+	+						+	+							Teasing
	♂	F	Adult	1	7 + 8	+	+		+												Aggressive play
	1	P	15	6	8	+	+						+	+							Tried to play with ♀ ferret
	♀	F	Adult	1		+	+						+	+							Tried to explore arena
	1	P	15	2	9	+	+		+	+									+		Tried to play
	5	F	7	2																	Ignored older animals
	1	P	15	2	9	+	+		+	+											Aggressive play
	3	F_3	8½	2									+	+							Defensive play
	2	F	9	2	9	+							+	+	+						Play. F_3 are aggressors
	3	F_3	8½	2		+	+			+											Newly introduced F are defensive
	3	F_3	8½	2	9	+	+														Older animals were aggressors
	5	F	7	2																	Younger animals followed and ignored older ones
6 ix	1	P	17½	1	10	+	+			+										+	Teased and jumped on younger animals
	6	F	8	1																	
	7	F	8	1																	Followed older animals
	7	F	8	5	10	+	+														7 were aggressors but later 6 attacked one of 7
	6	F	8	1		+	+						+	+							
	7	F	8	5	10																7 did not play
	6	F	8	4		+	+	+	+	+			+	+	+						6 played very actively especially with brown one

Appendix—*continued*

Date of expt.	Litter	Heredity	Age (weeks)	No. of animals in expt.	Film record	Neck-biting	Mounting	Shaking	Dragging	Chasing	Sustained neck-biting	Sideways attack	Rolling over	Playbiting	Flight	Hissing	Defensive threat	Screaming	Crying	Dancing	
10 ix	8	P	$4\frac{1}{2}$	7	—	+							+								Played, also indiscriminate biting (in nest)
17 ix	6	F	10	7	11	+	+	+		+			+	+	+					+	Very active play
	♂	F_1	Adult	1	11											+	+				No play, adult threatened young
	6	F	10	7																	

Key:
Column 2 "Litter": 1–8 order of age in particular year.
♀, ♂ Adults (born in previous years).
Column 3 "Heredity": F = Ferret
F_1, F_2, F_3 = Polecat × ferret hybrids
P = Litter of a wild caught polecat (1964); (undoubtedly polecat × ferret hybrids).
Column 6 "Film Record" Nos. 3–11 represent 8 mm ciné films.
Note. Both litter 1, 1964, and litter 1, 1965, were divided into two groups which were reared separately and only met briefly at intervals in the arena.

Symp. zool. Soc. Lond. (1966) No. 18, 45–59.

EXPLORATION AND FEAR IN THE RAT

M. S. HALLIDAY

Laboratory of Experimental Psychology, University of Sussex, Brighton, Sussex, England

SYNOPSIS

The hypothesis is advanced that fear may play an important role in the motivation of exploratory behaviour in rats, and that stimuli may be explored because they evoke fear rather than because they are novel. Evidence for and against this view is briefly discussed. Experimental results are presented on: (a) the differences in exploratory behaviour in elevated and enclosed mazes; (b) exploratory behaviour in rats with differential treatment in infancy; (c) the exploration of stimuli associated with electric shock. These results all suggest that exploratory behaviour in rats tends to vary with the fear evoking properties of stimuli rather than with their novelty.

Over the last twenty years a very large amount of information has been collected on the exploratory behaviour of a wide variety of mammalian species. (For general reviews see Berlyne, 1960, 1963; Welker, 1961; Fowler, 1963.) Most of this work has, however, been concerned with rats, and I shall largely confine my discussion to this species. These findings have provoked a great deal of theoretical discussion, much of which has centred round the question of the motivation of exploratory behaviour. As compared with other conventional drives the motivational system controlling exploratory behaviour presents a number of peculiar features. Drives or motivations are usually thought to have certain general features in common. (1) There are specifiable operations which will increase the level of the motivation; deprivation of food or water in the cases of hunger and thirst. (2) The motivation is associated with some physiological state, even though the details of this state may be poorly understood. (3) There are certain conditions which will reduce or eliminate the motivational state, for example feeding or drinking. In the case of exploration none of these conditions apply. It is by no means clear what arouses the motivation: is it the novel stimuli in the environment, or is there a "boredom" drive, produced by deprivation of interesting stimulation? The point is discussed in detail by Fowler (1963) who reaches the conclusion that both factors play a part. But even if this is so, we know little about what stimulus conditions are necessary either to arouse exploratory behaviour or to produce boredom. It is fairly certain that physiological conditions of arousal are connected with exploration, but it is still in doubt whether the function of exploratory behaviour is to increase the level of arousal, to reduce it, or to reach a happy mean of optimum arousal (see Berlyne, 1960, pp. 163–227). These confusions are paralleled by similar doubts about the goal of exploratory behaviour; rats will seek out novel stimulation (Montgomery, 1954; Montgomery and Segall, 1955), yet this appears to mean that they are seeking an increase in drive. Such a conclusion is so much at variance with the tenets of learning theory that it casts doubt on the usefulness of the idea of exploratory drive; this is essentially the point of the criticisms levelled against Montgomery's use of the concept (see e.g. Watson, 1961).

Faced with these difficulties it might seem prudent to abandon this rather theoretical approach and to try to account for the findings on exploratory behaviour without making any use of motivational concepts. Glanzer (1953) put forward a theory along these lines which dispensed with motivation; he suggested that all stimuli tend to be inspected by an animal and that, during exploration of a stimulus, satiation (on the analogy of Hull's reactive inhibition) builds up to this particular stimulus; this stimulus satiation dissipates with time, but its immediate effect will be to make the animal more likely to explore stimuli which it has not recently investigated and to which, therefore, no stimulus satiation is attached. A simple non-motivational theory of this sort can account for quite a wide range of experimental results and has obvious attractions, but it also has drawbacks which illustrate the necessity of having some motivational construct in order to account adequately for exploratory behaviour. Such a theory can only explain exploratory behaviour controlled by stimuli which are present to the animal at the time; but in some cases at least there is evidence that spontaneous alternation is not determined by stimuli at the choice point, but by stimuli in the goal boxes which are invisible from the choice point (e.g. Sutherland, 1957). A stronger objection to Glanzer's theory is that rats will learn in order to explore. Montgomery has shown that rats will learn a T-maze or a discrimination problem in order to get 2-min exploration in a Dashiell maze (Montgomery, 1954; Montgomery and Segall, 1955); various controls made it unlikely that these results could be attributed to position habits, or to reduction of some "activity drive". Chapman and Levy (1957), using rats, and Schneider and Gross (1964), using hamsters, found that the latency of running a straight alley decreased when novel stimuli were presented in the goal box. Berlyne and Slater (1957) failed to find any tendency for rats to prefer the side of a T-maze on which a novel card was presented; but Stretch (1960), using the same stimulus cards, found marked decreases in latency in running a straight alley, when the cards in the goal box were changed from trial to trial, and an increase in latency when the same card was shown on each trial. Berlyne and Slater's result cannot therefore be taken as conclusive, and may well be the result of test insensitivity. If rats will learn in order to explore it is hard to see how any satisfactory account of exploratory behaviour could be made without making use of some sort of motivational concept.

I do not intend to review the various theories of exploration. I have only discussed these theoretical issues in order to illustrate the type of difficulty that arises. All current theories have defects, and in general these defects arise over the identification of the motivation controlling exploratory behaviour. To make confusion worse confounded, I shall state the case for another candidate, at least in the limited area of locomotor exploration in rats. There is a striking association between exploratory behaviour and fear, and it seems possible that fear may play a much larger role than has commonly been thought in the control of such behaviour.

There is no lack of evidence to suggest that the same situations which elicit exploratory behaviour also evoke fear. In rats, defaecation is usually taken by psychologists as the most convenient indicator of fear. Defaecation, urination and other behaviour indicative of emotional arousal are characteristically found when a rat is placed in a novel situation; at the same time exploratory behaviour commonly occurs. The frequency of defaecation declines with time in a novel environment (Candland, 1958), so does the amount of exploratory behaviour. Both the amount of defaecation and the amount of activity decline when rats are given repeated exposures in an open field (Hall, 1934; Yoshioka, 1932). In other species too there are numerous reports of novel situations tending to produce both fear and withdrawal, and approach and exploration (e.g. Dolin *et al.*, 1958; Hebb, 1946; Melzack, 1952). The phenomena are, indeed, too common to need emphasizing. These findings have usually been taken to show that most novel stimuli activate two motivational systems, one mediating avoidance, and the other approach, and that the observed behaviour is the result of an approach–avoidance conflict. On the other hand, the conjunction between fear and exploratory behaviour is so common and so widespread that it seems very possible that there is a much closer connexion between them. I suggest that perhaps only one motivation is involved and that low levels of this motivation make the animal more likely to explore, while higher levels result in avoidance. The advantage of this suggestion is that the motivational system involved is already familiar in other contexts, and is detectable independently of the behaviour which it is supposed to explain. But there appears to be an insuperable objection; for surely it is the defining characteristic of fear that it induces withdrawal and avoidance. If this is so, it is quite impossible that fear of a stimulus could lead to exploration of that stimulus. To argue along these lines is, however, to take too narrow a view of the nature of motivational systems. It is not usually possible to use the frequency or amplitude of a single type of behaviour as the sole indicator of the strength of a motivation. It is better to think of a motivation as a state of the organism which affects the probability of the occurrence of a number of different sorts of behaviour, both learnt and unlearnt. Thus, for example, an increase in the level of fear may increase the probability of escape behaviour, but it may equally well result in the performance of a learnt avoidance response. Even in the unlearnt case we cannot use avoidance as the only indicator of fear, for, in the rat at least, high levels of fear may produce freezing rather than escape. In this case there is nothing inconsistent in the idea that under certain circumstances, and with certain levels of fear, an animal will approach and explore a stimulus because it arouses fear.

The suggestion is, therefore, that rats tend to explore novel stimuli, because they arouse low levels of fear, not simply because of their novelty. Most stimuli arouse fear in the rat on their first presentation, and such stimuli will be explored, and, if they are in fact harmless, they will cease to elicit fear and hence exploration. Stimuli which arouse higher levels of fear will give rise to both avoidance and exploration, while very alarming stimuli will be consistently avoided. One might say that the "biological function" of exploration was, therefore, to reduce the animal's fear of the environment. From an evolutionary point of view there would be advantages in animals approaching and exploring at least some of the situations which arouse fear. Obviously if a stimulus arouses extreme fear or has frequently been associated with pain it will not be explored at all. But if animals always reacted to stimuli which arouse fear in this way, they would never find out anything about their environment, since most novel stimuli also arouse fear. In particular an animal which behaved in this way would never find out which stimuli in the environment were genuinely dangerous and which were harmless, or even advantageous, for it to approach.

There is a certain amount of evidence to support such an idea. For example, Barnett has shown that if novel stimuli are introduced into a familiar keeping cage wild rats show a great deal of fear and prolonged refusal to eat (Barnett, 1958). Yet he reports (Barnett, 1963) that "wild rats ordinarily take cover when disturbed, but if they are placed in a completely unfamiliar enclosure they usually explore before settling in a concealed place. This is not because they have had no previous experience of where cover is to be found: in large cages fitted with nest boxes, the boxes may be visited during the exploration, but the rat is so stimulated by the new surroundings that it emerges again, despite the presence of the experimenter, and resumes its wanderings". Such a reaction in wild rats, which are notorious for their "neophobia" confirms the idea that the function of exploratory behaviour is to reduce the rats' fear of the environment. Further evidence of the same sort is supplied by various experiments in which rats have explored a novel environment in which food was present. The general finding is that, even after they have located the food, the animals explore for some time before they will eat (Majorana, 1950; Chance and Mead, 1955; Zimbardo and Montgomery, 1957). For example, Whiting and Mowrer (1943) say that in a situation of this sort using an elevated maze, the rats showed initial fearfulness followed by a period of great exploratory activity during which they ignored the food, although they were 36 h hungry; only after this did they begin to eat. Once again it seems natural to say that since fear and eating are incompatible, it was necessary for the rats to reduce their fear before they could eat; the adaptive response was therefore to explore, thus reducing fear and making it possible to eat. Berlyne and Walley (reported in Berlyne, 1960, p. 115) found that if rats were given a brief electric shock in an alcove in the course of exploring a maze, they would explore the alcove less than unshocked rats, but they did a greater proportion of their exploration in the first three minutes after the shock. Thus the immediate effect of the shock was to make the rats explore more in the place where they had been shocked. Hudson (1950), in an experiment on one trial avoidance learning, found a similar tendency for rats to explore the stimulus near which they had been shocked. A rather different line of evidence is provided by an experiment by Candland and Campbell (1962). They tested groups of rats of various ages in an open field in which they measured exploratory activity and also defaecation. The ages of the groups of animals at the time of testing varied from 18 to 200 days. At the same time the animals' home cage activity and defaecation were also recorded. They found that these last two measures remained constant for all groups. But both defaecation and activity scores in the open field rose steadily up to 54 days and declined very slightly thereafter; the two graphs were strikingly similar in appearance. If defaecation is accepted as a rough measure of emotionality, it appears that the exploratory activity of rats in an open field and the fear that they experience in the field show an almost perfect correlation over a wide range of different ages. The control measurements in the home cages showed that these changes were specific to the situation and were not the effect of maturation of functions unrelated to exploratory behaviour. Such a close correspondence gives one good reason for suspecting that there is a close relation between the fear that an animal feels of an environment and the amount of exploration that it will do.

The possibility that there may be a relationship between exploratory behaviour and fear has already been investigated by Montgomery and by Baron (Montgomery and Monkman, 1955; Montgomery, 1955; Baron, 1963, 1964). They are agreed that fear inhibits exploratory behaviour. It would not be appropriate to review this evidence now, but there are two reasons why it is not entirely conclusive. In some of the experiments there are good grounds for thinking that the situation was made too aversive. For example, both Montgomery (Montgomery and Monkman, 1955) and Baron (Baron, 1964) gave electric shocks to their rats in the exploratory situation itself; they found that the rats which had been shocked explored less than those which had not. But in this case, not only is it probable that the level of fear resulting from the electric shock was too high to produce exploration, but also, since the rats were exploring at the time that they were shocked, exploratory behaviour was in fact being punished. Other experiments purporting to show the inhibitory effect of fear on exploratory behaviour have used situations in which the rat is in its home cage and is able to venture out into a new environment and explore it (e.g. Montgomery, 1955). Here, the more alarming this new environment the longer it is before the rat begins to explore. This is a very different experimental situation from the more usual one in which all parts of the environment are more or less equally familiar to the rat; in particular the rat can avoid encountering any new or frightening stimuli at all by staying in the home cage. By doing this it can reduce the alarmingness of the environment, which, if I am correct, is the aim of exploration; but clearly this alternative method of achieving the aim will have an important effect and change the nature of the analysis of the situation. That such a view is not far-fetched is evidenced by the quotation from Barnett in which it appears that the two types of situation produce strikingly different results in wild rats. I do not feel therefore that these results need invalidate my hypothesis, at least until the differences between these two situations are better understood.

There are some further results which would appear to go against my proposal. It is widely believed that in the open field there is a negative correlation between activity and defaecation, which I am accepting respectively as indicators of exploration and fear. Hall (1936) found that there was an inverse relationship between the number of days on which an animal defaecated and its average activity during those days. But he reports no negative correlation between activity and defaecation on any one day; and indeed a number of investigators have failed to find any correlation of this sort (Evans and Hunt, 1942; Candland, 1958; Pare, 1964). Candland comments on these results that there appears to be a bivariate population, with some animals which "cower on a single square and deposit a large number of boli, while other animals race around the field and also deposit a large number of boli". This finding is fully in accord with the hypothesis that I have proposed, if it is accepted that some of the rats were too frightened to explore while others were just frightened enough to do so. In any case Hall's results are not a very powerful objection.

Nevertheless, even if it is possible to discount most of the apparently contrary evidence, there is little direct evidence that fear and exploration are linked in the way that I have suggested. The best test of the hypothesis would be to vary independently the novelty and the fear evoking properties of the situation, predicting from this theory that exploratory behaviour should vary with the latter rather than with the former. I have attempted to do this in a number of different situations, and I will briefly report some of the results.

It is generally agreed that an elevated maze is more fear evoking for a rat than an enclosed one; presumably this is because it is a very open situation and rats dislike open spaces. This difference in the capacity to evoke fear should, according to my hypothesis, result in differences in the exploration of the two types of maze. In a number of experiments using both types of maze I have found such differences. In all these experiments the subjects were satiated, naive, female, hooded rats, about 100 days old. Y-mazes were used, with arms 18 in. long and 4 in. wide meeting at 120°; the elevated maze was 18 in. above the floor, the enclosed maze had 6 in. high metal walls and a transparent removable roof. Either maze was used under an enclosure 4 ft × 4 ft × 4 ft 6 in. high, covered with black material and lit by a 60 W bulb on the centre of the roof. The rats' movements were recorded by dividing each of the arms of the maze into two sections by a line on the floor and recording the number and sequence of entries made to these sections during any one trial. It was found that during a single long exploratory trial (30 min) activity declined with time in the maze in each group, and in each case reached a steady low level after about 15 min; the rats also stopped alternating their choice of maze arms after 10–15 min in both mazes. It seems, therefore, that they gave up exploring each type of maze after about the same length of time, which implies that the two mazes did not differ in intrinsic interest. In another experiment twelve rats were given daily 3-min trials in the enclosed maze and twelve in the elevated maze. It was found that the elevated group showed a constant amount of activity from day to day, while activity in the enclosed group declined steeply and significantly over the first three days; there was then a recovery in exploratory activity in this group which remains unexplained (see Fig. 1).The proportion of

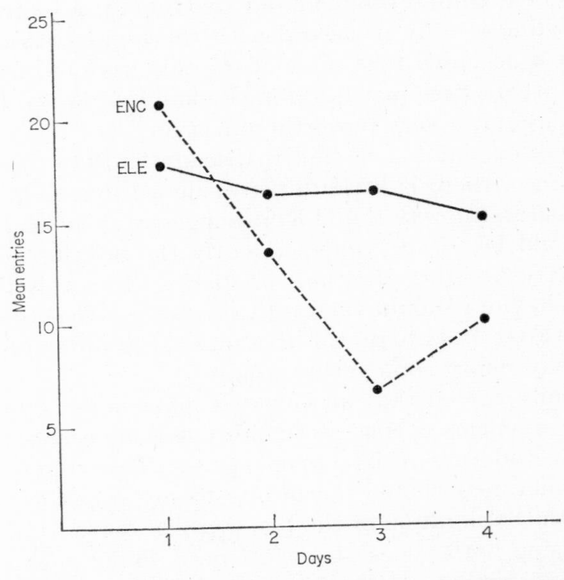

Fig. 1. Mean daily activity in elevated (ELE) and enclosed (ENC) mazes.

animals defaecating in the enclosed maze dropped from 8/12 on the first day to 3/12 on the sixth; while the number of animals defaecating in the elevated maze remained rather constant throughout, never dropping below 8/10; the differences in defaecation between the groups were significant. It thus appears that the enclosed maze lost its capacity to evoke fear as it became increasingly familiar to the rats, while the elevated maze continued to evoke as much fear on the last day of the experiment as it did on the first. Yet by this stage it must have been familiar to the rats, since the enclosed maze, which it has been shown was no more intrinsically interesting, had clearly become familiar. It thus appears that the main difference between the fear evoking properties of the two types of maze is that familiarity with the enclosed one leads to a reduction in its capacity to evoke fear, while familiarity with the elevated maze does not change this capacity; or if it does, it does so only very temporarily. This sort of difference between fear evoking stimuli is familiar in other contexts; the rate at which an alarming stimulus loses its capacity to evoke fear as a result of experience, seems to vary. In some cases a stimulus loses this property very slowly if at all (as with fear of snakes in monkeys or heights in human beings); while in others, although the stimulus may initially be very alarming it soon becomes innocuous. If the elevated and enclosed mazes differ in this way, then, for the first three days at least, the differences in exploratory activity in the two mazes vary with the rats' fear of the situation rather than with its novelty.

In further experiments with elevated and enclosed mazes the interval between two 3-min exposures to the same maze was varied between $\frac{3}{4}$ min and 21 hr 20 min for various groups of animals. One hundred and thirty-three animals were used in the elevated maze and seventy-one in the enclosed one. In this case it was found that $\frac{3}{4}$ min after a single 3-min exposure to either of the mazes the rats were only about 25% as active on the second trial as they had been on the first. As the inter-trial interval grew longer they were increasingly active on the second trial, until with an inter-trial interval of 10 min the animals in the elevated maze were as active on the second trial as they had been on the first; there were further changes in activity with longer delays, but these could be shown to be non-exploratory in nature and need not concern us further here; the results for delay up to 20 min are summarized in Table I. It appears that after a single 3-min trial in the elevated maze, the tendency to explore has completely recovered after as little as 10 min; furthermore this temporary decrement in exploratory activity can be shown to be specific to the particular situation since it does not appear if the two trials are given at a short interval in different environments (Halliday, 1966). Thus it is not the result of the satiation

TABLE I

*Inter-trial delay**

Group	$\frac{3}{4}$ min	2 min	5 min	10 min	20 min
Elevated	−75·3%	−51·6%	−17·7%	+3·2%	+0·25%
Enclosed	−65·6%	—	−45·7%	−17·6%	—

* The scores are the percentage change in activity between first and second trials.

of a "boredom" drive or of an activity drive but is rather a decrement in the tendency to explore the particular stimuli in the environment. Precisely analogous effects are found in the enclosed maze, except that in this case the recovery in exploratory activity is not complete, reaching only about 80% after 10 min. As in the case of daily trials there are therefore important differences in the exploration of the two sorts of maze; and once again they cannot plausibly be explained by supposing that they are due to differences in the novelty of the mazes. The results are, however, easily explicable if it is assumed that it is not the novelty of the maze which determines how much it will explore, but rather its capacity to evoke fear. In this case the recovery in tendency to explore after a single trial could be attributed to recovery from habituation of fear occurring during the first trial. This recovery reaches a different level in the two mazes because in the elevated maze the rats' familiarity with the maze make little difference to the final level to which fear will recover after habituation; while in the enclosed maze the rats' experience of the maze produces a permanent decrement in the maze's capacity to evoke fear and hence exploration.

In other experiments on elevated and enclosed mazes, rats have been given first trials of varying lengths in either type of maze, these were followed after 10 min by a second 3-min trial in the same maze. The same pattern appeared once again; in the elevated maze the length of the first trial had only a small effect on the amount of exploratory activity 10 min later, while in the enclosed maze there were large decrements in exploratory activity on the second trial for the groups which had had long first trials (see Table II). Once again the differences in exploratory activity between the two types of maze are inexplicable in terms of the novelty of the mazes alone, while they are easily accounted for in terms

TABLE II

Group	Length of first trial	% Decrease on second trial*
Elevated	5 min	10·0
	15 min	23·4
	30 min	34·3
Enclosed	5 min	49·0
	15 min	65·7
	30 min	67·5

* The second trial lasted 3 min and the percentage decrease score is derived from comparison with the first 3 min of the first trial in each case.

of my hypothesis. The interpretation of these results may appear highly speculative, but an explanation somewhat along these lines is forced on us by the facts. Exploration in elevated and enclosed mazes differs in certain systematic ways; these differences cannot be explained in terms of differential novelty or familiarity alone, some other motivational factor seems to be required which can vary independently of the information that the animal has about the maze. There is good reason to think that fear of the maze varies appropriately in the two types of maze. It is not, therefore, a long step to suppose that fear of the environment does act as the motivation controlling the exploratory behaviour in these experiments.

The hypothesis that I have proposed could also be tested, not by varying the fear evoking properties of the maze, but by comparing the behaviour of differentially fearful rats in exploratory situations. Strains of rats which differ in "emotionality" have been bred (Broadhurst, 1960) and it is also possible to produce differences in emotional reactivity by differential treatment in infancy (Levine, 1962). It has been found that rats stimulated in infancy are less emotional, by a number of measures, than unstimulated ones; they are also more active in exploratory situations (e.g. Denenberg and Morton, 1962). This would appear to go against my hypothesis, but in the experiments so far reported the only measure of exploration has been the amount of activity; it is therefore possible that the differences arise from differences in general activity level, unrelated to exploratory tendencies, and that if the tendency to explore was to be measured in some other way the relationship would be reversed and the unstimulated (emotional) animals be found to be the more exploratory. I have carried out some pilot studies on these lines with positive results. The rats were bred under controlled conditions and were completely undisturbed for the first 3 weeks of life; the only difference between the stimulated and unstimulated animals was that the former were removed from the cage each day for these 3 weeks and gently handled for about half a minute each. They were all weaned at 21 days and after that were handled only twice, for the purpose of changing cages, until the time they were tested at around 100 days. At this time it was found that the stimulated rats were far more active in an open field than the unstimulated ones. This difference persisted over as many as thirty daily trials. But when home cage activity was measured (by means of a phototransistor and a beam of infrared light crossing the cage) it was found that there was an equally large activity difference in the home cages. The differences in activity found in the open field probably do not, therefore, represent real differences in the tendency to explore. In a further experiment sixteen female rats, eight stimulated and eight unstimulated, explored an enclosed Y-maze on 5 days, for 5 min per day. The maze had arms 2 ft long and 4 in. wide; two of the arms were painted grey and the third was covered with vertical black and white stripes. The stimulated animals were once again consistently more active than the unstimulated ones, but, while the stimulated animals never showed a significant preference for the striped arm of the maze, the unstimulated animals showed such a significant preference on 3 of the 5 days of the experiment; and on days 2 and 3 they preferred it significantly more than the stimulated rats. Here again, therefore, there is some evidence in favour of the idea that a rat will explore according to the level of fear aroused by the environment.

Another experiment furnished a rather direct test of my hypothesis. In this experiment four groups of rats explored a Y-maze for 5 min per day over 6 days. As in the last experiment, two arms of this maze were painted grey and the third was striped. Between the 3rd and 4th days of the experiment, the rats in group 1 ($n = 16$) were given two 15-sec electric shocks* in a box with striped walls. The rats in group 2 ($n = 16$) were given two shocks in a similar box with plain wood walls; those in group 3 ($n = 8$) were placed in a striped box but given no shock, while the rats in group 4 ($n = 8$) were placed in the plain box without shock. Since the scores of these last two groups did not differ in any significant way, the results have been combined for simplicity of presentation. The prediction from my hypothesis is that in group 1 the association of shock and stripes should increase the capacity of the striped arm of the maze to evoke fear. This, in turn, should lead group 1 to explore this arm more than other groups on the days following the shock. The results on the whole confirmed this prediction. On the day following shock, group 1 showed no special preference for the striped arm, but on the 5th and 6th days the animals in group 1 had a highly significant preference for this arm as compared with the other groups (see Fig. 2). This preference cannot have been the result of shock alone, since in this case it should have appeared in group 2 as well; nor could it be the result of experience of a striped environment outside the maze, since in this case the preference should have appeared in group 3. It appears that this result cannot easily be explained except by supposing, as my hypothesis requires, that rats will explore stimuli because they are fear-evoking rather than because they are novel.

The experimental results reported here are, of course, in no sense conclusive evidence for the hypothesis that has been proposed. Nevertheless, they do show, in various types of experimental situation, that

* 175 V d.c. with a resistance of 200 kΩ in series with the rat.

locomotor exploration in rats is not determined simply by the novelty or familiarity of the stimuli in the environment, as has commonly been supposed. The results also suggest that fear of the environment can, in some circumstances at least, increase the rats' tendency to explore.

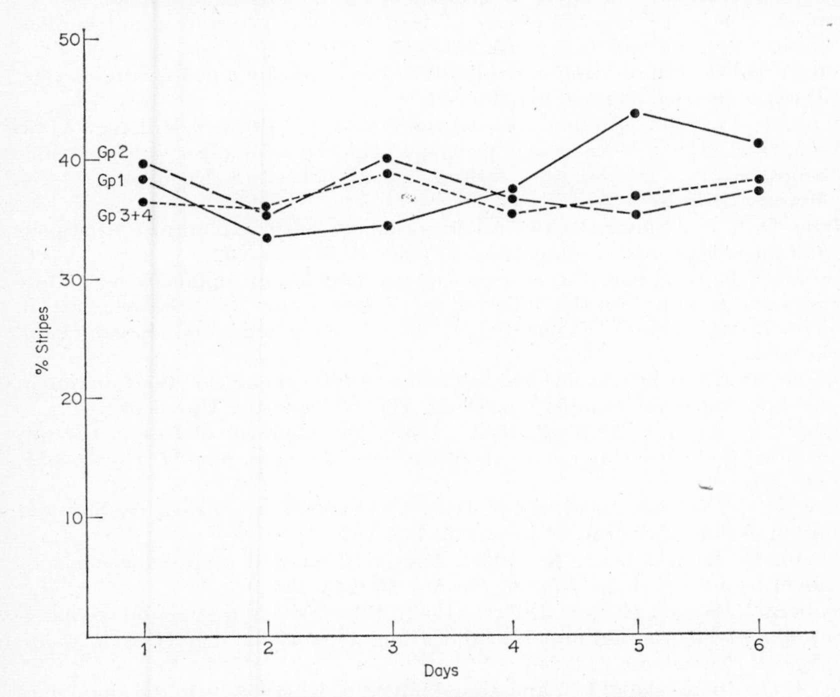

FIG. 2. Percentage activity in striped arm of Y-maze.

I have argued that the idea that fear of the environment motivates exploratory behaviour cannot be rejected on theoretical grounds, nor is there any conclusive experimental evidence against it. There are, therefore, good reasons for taking seriously the suggestion that at least one of the reasons that rats explore is because the stimuli that elicit exploration evoke fear.

ACKNOWLEDGEMENTS

The experimental work reported in this paper was carried out at the Laboratory of Experimental Psychology, Cambridge, and was supported by a Training in Research grant from the Medical Research Council. I am most grateful to Mr. A. J. Watson for his help and advice in carrying out this research.

References

Barnett, S. A. (1958). Experiments on "neophobia" in wild and laboratory rats. *Br. J. Psychol.* **49**, 195–201.

Barnett, S. A. (1963). "A Study of Behaviour", p. 26. Methuen, London.

Baron, A. (1963). Differential effects of fear on activity in novel and familiar environments. *Psychol. Rep.* **13**, 251–257.

Baron, A. (1964). Suppression of exploratory behaviour by aversive stimulation. *J. comp. physiol. Psychol.* **57**, 299–301.

Berlyne, D. E. (1960). "Conflict, Arousal and Curiosity." McGraw-Hill, New York.

Berlyne, D. E. (1963). Motivational problems raised by exploratory and epistemic behaviour. *In* "Psychology—A Study of a Science" (S. Koch, ed.), Vol. 5. McGraw-Hill, New York.

Berlyne, D. E. and Slater, J. (1957). Perceptual curiosity, exploratory behaviour and maze learning. *J. comp. physiol. Psychol.* **50**, 228–232.

Broadhurst, P. L. (1960). Experiments in psychogenetics: applications of biometrical genetics to the inheritance of behaviour. *In* "Experiments in Personality" (H. J. Eysenck, ed), Vol. 1. Routledge and Kegan Paul, London.

Candland, D. K. (1958). 'Emotional behaviour' in the 'open field' as a function of age and traumatic stimulation. Ph.D. Thesis, Princeton University.

Candland, D. K. and Campbell, B. A. (1962). Development of fear in the rat, as measured by behaviour in the open field. *J. comp. physiol. Psychol.* **55**, 593–596.

Chance, M. R. A. and Mead, A. P. (1955). Competition between feeding and investigation in the rat. *Behaviour* **8**, 174–182.

Chapman, R. M. and Levy, N. (1957). Hunger drive and reinforcing effect of novel stimuli. *J. comp. physiol. Psychol.* **50**, 233–238.

Denenberg, V. H. and Morton, J. R. C. (1962). Effects of environmental complexity and social groupings upon modification of emotional behaviour. *J. comp. physiol. Psychol.* **55**, 242–246.

Dolin, A. O., Zborovskaia, I. I. and Zamakhover, S. K. (1958). (On the characteristics of the role of the orienting-investigatory reflex in conditional-reflex activity). *In* "Orientirovochny refleks i orientirovochno-issle dovatelskaia deiatelnost" (L. G. Voronin *et al.*, eds.). Acad. Pedag. Sci., Moscow. (Reported in Berlyne, 1960).

Evans, J. T. and Hunt, J. McV. (1942). The 'emotionality' of rats. *Am. J. Psychol.* **55**, 528–545.

Fowler, H. (1963). "Curiosity and Exploratory Behaviour." Macmillan, New York.

Glanzer, M. (1953). The role of stimulus satiation in spontaneous alternation. *J. exp. Psychol.* **45**, 387–393.

Hall, C. S. (1934). Emotional behaviour in the rat. I. Defecation and urination as measures of individual differences in emotionality. *J. comp. Psychol.* **18**, 385–403.

Hall, C. S. (1936). Emotional behaviour in the rat. III. The relationship between emotionality and ambulatory activity. *J. comp. Psychol.* **22**, 345–352.

Halliday, M. S. (1966). The effect of previous exploratory activity on the exploration of a simple maze. *Nature, Lond.* **209**, 432–433.

Hebb, D. O. (1946). On the nature of fear. *Psychol. Rev.* **53**, 259–276.

Hudson, B. B. (1950). One trial learning in the domestic rat. *Genet. Psychol. Monogr.* **41**, 99–145.
Levine, S. (1962). The effects of infantile experience on adult behaviour. *In* "Foundations of Clinical Psychology" (A. J. Bachrach, ed.). Basic Books Inc., New York.
Majorana, A. (1950). Richerche sull'apprendimento dei ratti in labirinto sul comportamento investigativo dei ratti. *Riv. Psicol.* **46** (4), 1–19.
Melzack, R. (1952). Irrational fear in the dog. *Can. J. Psychol.* **6**, 141–147.
Montgomery, K. C. (1954). The role of the exploratory drive in learning. *J. comp. physiol. Psychol.* **47**, 60–64.
Montgomery, K. C. (1955). The relation between fear induced by novel stimulation and exploratory behaviour. *J. comp. physiol. Psychol.* **48**, 254–260.
Montgomery, K. C. and Monkman, J. A. (1955). The relation between fear and exploratory behaviour. *J. comp. physiol. Psychol.* **48**, 132–136.
Montgomery, K. C. and Segall, M. (1955). Discrimination learning based upon the exploratory drive. *J. comp. physiol. Psychol.* **48**, 225–228.
Pare, W. P. (1964). Relationship of behaviours in the open field test of emotionality. *Psychol. Rep.* **14**, 19–22.
Schneider, G. E. and Gross, C. G. (1964). Curiosity in the hamster. *J. comp. physiol. Psychol.* **59**, 150–152.
Stretch, R. G. A. (1960). An experimental analysis of perceptual curiosity and exploratory behaviour in the rat. Ph.D. Thesis, University of Sheffield.
Sutherland, N. S. (1957). Spontaneous alternation and stimulus avoidance. *J. comp. physiol. Psychol.* **50**, 358–362.
Watson, A. J. (1961). The place of reinforcement in the explanation of behaviour. *In* "Current Problems in Animal Behaviour" (W. H. Thorpe and O. L. Zangwill, eds.). Cambridge University Press.
Welker, W. I. (1961). An analysis of exploratory and play behaviour in animals. *In* "Functions of Varied Experience" (D. W. Fiske and S. R. Maddi, eds.). Dorsey Press, Homewood, Illinois.
Whiting, J. W. M. and Mowrer, O. H. (1943). Habit progression and regression—a laboratory study of some factors relevant to human socialization. *J. comp. physiol. Psychol.* **36**, 229–253.
Yoshioka, J. G. (1932). Learning versus skill in rats. *J. genet. Psychol.* **41**, 406–416.
Zimbardo, P. G. and Montgomery, K. C. (1957). The relative strength of consummatory responses in hunger, thirst and exploratory drive. *J. comp. physiol. Psychol.* **50**, 504–508.

Symp. zool. Soc. Lond. (1966) No. 18, 61–81.

EXPLORATION AND PLAY IN CHILDREN

CORINNE HUTT

Park Hospital for Children, Oxford, England

SYNOPSIS

Exploration and play are concepts often used synonymously. Exploration itself is seen to be at least two different classes of behaviour, viz. specific exploration and diversive exploration. Discrepancies in the literature are shown to be due to a failure to make this distinction. It is suggested that play may be similar to the latter but contrasts with the former. A study of exploratory behaviour in 3–5-year-old nursery school children is reported. The primary aim of the study was the investigation of exploratory activity elicited by a novel object and the habituation of this activity with repeated exposure. The results also threw some light on the determinants and genesis of "play" activities. Auditory feedback was found to be more potent than visual feedback in eliciting and maintaining "play" responses. It was thus possible to distinguish investigative or specific exploration from play on several grounds. By reference to the probable ontogenetic course of these behaviours, an explanation is offered for the traditional view of them as synonymous activities. It is not fruitful to label behaviours as "playful" simply because they are performed by young and immature animals.

INTRODUCTION

Exploration and play are often regarded as one class of behaviour. Welker (1956a, b) in describing some determinants of exploration and play in chimpanzees, as well as the variability manifested in these behaviours, treats them as indistinguishable. More recently (1961) he has acknowledged this more explicitly: "the term play is often used in conjunction with, or in place of, the term exploration. In other instances play is used as the generic term, exploration being only one type of play". On the grounds that a distinction between play and exploration is not always ready-made, he justifies a perfunctory attempt to define these behaviours. Hayes (1958) in studying the maintenance of play activities in children, included games with marbles as well as visual exploration of pictures. Thorpe (1963), too, implicitly assumes the equivalence of exploration and play; he states that where appetitive behaviour and consummatory behaviour are not too strictly tied, we may begin to get general exploration of the environment which often takes the form of play, and he sees learning deriving from this process of play or exploration. Berlyne (1960) has discussed the perceptual and intellectual activities which are engaged in for their own sake, and calls them comprehensively "ludic behaviour", defining this category as "any behaviour that does not have a biological function that we can clearly recognize".

At the same time, it is clear that these authors are aware of this conceptual confusion and of the need for clarification and distinction. Thorpe says "there are various possible explanations for behaviour which can be described as play, and it would be a mistake to think that at present they can all be brought together in one category". Berlyne states "ludic behaviour forms such a motley assortment that it is highly unlikely that all of it has just one function . . . so far it is mainly our ignorance that binds them all together". But in general theories of exploration have subsumed play and theories of play have failed to take cognisance of exploratory activities. Since these two classes of behaviour are likely to differ in terms of their determinants, morphology and function, we might consider briefly the empirical data and theoretical arguments concerning them.

EXPLORATION

Most definitions of exploratory behaviour have tended to be over-inclusive: exploratory behaviour is defined as "any behaviour which tends to increase the rate of change in the stimulation falling on the animal's receptors which is not impelled by homeostatic or reproductive need" (Barnett, 1963), or "those responses that alter the stimulus field" (Berlyne, 1960). These are hardly operationally useful definitions, but attempts have been made to classify these behaviours more precisely in terms of the receptors involved, e.g. orienting, locomotor, and investigatory responses (Berlyne, 1960; Hayes, 1960; Welker, 1961). Whatever the measure of behaviour used it is generally accepted that novel situations and objects elicit exploratory behaviour (Berlyne, 1950; Montgomery, 1953; Carr and Brown, 1959a), that this responsiveness shows a decrement with continued exposure (Adlerstein and Fehrer, 1955; Inhelder, 1955; Welker, 1956b; Glanzer, 1961), and a recovery after a period of non-exposure (Montgomery, 1951; Berlyne, 1955). This habituation of exploratory behaviour has been interpreted in terms of Hullian principles of reactive and conditioned inhibition by Berlyne (1950); in terms of the Pavlovian theory of inhibition by Danziger and Mainland (1954); in terms of stimulus satiation by Glanzer (1958); and in terms of the weakening of the exploratory drive elicited by novel stimuli by Montgomery (1953). This type of behaviour directed at particular features of the environment and showing the properties mentioned above, has been termed *specific exploration* by Berlyne (1960).

On the other hand, workers from the Wisconsin Laboratory have shown that visual exploration persists in the monkey over a long period of time (Butler and Harlow, 1954) and shows a non-decremental steady pattern from day to day (Butler and Alexander, 1955). Similar results were reported for manipulatory investigation by Harlow *et al.* (1956), and Carr and Brown (1959b). At first sight, these two sets of results appear contradictory, and Harlow's (1956) conclusion that "manipulatory behaviour is self-sustaining", adds little to the description of the behaviour. If, however, one examines the conditions under which the animal is reported as showing a maintenance or increase in exploratory activity with time, these are in general those we would describe as sensorily depriving or at least unstimulating; typically, small bare cages were used. The animal was therefore deprived of the opportunity of alternative activities other than those directed towards himself or to the predetermined stimulus objects. Under these conditions, the animal strives to vary sensory input: rats press a lever for no other "reward" than microswitch clicks and relay noises (Kish and Antonitis, 1956); monkeys bar press for a change in brightness (Moon and Lodahl, 1956), or show increasing manipulation and chewing of a door which is the only variable object in its restricted environment (Symmes, 1959); children in an empty room engage in bodily manipulations and gestural patterns (Hutt *et al.*, 1965); adults in sensory deprivation experiments talk and whistle to themselves (Bexton *et al.*, 1954). Moreover, since we are usually told *how much* of an activity is performed, and not *in what manner*, the interpretation of the behaviours in restricted environments as specific types of exploration needs to be questioned. For example, in the Butler and Harlow study the monkey was said to be visually exploring when the trap door was held open for relatively long periods of time. Symmes, however, reports that in a similar situation, the monkeys "very commonly sat near the door holding it open with one hand, and moving it against the spring resistance, and only occasionally turning to look through the opening". The animals continued to do this even if there was complete darkness outside the door. Such efforts to vary stimulation are similar in effect to, and differ only in complexity from, human recreational and entertainment activities. It is this behaviour that Berlyne (1960) terms *diversive exploration*, to distinguish it from specific exploration.

PLAY

The term "play" covers a heterogeneous assortment of activities from the darts and gambols of young birds and mammals to the extremely ritualized games of adult humans. In his review, Beach (1945) lists five characteristics of play, only three of which are relevant to its definition. These are: (1) that it carries an emotional element of pleasure; (2) that it is characteristic of the immature animal rather than the adult; (3) that it differs from non-playful responses in having no relatively immediate biological result.

The first characteristic has clearly impressed many authors: Bally (1945) refers to play as appetitive activity in a "relaxed field" ("im entspannten Feld"), Bertalanffy (1960) as activities which are accompanied by "functional pleasure", Meyer-Holzapfel (1956) as activities which are characterized by the "disinterested" atmosphere concerning the consummatory act, and Lorenz (1956) comments that "the usual opposition between play and being serious has a very real background". Although, as Beach points out, systematic studies of play activities and the environmental factors that elicit them are lacking, theories to explain the occurrence and function of this behaviour in young mammals have always been forthcoming.

Perhaps the earliest of them is that of Spencer in 1855, who regarded play as an outlet for surplus energy. In 1891 Stanley Hall, influenced by evolutionary principles and Haeckel's biogenetic law, stated that the play of children passed through a series of stages comparable to those appearing in the evolution of the social group (see Rogerson, 1939). Hall (1904) stated "I regard play as the motor habits and spirit of the past of the race, persisting in the present, as rudimentary functions sometimes of and always akin to rudimentary organs. The best index and guide to the stated activities of adults in past ages is found in the instinctive, untaught, and non-imitative plays of children . . .". Groos (1898, 1901) regarded play activities as incomplete in themselves, i.e. lacking a consummatory act, but as a rehearsal of patterns which would be of future biological significance. McDougall (1931) questioned Groos's assumption of an instinct to play, and disputed the notion that motor patterns associated with specific instincts were being exercised. He argued that play was non-purposive and involved the expenditure of surplus neural energy. Schlosberg (1947) has argued that play can more parsimoniously be conceptualized in S–R terms, that is as responses initially readily elicited by certain stimulus configurations, but which gradually acquire more specificity by differential reinforcement. Thomae (1956) has formulated the hypothesis that inner, organismally determined behaviour has periodicity or rhythm whereas outer, environmentally determined behaviour is aperiodic and sporadic, an hypothesis that underlies the studies of children's play by Lehr, Erfmann, and Schapitz; from Lehr's work it is concluded that with maturation the focus of young children's play shifts from movement periodicity, through object and location periodicity, to "activity level" periodicity. Brownlee (1954) has reiterated the postulate of a play drive and Haldane (1956) has suggested that games or play may result in the loss of negative entropy.

The category of play commonly includes bodily activities, activities involving inanimate objects (investigation or games), animate objects (social play), and competitive sports. When to this heterogeneous category is added yet another, such as exploration (which in turn includes topographical, object and social exploration), there seems little likelihood of arriving at general principles governing the nature, occurrence and function of these behaviours. It seems essential therefore that we attempt a more precise conceptualization and inquiry of these behaviours.

The study to be described here, although primarily designed to investigate specific exploration in children, does throw some light on those behaviours customarily called play.

EXPERIMENT

The main aim of the experiment was the study of curiosity or exploratory behaviour elicited in young children by the presentation of a novel object, and the habituation of this behaviour with time. Since we were concerned with the attraction of novelty to the child, rather than a forced responsiveness, it was decided to allow it alternative choices. These consisted of five familiar toys.

Subjects

The subjects were all nursery school children between the ages of 3 and 5 years. They were seen in a small room in the school which was relatively familiar to them. The furniture was stacked against one wall, leaving most of the floor area free for the child to move around in. Altogether thirty nursery school children were studied under the conditions to be described. Five children of friends were also seen in a playroom specially constructed to enable film records to be made (Lee and Hutt, 1964).

Apparatus

The novel object was designed to allow for the assessment of both novelty and complexity variables, although the latter was not parametrically varied. The object consisted of a red metal rectangular box on four brass legs (Fig. 1). On the top was mounted a lever at the end

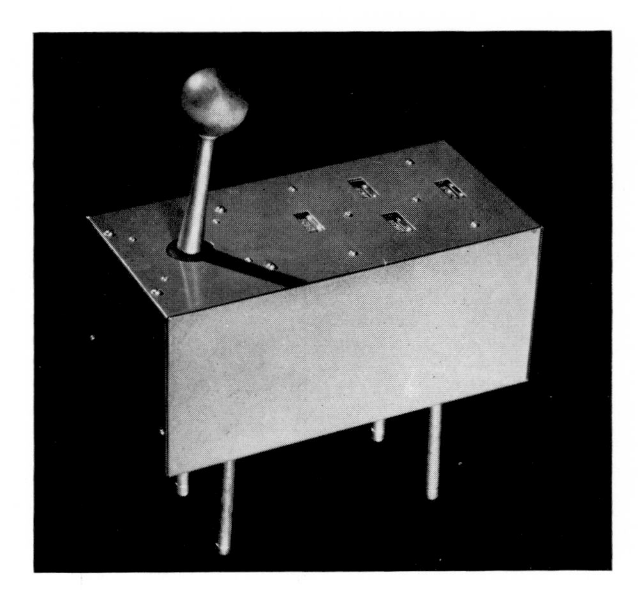

FIG. 1. The novel object: a red metal box on four brass "legs" and a lever ending in a blue wooden ball. The directional manipulations of the lever are registered on four counters which could be left open as here, or covered up.

of which was a blue wooden ball. The four directional movements of the lever were registered by four Post Office counters which could be made visible to the child. It was also possible to allow the child differential auditory feedback contingent upon specific manipulatory movements (a bell in one of the horizontal directions and a buzzer in one of the vertical). Four conditions of relatively increasing complexity were thus available:

(i) No sound or vision: the bell and buzzer switched off and the counters covered up.
(ii) Vision only: noises off, but counters visible.
(iii) Sound only: bell and buzzer on, but counters covered.
(iv) Sound and vision: noises on and counters visible.

Procedure

The six experimental sessions were preceded by two pre-exposure sessions which additionally served to familiarize the child with the room and the five toys. These pre-exposure sessions were procedurally identical to the experimental sessions, except for the presence of the novel object. All sessions were of 10 min duration. An experimental design was used that ensured that the week-ends were equally distributed over the experimental sessions under each condition. The experimental sessions were otherwise 48 h apart. In the nursery school observations were entered in check-lists, an entry being made every 10 sec by the observer who sat in a corner of the room. The child was asked if he would like to play for a few minutes while the observer finished off some work. Further details were recorded at the end of each session. The four children seen in the film unit were left to play by themselves, but knew the observer was in the adjoining room. The counters on the object were read at the end of each session.

RESULTS

In general, when the children entered the room they looked at the novel object immediately, or approached it, often asking the observer what it was. They would then examine the object manually or inspect it visually while holding the lever, and finally engage in active manipulation of the lever.

The amounts of time spent exploring the object under conditions (i) and (ii) are shown in Fig. 2. There is a progressive decrement of exploratory activity with repeated exposure. If the counter readings are used as a measure of investigatory manipulation, a similar trend is seen under both these conditions (Fig. 3).

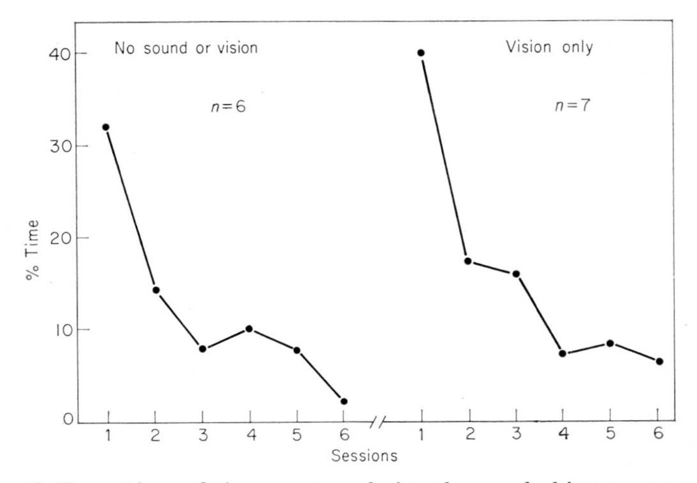

FIG. 2. Proportions of time spent exploring the novel object on successive trials under (i) no sound or vision, and (ii) vision only, conditions. n = Number of subjects.

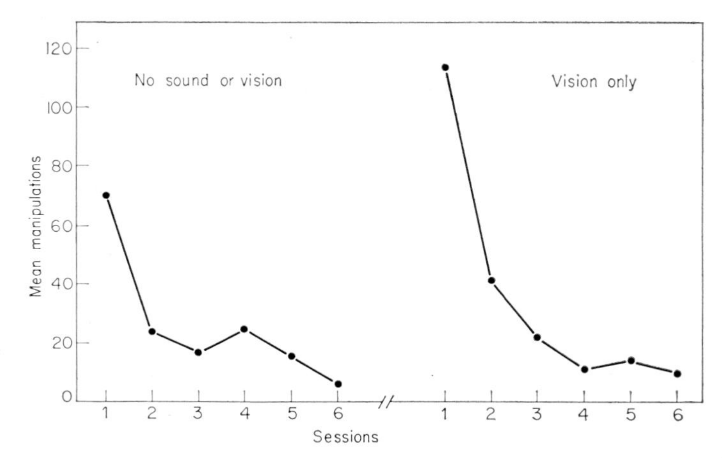

FIG. 3. Mean amounts of manipulatory exploration under (i) no sound or vision, and (ii) vision only, conditions.

These decay curves, whether of time or manipulatory activity, are exponential functions of time, and if a Naperian logarithm transformation of the number of manipulations is used to plot manipulations against trials, the two lines of best fit are seen to have different slopes (Fig. 4). The regressions of manipulations on trials are significant under

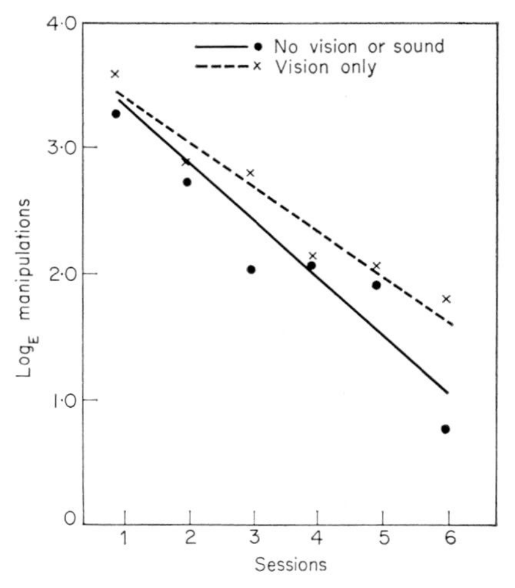

FIG. 4. Linear regressions of manipulations on trials under (i) no sound or vision, and (ii) vision only, conditions, when a Naperian logarithmic transformation of manipulations is used.

both conditions (i) (variance ratio = 11·5, d.f. = 4, $P < 0{\cdot}05$), and (ii) (variance ratio = 27·56, d.f. = 4, $P < 0{\cdot}01$). Thus, addition of the visual feedback slightly decreased the rate of habituation to the novel object. The initial amount of exploration was greater with the visual incentive, than with no such incentive.

Under both conditions (iii) and (iv) the object was increasingly manipulated, and only after the fifth exposure was there a decrease in this responsiveness (Fig. 5). It appeared that simply making noise

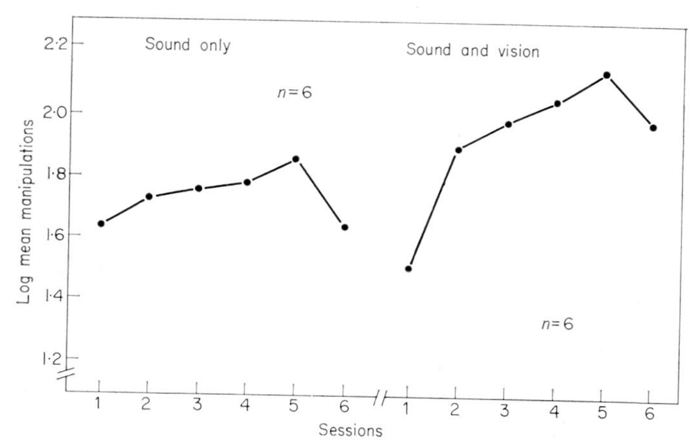

FIG. 5. Manipulatory exploration of the novel object on successive trials under (iii) sound only, and (iv) sound and vision, conditions. n = Number of subjects.

contingent upon certain manipulatory responses completely altered the temporal pattern of activity towards the object. Addition of the visual to the auditory feedback only served to enhance this pattern.

Analysis of activities

It was clear that under conditions (iii) and (iv) the nature of activities engaged in changed markedly over the six sessions. Investigative responses gave way to other behaviours, and it was decided to separate the time spent investigating the object from other activities involving it. Investigative responses were those responses that involved visual inspection, and feeling, touching or other manipulations accompanied by visual inspection. These had in common the characteristic of "learning the properties" of the object. Whereas under the two no-sound conditions nearly all the activity directed towards the object was of this kind, this was not so under the sound conditions. The time spent in investigatory responses decreased progressively from session 1 to 6 under both conditions (iii) and (iv) (Fig. 6); Grant's analysis of variance (1956) involving the use of orthogonal polynomials indicates that the linear components of these trends are significant ($F = 557{\cdot}5/31{\cdot}24$, d.f. = 1 and 30, $P < 0{\cdot}001$; $F = 1457/94{\cdot}5$, d.f. = 1 and 30, $P < 0{\cdot}001$ respectively).

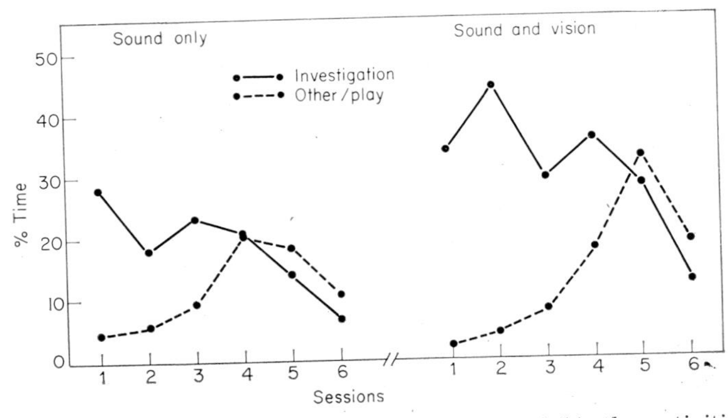

FIG. 6. Proportions of time spent in (a) investigating and (b) other activities involving the novel object under conditions (iii) and (iv).

As investigation of the object decreased other activities involving it increased. When analysed these consisted of repetitive motor movements, manipulations of long duration accompanied by visual inspection of other objects, and a sequence of activities incorporating both the novel object and other toys—in other words a "game". Examples of these were respectively: patting the lever repeatedly, leaning on the lever making the bell ring continuously while looking around the room, and running round with the truck ringing the bell each time the object was passed. There is another group of responses which can be termed "transposition-of-function"—those responses which resulted in the object explicitly fulfilling another function, e.g. something to climb, a bridge, or a seat. All these activities (i.e. repetitive movements, "games" and "transposition-of-function" responses) are those which an observer would recognize and label as *play*. They occurred hardly at all under the no-sound conditions, and when they did they were entirely of the "transposition-of-function" kind. By the sixth session, however, even "play activities" directed towards the object decreased and it seems likely that these responses are a quadratic function of time, though more results are required to demonstrate this.

In all children, once active investigation had commenced, it generally proceeded vigorously, all aspects of the object being explored. It was only once the child had apparently learned all there was to know about the object that it was incorporated in play activities, and any further learning was purely incidental. In fact one boy who started a "game" after a relatively brief period of investigation failed to find the buzzer. However, if during play a new property or aspect of the object was chanced upon, a further spell of investigation would follow.

The transition from investigative exploration to playful activities was marked by certain features: during investigation all receptors were oriented towards the object, the general expression being one of "concentration" (see Fig. 7); at a later stage (intermediate between investigation and play), manipulation might occur with simultaneous visual exploration of other stimuli, and the intent facial expression changed to a more relaxed one. Finally in play for much of the time, the receptors were desynchronized (i.e. vision and manipulation were no longer simultaneously directed towards the object) and the behaviour towards the object might almost be described as "nonchalant" (see Fig. 8).

The relative amounts of time spent on other activities from session to session are shown in Figs. 9 and 10. Under the no-sound conditions gestures increased with continued exposure to the same situation; this was probably a reflection of the child's boredom, particularly as yawning and stretching figured prominently in the latter sessions. That the situation had become less attractive under these conditions was indicated by two children who showed some reluctance to being exposed to it for the fifth or sixth time. Under the sound conditions, however, locomotion progressively increased over the sessions; presumably once the children had started moving about as they did when playing a game, they continued to do so, even when they had tired of the object. On the whole, orienting responses towards the adult were most frequent in the first and last experimental sessions, i.e. at the initial presentation of the novel object, and when the child had become more or less tired of the situation. In the first case the adult provided assurance, in the second the possibility of further stimulation when other objects had lost their attraction.

Pattern of approach

There was a marked difference in the pattern of initial approach towards the object between the nursery school children and the children seen in the film unit. The presence of the adult in the room appeared to make the nursery school children more adventurous and

FIG. 7A

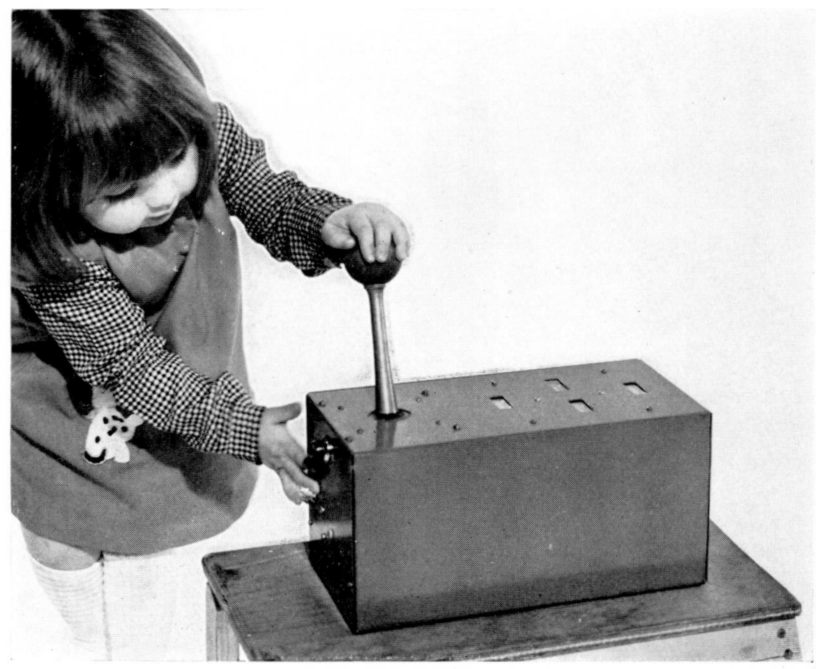

FIG. 7B

FIG. 7C

FIG. 7, A–C. Characteristic patterns of exploration. Note synchrony of visual and manual receptors, and "intent" facial expressions and postures.

less apprehensive of novelty; they approached and investigated the object readily. The latency of approach for the two groups of children is given below.

School (adult present)	Film unit (no adult)
30·0 sec	108·0 sec

The children who were by themselves showed more neophobia and even when they did approach the object their early responses were tentative. All of them also first approached the object with a familiar toy—the boys with the truck and the girls with the panda.

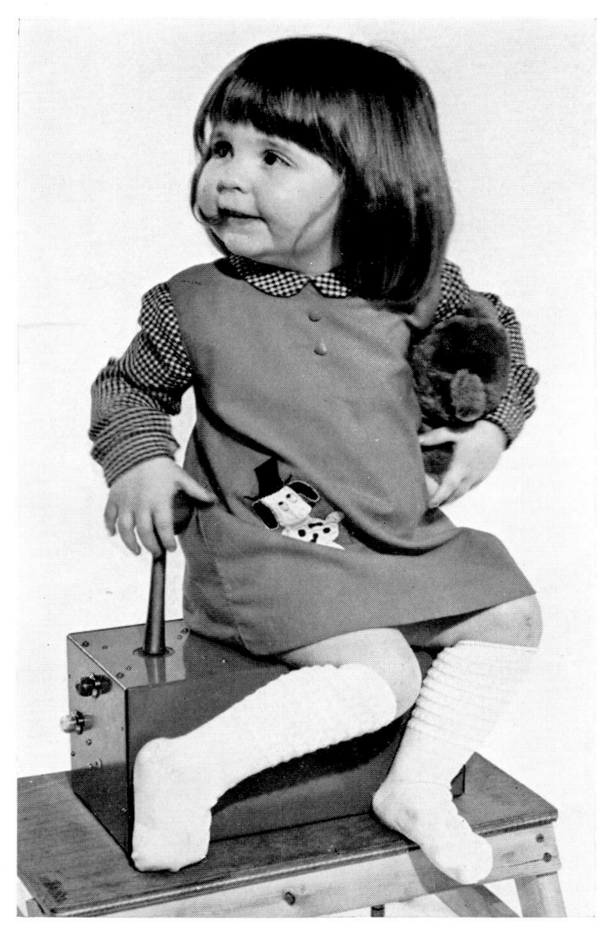

FIG. 8. The characteristic pattern of play: in this case of the "transposition-of-function" kind. Note desynchrony of different receptors: child looks around the room while sitting on the object, holding the lever, and cuddling another toy.

Non-explorers

The children discussed so far are those who sooner or later engaged in active exploration of the novel object. There was another subgroup of children who might be termed "non-explorers". There were five such children under these conditions, and three in another part of the study using other conditions (Hutt and Level, in preparation). These children appeared distinctly inhibited: they moved about hardly at all, watched the adult and smiled at her for a good deal of the

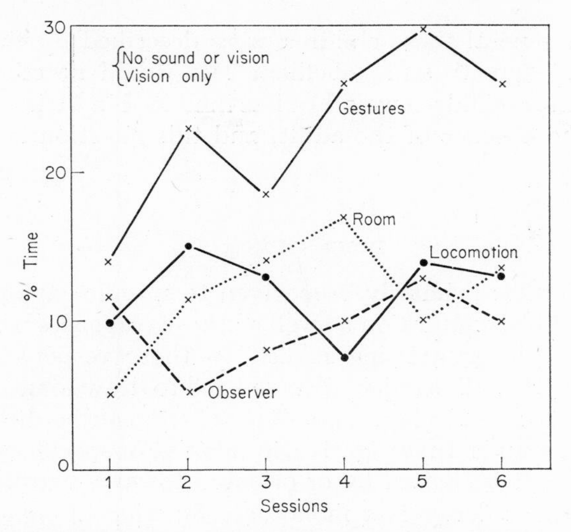

Fig. 9. Proportions of time spent gesturing, exploring the room, looking at the observer, and in locomotion, from session to session under conditions (i) and (ii).

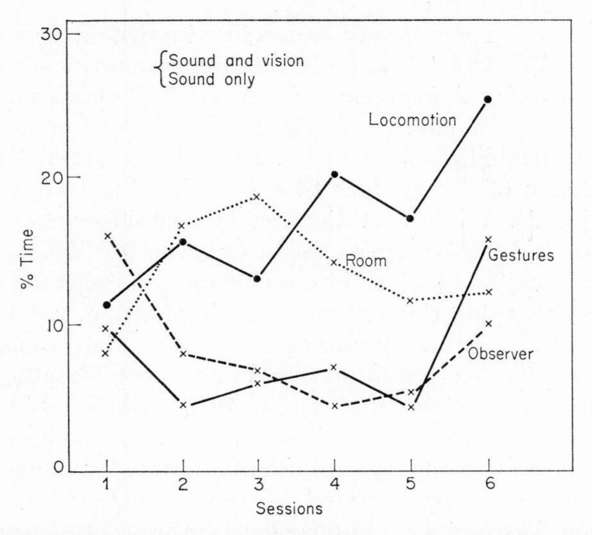

Fig. 10. Proportions of time spent gesturing, exploring the room, looking at the observer, and in locomotion, from session to session under conditions (iii) and (iv).

time, and often engaged in stereotyped activities like twining a piece of string round their fingers. When they did make any approaches to the object, these were of a tentative nature, and hardly ever led to active exploration. In general these children were described by other adults in the school as "good" and "obedient". It would be of interest to know whether these children would be less inhibited in their exploratory behaviour in the absence of the adult, and this question is shortly to be investigated.

DISCUSSION

Consideration has primarily been given to specific exploration of a novel object and its habituation as well as those responses which might be termed play. By restricting myself to those responses directed towards the same stimulus object, I have tried to draw some distinction between exploration and play. These behaviours can be differentiated on a number of grounds. Investigative, inquisitive or specific exploration is directional, i.e. it is elicited by or oriented towards certain environmental changes. Its decay is a monotonic function of time, and any overall response measure would mask this. The goal is "getting to know the properties", and the particular responses of investigation are determined by the nature of the object.

Play, on the other hand, only occurs in a known environment, and when the animal or child feels he knows the properties of the object in that environment; this is apparent in the gradual relaxation of mood, evidenced not only by changes in facial expression, but in a greater diversity and variability of activities. In play the emphasis changes from the question of "what does this *object* do?" to "what can *I* do with this object?". While investigation is stimulus-referent, play is response-referent. In this respect an observation of Mead's (1956) is pertinent: "you will find with children who are spinning a top or bouncing a ball that stopping the action is the deprivation, not taking the ball away". Again, while investigative exploration demonstrably results in the acquisition of information, in play such learning is largely incidental (see also Jackson and Todd, 1946). Haldane's hypothesis quoted earlier thus seems a valid one. Indeed, by being repetitive, play is by definition a highly redundant activity, and can actually prevent learning as was illustrated by one of our subjects. Schiller (1957) too describes how his chimpanzee Don failed to learn to use a stick to solve a problem because he was preoccupied with the play activity of "weaving".

It is of interest then to enquire why play has traditionally been regarded as an exploratory activity. In infancy and early development most of the animal's environment is novel, and it has also an inadequate memory store against which to match new objects; thus, much of its behaviour is likely to be investigatory. Harlow (1953) is less equivocal about this in his observations of a young child: "Perhaps the most striking characteristic of this particular primate has been the power and persistence of her curiosity-investigatory motives". At the same time, many of the young animal's responses are of a repetitive nature—a pattern which commonly characterizes play (see, for example, primary, secondary and tertiary circular reactions described by Piaget, 1953). Thus, in infancy it is perhaps difficult to distinguish between investigatory responses and play responses. During ontogeny, however, these two activities diverge, and become more easily separable, until in the adult there is a sharp distinction between investigatory activities on the one hand, and play activities on the other, which are often of an extremely ritualized kind. There may indeed be many instances where both features of exploration and play are present, but these should not prevent us from attempting to make the distinction. It may be that many of the young animal's responses are investigatory rather than playful. Certainly, so-called play activities in the developing organism may be a preparation for future skills in the sense that any motor activity is, e.g. walking. Lorenz (1956) points out that such activities in any animals cannot be regarded simply as a rehearsal of instinctive or innate behaviour patterns, since "play is most prominent in species which combine a minimum of equipment of instinctive movements with a maximum of exploratory learning". They may also utilize much energy, but to consider this as "surplus" is to regard the organism as a closed system (Bertalanffy, 1960). It does seem, however, that play is relatively low in the motivational hierarchy, i.e. it can be inhibited by fear, hunger, curiosity or almost any other drive. Morris (1956) makes a similar point more neatly: he suggests that in play "the mechanisms of mutual inhibition and sequential ordering", evident in other drive states, are not operational and hence there is less control over the nature and sequence of motor patterns.

In the human species there are many kinds of play that are not engaged in by other mammals. Certain forms of imitative play and dramatic play are associated with a greater degree of conceptual sophistication in the human, and it may be that for a better understanding of these activities, which have their analogies more on the stage that in the cot, we need an analysis of their linguistic content as well. My concern up to the present has been with less symbolic forms of play.

A difference between the determinants of exploration in children and in lower mammals, chiefly rodents, may be noted *en passant*. Rodents will explore a new environment but not a new object in a familiar setting (Chitty and Southern, 1954; Shillito, 1963). Children, on the other hand, will not readily explore a new environment on their own, but will explore a new object if placed in a relatively familiar environment. This difference may represent a shift in biological emphasis from prey to predator.

CONCLUSIONS

Studies of exploration have been concerned with *at least* two different kinds of behaviour having somewhat contrary functions. In psychophysiological terms diversive exploration has been seen by Hebb (1955) as an attempt to avoid states of monotony or low arousal; by Fiske and Maddi (1961) as an attempt to vary stimulation in order to sustain a certain level of activation; and by Berlyne (1960) as an effort to increase sensory input so as to avoid a state of boredom or high arousal. Investigative or specific exploration, on the other hand, seeks to reduce uncertainty and hence arousal or activation produced by the novel or complex stimulation. Play in its morphology, determinants and functions often appears to be more similar to diversive exploration than specific exploration. Extending Bertalanffy's (1960) model of the psychophysical organism as an open system tending to a steady state and allowing for "anamorphosis" (i.e. spontaneous transition toward higher order), we might suggest that play represents a steady state, and exploration a process of anamorphosis. At other times, by its repetitive nature and practice effects, play may more parsimoniously be considered conceptually in the category of skills. Until we are able to use a more precise terminology, it may be premature to conclude as Thorpe (1963) does that true play, both in a phylogenetic and an ontogenetic sense, can lead "to the development of exploratory drive". In certain cases the opposite can be true. In the human species a systematic investigation of play is still lacking and a satisfactory understanding of this class of behaviour awaits, as Beach (1945) has pointed out, an analysis of the motor patterns, their situational determinants and ontogenetic development. We must beware too of the danger of circularity in describing an activity as play simply because a young animal performs it.

ACKNOWLEDGEMENTS

I am indebted to Miss Megan Level for invaluable help at every stage of the study. I acknowledge with thanks the co-operation of the Chief Education Officer, Oxford, and in particular the help and encouragement we have received from Miss Joan Lawrence and her staff at The Slade Nursery School, Oxford. My thanks are also due to S. J. Hutt for valuable criticism and statistical help, and to Dr. C. Ounsted for comments on the manuscript. The work was supported by grants from the Nuffield Foundation, Smith, Kline & French Foundation, and the British Epilepsy Association.

References

Adlerstein, A. and Fehrer, E. (1955). The effect of food deprivation on exploratory behaviour in a complex maze. *J. comp. physiol. Psychol.* **48**, 250–253.

Bally, G. (1945). "Vom Ursprung und den Grenzen der Freiheit". Schwabe, Basel.

Barnett, S. A. (1963). "A Study in Behaviour." Methuen, London.

Beach, F. A. (1945). Current concepts of play in animals. *Am. Nat.* **79**, 523–541.

Berlyne, D. E. (1950). Novelty and curiosity as determiners of exploratory behaviour. *Br. J. med. Psychol.* **41**, 68–80.

Berlyne, D. E. (1955). The arousal and satiation of perceptual curiosity in the rat. *J. comp. physiol. Psychol.* **48**, 238–246.

Berlyne, D. E. (1960). "Conflict, Arousal and Curiosity." McGraw-Hill, New York.

Bertalanffy, L. von. (1960). *In* "Discussions on Child Development" (J. M. Tanner and B. Inhelder, eds.), p. 73. Tavistock Publications, London.

Bexton, W. A., Heron, W. and Scott, T. H. (1954). Effects of decreased variation in the sensory environment. *Can. J. Psychol.* **8**, 70–76.

Brownlee, A. (1954). Play in domestic cattle in Britain: an analysis of its nature. *Br. vet. J.* **110**, 46–68.

Butler, R. A. and Alexander, H. M. (1955). Daily patterns of visual exploratory behaviour in the monkey. *J. comp. physiol. Psychol.* **48**, 247–249.

Butler, R. A. and Harlow, H. F. (1954). Persistence of visual exploration in monkeys. *J. comp. physiol. Psychol.* **47**, 258–263.

Carr, R. M. and Brown, W. L. (1959a). The effect of the introduction of novel stimuli upon manipulation in rhesus monkeys. *J. genet. Psychol.* **94**, 107–111.

Carr, R. M. and Brown, W. L. (1959b). Manipulation of visually homogeneous stimulus objects. *J. genet. Psychol.* **95**, 245–249.

Chitty, D. and Southern, H. N. (1954). "Control of Rats and Mice," Vols. 1 and 2. Clarendon Press, Oxford.

Danziger, K. and Mainland, M. (1954). The habituation of exploratory behaviour. *Aust. J. Psychol.* **6**, 39–51.

Fiske, D. W. and Maddi, S. R. (1961). A conceptual framework. *In* "Functions of Varied Experience" (D. W. Fiske and S. R. Maddi, eds.). Dorsey Press, Homewood, Illinois.

Glanzer, M. (1958). Curiosity, exploratory drive and stimulus satiation. *Psychol. Bull.* **55**, 302–315.

Glanzer, M. (1961). Changes and interrelations in exploratory behaviour. *J. comp. physiol. Psychol.* **54**, 433–438.

Grant, D. A. (1956). Analysis-of-variance tests in the analysis and comparison of curves. *Psychol. Bull.* **53**, 141–154.

Groos, K. (1898). "The Play of Animals" (E. L. Baldwin, trans.). Appleton, New York.

Groos, K. (1901). "The Play of Man" (E. L. Baldwin, trans.). Appleton, New York.

Haldane, J. B. S. (1956). Discussion on plays and vacuum activities. *In* "L'Instinct dans le comportement des animaux et de l'homme". Masson, Paris.

Hall, G. S. (1891). "Pedagogical Seminary." Worcester, Mass.

Hall, G. S. (1904). "Adolescence: Its Psychology and Its Relations to Physiology, Anthropology, Sociology, Sex, Crime, Religion, and Education." Vol. 1, p. 202. Appleton, New York.

Harlow, H. F. (1953). Mice, men, monkeys and motives. *Psych. Rev.* **60**, 23–32.

Harlow, H. F., Blazek, N. C. and McClearn, G. E. (1956). Manipulatory motivation in infant rhesus monkeys. *J. comp. physiol. Psychol.* **49**, 444–448.

Hayes, J. R. (1958). The maintenance of play in young children. *J. comp. physiol. Psychol.* **51**, 788–79.

Hayes, K. J. (1960). Exploration and fear. *Psychol. Rep.* **6**, 91–93.

Hebb, D. O. (1955). Drives and the C.N.S. (conceptual nervous system). *Psychol. Rev.* **62**, 243–254.

Hutt, C., Hutt, S. J. and Ounsted, C. (1965). The behaviour of children with and without upper C.N.S. lesions. *Behaviour* **24**, 246–268.

Inhelder, E. (1955). Zur Psychologie einiger Verhaltensweisen—besonders des Spiels—von Zootieren. *Z. Tierpsychol.* **12**, 88–144.

Jackson, L. and Todd, K. M. (1946). "Child Treatment and the Therapy of Play." Methuen, London.

Kish, G. B. and Antonitis, J. J. (1956). Unconditioned operant behaviour in two homozygous strains of mice. *J. genet. Psychol.* **88**, 121–129.

Lee, D. and Hutt, C. (1964). A play-room designed for filming children: a note. *J. Child Psychol. Psychiat.* **5**, 263–265.

Lorenz, K. (1956). Plays and vacuum activities. *In* "L'Instinct dans le comportement des animaux et de l'homme". Masson, Paris.

McDougall, W. (1931). "Introduction to Social Psychology." Methuen, London.

Mead, M. (1956). *In* "Discussion on Child Development". (J. H. Tanner and B. Inhelder, eds.), p. 139. Tavistock Publications, London.

Meyer-Holzapfel, M. M. (1956). Uber die Berichschaft zu Spiel und Instinkthandlunge. *Z. Tierpsychol.* **13**, 442–462.

Montgomery, K. C. (1951). Spontaneous alternation as a function of time between trials and amount of work. *J. exp. Psychol.* **42**, 82–93.

Montgomery, K. C. (1953). Exploratory behaviour as a function of "similarity" of stimulus situations. *J. comp. physiol. Psychol.* **46**, 129–133.

Moon, L. E. and Lodahl, T. M. (1956). The reinforcing effect of changes in illumination on lever-pressing in the monkey. *Am. J. Psychol.* **64**, 288–290.

Morris, D. J. (1956). Discussion on plays and vacuum activities. *In* "L'Instinct dans le comportement des animaux et de l'homme". Masson, Paris.

Piaget, J. (1953). "The Origin of Intelligence in the Child." Routledge and Kegan Paul, London.

Rogerson, C. H. (1939). "Play Therapy in Childhood." Oxford University Press, London.

Schiller, P. H. (1957). Innate motor action as a basis of learning: manipulative patterns in the chimpanzee. *In* "Instinctive Behaviour" (C. H. Schiller, ed.). Methuen, London.

Schlosberg, H. (1947). The concept of play. *Psychol. Rev.* **54**, 229–231.

Shillito, E. E. (1963). Exploratory behaviour in the short-tailed vole *Microtus agrestis*. *Behaviour* **21**, 145–154.

Spencer, H. (1855). "Principles of Psychology." Longmans, Green, London.

Symmes, D. (1959). Anxiety reduction and novelty as goals of visual exploration by monkeys. *J. genet. Psychol.* **94**, 181–198.

Thomae, H. (1956). "Die Periodik im kindlichen Verhalten." Verlag für Psychologie Dr. Carl-Jürgen Hogrefe, Göttingen.

Thorpe, W. H. (1963). "Learning and Instinct in Animals." Methuen, London.

Welker, W. I. (1956a). Some determinants of play and exploration in chimpanzees. *J. comp. physiol. Psychol.* **49**, 84–89.

Welker, W. I. (1956b). Variability of play and exploratory behaviour in chimpanzees. *J. comp. physiol. Psychol.* **49**, 181–185.

Welker, W. I. (1961). An analysis of exploratory and play behaviour in animals. *In* "Functions of Varied Experiences" (D. W. Fiske and S. R. Maddi, eds.). Dorsey Press, Homewood, Illinois.

Symp. zool. Soc. Lond. (1966) No. 18, 83.

ANTING AND THE PROBLEM OF SELF-STIMULATION*

K. E. L. SIMMONS

Department of Psychology, University of Bristol, England

SYNOPSIS

Anting behaviour has been claimed for mammals but the evidence suggests that, in its characteristic forms, it is confined to birds and, in particular, to passerine birds. True anting consists of highly stereotyped movements whereby the birds apply ants to their feathers or expose their plumage to the ants. A variety of other, mainly pungent substances have also been recorded as being used (anting with substitutes).

Several authors have maintained that anting is non-functional and self-stimulating and the evidence for this interpretation is given. However, a general objection is made on evolutionary grounds and then a more detailed case constructed against the theory of self-stimulation, consisting of a review of true anting with special reference to its adaptive significance and ontogeny.

It is concluded that true anting is strictly functional and probably belongs to the feather-maintenance group of behaviour-patterns. Anting with substitutes, however, is thought to be non-functional, arising from developmental "error" in the learning process during the ontogeny of anting responses.

EDITORS' NOTE

Amongst the topics considered for inclusion in the symposium was the apparently aberrant behaviour of animals which anoint themselves with pungent smelling substances, with ants, or with burning twigs. The phenomenon has been studied most closely in birds, and Dr. K. E. L. Simmons was invited to contribute on this topic. It subsequently became clear to the editors, however, that to keep the subject within reasonable bounds it would be necessary to concentrate on the mammals, and the title of the symposium was restricted accordingly. Dr. Simmons delivered his paper at the meeting, but kindly agreed that it should be published separately in the *Journal of Zoology*.

* Published in full in *J. Zool., Lond.* (1966) **149,** 145.

Symp. zool. Soc. Lond. (1966) No. 18, 85–109.

THE CONCEPT OF HOME RANGE IN MAMMALS

P. A. JEWELL*

Wellcome Institute of Comparative Physiology,
The Zoological Society of London, London, England

SYNOPSIS

The concept of home range is an important one in the interpretation of the behaviour of mammals: it relates to the restricted area within which individuals or groups live and the manner in which they use this living space. A territory, in the sense of a defended area, may not be involved, but a part of the home range may, nevertheless, be monopolized by the occupants. Home range bears a relation to the density at which given populations exist and is fundamentally connected with the energy requirements of animals. Methods of studying home range are examined and are illustrated with information obtained from recent studies on the Soay sheep, the field mouse, and the Skomer vole. Examples from the literature of the area of the home range for a number of species are tabulated, and an examination is made of the terms used in describing these home ranges. The types of activity in which mammals engage in creating home ranges are discussed.

INTRODUCTION

All terrestrial mammals spend their lives in a confined area. For some this may be no more than a few acres, but for others, especially those that are involved in annual migrations, the familiar area may be greatly extended. This area forms an individual's home range although it may be shared with a family or larger group.

It is tempting to represent an animal's home range in the form of an occupied area on a map, but this raises the problem of where to draw the boundary lines and of what they may mean. The home range is an arena for activity with spatial qualities that vary throughout its extent, and that is subject to great irregularity in intensity of use. For most species of mammals, the extent and nature of the home range can only be defined from intensive behavioural studies, although in a few species a clearly defined boundary may enclose an area that is functionally similar to the territory of many birds.

Fundamentally the home range is an area with a certain productivity that meets the energy requirements of the individual, or group, that occupies it. It is useful, therefore, in discussing home range to have some impression of the densities at which animals may normally exist, and to be aware of such measures as biomass, or standing crop, that indicate the numbers of animals a given habitat can support.

* Present address: Department of Zoology and Comparative Anatomy, University College, London, England.

In the present paper some examples of these parameters will be given to indicate their value as background information against which to set crude measures of home range in terms of ground area. The nature of the home range will then be briefly considered and some definition of terms attempted. Most illustrative examples will be taken from the literature, but some previously unpublished data from my own observations on feral Soay sheep, on the Skomer vole (*Clethrionomys glareolus*) and on the field mouse (*Apodemus sylvaticus*) will also be presented.

DENSITY AND BIOMASS

The shortcomings of information on the density at which a given population of a particular species exists, must be fully appreciated to avoid making unwarranted deductions. The information itself may derive from a single short study, and be obtained by a method with great margins of error. Some species exhibit marked cycles in density that may be seasonal or extend over several years. Perhaps more difficult to accommodate is the fact that observed densities may in no way reflect the optimal densities at which the species evolved. For example, interference by man has completely disrupted the distribution of most large mammals, so that they are harassed in their preferred habitats or may live at ill-adjusted densities in refuge areas. Notwithstanding these difficulties, density figures may be useful in gauging the status of species for purposes of comparison. Figure 1 is set out as an example.

There are several points illustrated by this figure. The low density of a carnivore compared with herbivores is apparent. Man as a hunter-gatherer (bushman and aborigines) has densities similar to the large hunting mammals, although no doubt specialized primitive communities, for example mammoth hunters, could achieve locally high densities. Lion may be more concentrated, as in the Nairobi National Park, but it is interesting that strife is then not uncommon amongst them and they occasionally kill one another (Schenkel, pp. 19–20). The vegetarian gorilla and omnivorous baboon illustrate the moderate densities achieved by large primates, but amongst large mammals it is the grazing herbivores, represented by the wildebeest, that reach the most impressive concentrations. In showing three small ruminants alongside one another, Fig. 1 illustrates the aberrant density of feral sheep on St. Kilda. Whitetail deer in North American woodland and Thompson's gazelle in African savanna grassland happen to show comparable densities but the feral sheep are ten times more concentrated.

The numbers of the sheep are regulated naturally and there is no husbandry, but equally there are no predators on St. Kilda and the fact that the sheep are feral domestic animals may be an important factor in determining the densities they tolerate (see Jewell, 1966, p. 113). Another contrast in density is seen in the two small mammals illustrated; some of the factors involved in this particular contrast will be discussed later.

An inverse relationship exists between the body weight of an animal and the numbers that a given area can maintain, so that for many purposes the density alone is not a very useful variable to manipulate. In order to compare populations of animals of different size, a convenient measure is obtained by summating individual body weights to give a total biomass figure for the species in an area. Further, the biomass of the several species occupying an area can be calculated and used as a measure of its carrying capacity. Some refinement is achieved by converting biomass figures into metabolic energy expenditure since this factor is more closely related to food requirements, and whilst food requirement increases with body weight it is, like metabolic energy expenditure, less than proportional to it. An example of these transformations from numbers, through biomass, to metabolic energy expenditure has been presented recently by Lamprey (1964) for a complex of herbivores in the Tarangire Reserve, Tanzania. In order of numerical importance, the species are buffalo, zebra, wildebeest and impala with insignificantly few elephant. In terms of biomass, elephant are second only to buffalo but this dramatic change of role is tempered slightly in the further transformation to metabolic energy expenditure when elephant fall third in importance to buffalo and zebra but have requirements that exceed the more numerous wildebeest. These considerations are relevant to an interpretation of the size of an animal's home range in so far as a large energy demand is likely to require a large area for food gathering. McNab (1963) has considered the relations between body weight, energy requirements, and home range size, using information on twenty-six species of mammals. He found that home range size could be expressed as a function of body weight which was directly comparable with the function relating basal metabolic rate to body weight. When the data for "hunters" and "croppers" were separated, the calculated relations between body weight and home range size remained similar but the home range for hunters was about four times that of croppers at a given body weight. Treatments of this kind are at a preliminary, exploratory stage, but they indicate one way in which the relation between an animal and its range can be quantified.

in 20 sq. miles

in 1 sq. mile

FIG. 1. A comparison of the density of certain mammalian populations. These densities are idealized and simply indicate an order of magnitude achieved in particular areas. In fact there are wide fluctuations in numbers from year to year and with the seasons. *Man*, hunters and food-gatherers, information from sources in Lee (1963); *Lion*, in the Serengeti, Tanzania (Talbot and Stewart, 1964); *Gorilla*, Congo, mountain area (Schaller, 1963); *baboon*, Nairobi National Park, Kenya (De Vore and Washburn, 1963); *wildebeest*, Serengeti (Talbot and Stewart, 1964); *Whitetail deer*, North American woodland (Severinghaus and Cheatum, 1956); *Thompson's gazelle*, Serengeti (Talbot and Stewart, 1964); *Soay sheep*, Hirta, Outer Hebrides (Boyd *et al.*, 1964); *wood mouse*, English woodland (Brown, p. 113); *Skomer vole*, Skomer island, Wales (Jewell, 1966).

The numbers of animals that can be supported by an area are also affected by the manner in which biomass is distributed within the population. In the baboon *Papio cynocephalus* there is marked sexual dimorphism in which adult males weigh about 80 lb and females about 35 lb. De Vore and Washburn (1963) have suggested that this is the optimum distribution of the biomass of the species in that it accommodates large males serving a protective role to the troop but allows a greater number of females to be maintained on a given food supply. This view can hold if food supply is a major factor limiting the number of baboons and if survival is more likely when there are many individuals in a group.

It seems possible that seasonal dimorphism serves a similar purpose and this kind of adaptation is particularly well seen in small mammals in temperate zones. These animals usually breed in one season only and then die. The over-wintering population is comprised of immature individuals that exhibit an arrested development and that remain small until the following spring. Adult body weights are then rapidly assumed as the animals mature to form the breeding population. An example of this seasonal dimorphism is well illustrated in charts for *Microtus agrestis* presented by Baker and Ranson (1933) where adult weights range from 25 to 40 g but the weights of over-wintering animals cluster about 18 g. The same phenomenon is seen in the autumn weight distribution of the Skomer vole (*C. glareolus*) where immature animals accumulate at weights of 21–24 g, whereas adults are characteristically ten or more grams heavier (Jewell, 1966, Fig. 12). Seasonal dimorphism could provide a means of carrying the maximum number of individuals through the winter months when their small size will minimize their food requirements.

RECORDING HOME RANGE

The simplest situation in which to record home range is one where the animals can be watched at any time and their positions plotted on a map. This elementary procedure has been followed at St. Kilda in studies on the Soay sheep (Grubb and Jewell, pp. 179–210). A number of sheep were given distinctive bright collars and their positions were frequently recorded. On the steep slopes at St. Kilda it is an easy matter to find a good vantage point, and the complete absence of trees or bushes makes the marked animals easy to spot. The range of some sheep has been recorded in successive years by plotting sightings of the animals on a map and an example for one ewe is given in Fig. 2.

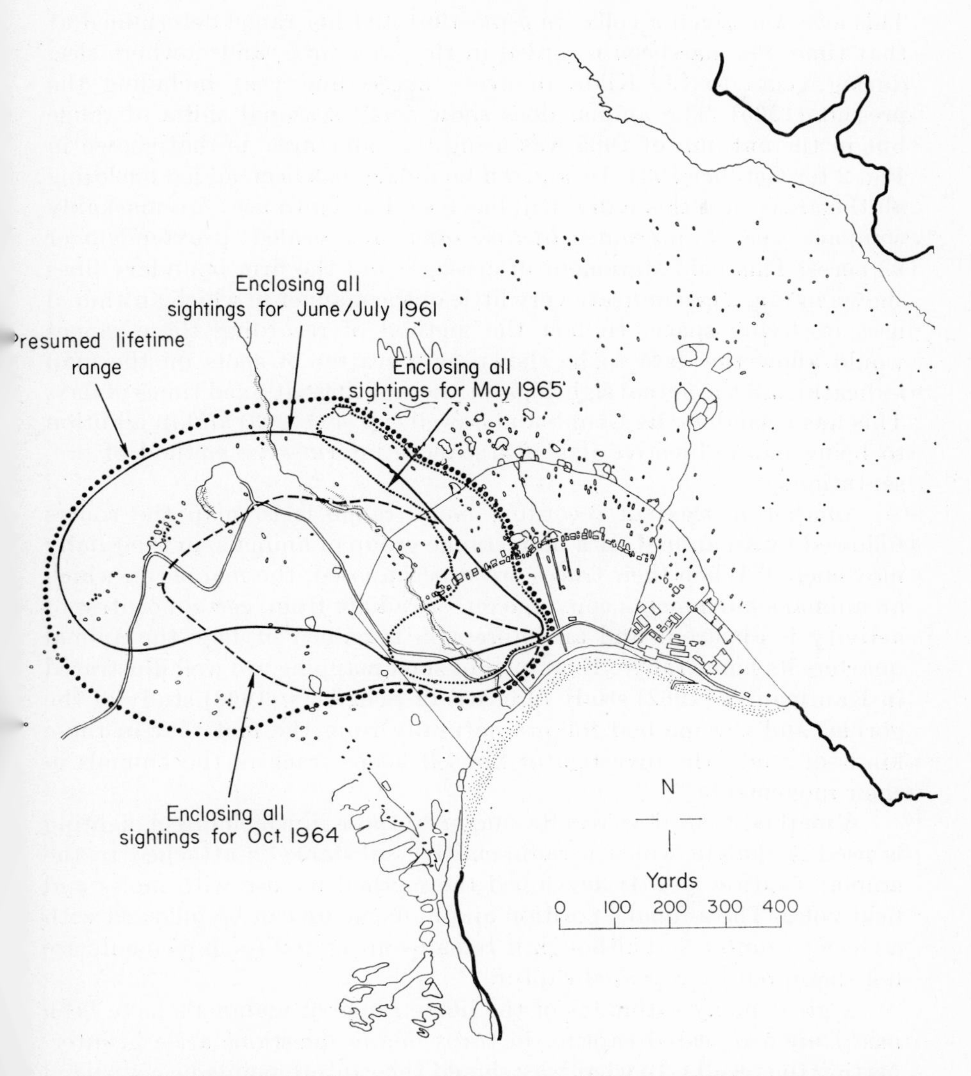

FIG. 2. The home range of a mature Soay ewe on the island of Hirta, St. Kilda. The lines have been drawn to enclose all the sighting of a given period. Seasonal changes of range are illustrated. A line of heavy dots has been drawn to enclose all recorded sightings of this ewe between June 1961 and October 1965; this area of 83 acres is presumed to be close to the lifetime range of this individual. The map shows the village area of Hirta; drystone walls, village houses, and scattered cleits are indicated, and the coast line of beach (dots) and cliffs (heavy line) is shown. (For more detailed description of the terrain, see Grubb and Jewell, p. 180.)

This ewe was given a collar in June 1961 and her range determined at that time. She has been recorded in the same area, and nowhere else, during visits to St. Kilda in every succeeding year including the present (1965). The animal does show small seasonal shifts of range but in the autumn of 1965 was using the same area as that shown in Fig. 2 for October 1964. In Fig. 2 a boundary has been added enclosing all the areas that this individual has been known to use. A remarkably compact area, its presumed *lifetime range*, is revealed: it extends over 83 acres. This bald statement of acreage, and the firm boundary lines shown in Fig. 2 can indicate very little of the manner in which an animal uses its living space. In fact the method of recording these ranges would allow the data to be shown as a scatter of spots on the map indicating all the actual sightings, or the sightings at fixed times of day. This has been done by Grubb and Jewell (pp. 187–203) and in addition to being more objective it is also a more informative method of presentation.

Another method of recording home range is to map the routes followed by an animal, or a home range group of animals, in their daily movements. When their traces are superimposed, the manner in which an animal's movements converge on, or radiate from, certain centres of activity is apparent and an impression is gained of how the animal quarters its home range. Examples of such mapping are well illustrated in Kaufmann's (1962) study of coatis or Schaller's (1963) study of the gorilla, and the method follows naturally from the fact that in these kinds of study the investigator himself keeps track of the animals in their movements.

A method that gives results similar to those in which direct sighting is used is that in which a radio-emitive substance is attached to the animal. Godfrey (1954) developed the method for use with moles and field voles. The animal's position and movements can be followed with a Geiger counter and although it remains unsighted its movements are not disrupted by repeated capture.

A great many estimates of the home range of mammals have been based upon repeated capture in traps. Many questions arise in interpreting the results. In what way should the capture points be connected to give a diagrammatic plan of the home range area? What area outside the zone of capture is known to the animal? What has been the effect of holding an animal in a trap? These problems have been considered in a recent review by Brown (1962) and will not be elaborated here, but I would like to present a particular instance of the way in which quite false results may arise in trapping. These observations were made during a collaboration study between Dr. P. J. Fullagar and myself on the vole (*C. glareolus*) and field mouse (*Apodemus sylvaticus*) of Skomer island.

The Skomer vole is a sedentary animal and exists at high densities (see Fig. 1). By trapping on a grid pattern (100 × 100 yd) at intervals of 10 yd, it is possible to capture repeatedly a large number of voles at points all well within the borders of the area. It was found over a period of 16 days that the estimated area of a trap-revealed home range increased with the number of times an animal was caught, but after nine recaptures the further extensions of home range were not so marked. The placing of traps was manipulated in various ways and the results, together with other information (see later), suggested that the trap-revealed home ranges could be taken with confidence to correspond to the real areas used by the voles. The ranges were of the order of 30–40 yd in diameter (see Figs. 5, 6 and 7).

The determination of home range in the field mouse was approached in a similar way. It was known to make longer movements than the vole and so a trapping area of 154 × 154 yd was set out with an interval of 22 yd between the rows of the grid lattice. Traps were set for 12 nights and the resultant captures and recaptures of mice permitted a number of apparently compact and well-defined home ranges to be drawn (Fig. 3). At the end of this period of trapping, however, ten traps were set on four consecutive nights around a single point at the centre of the grid. Sixteen mice were captured here despite the fact that many of them had "home ranges" that did not include the point and that were on the borders of the study area. Other trapping results showed us that field mice would readily travel 100 yd or more in a night. There was clear indication, then, that reliable information about home range was not being obtained. Our next step, therefore, was to treat the whole island as a "grid" and, with the aid of measuring tape and prismatic compass, posts were set out over the island at intervals of 300 yd. Traps were set at all these sites, and at some of them, together with intervening points at 150 yd intervals, re-trapping was carried out. Time did not permit the protracted period of study that would have been required to construct home range areas for individual mice, but Fig. 4 shows some of the movements recorded. It is evident that the previous trapping for the field mouse on a small restrictive grid had produced quite spurious "home ranges".

To return to observations on the Skomer vole, David Saunders, Warden of the island, has confirmed the value of set grid trapping for studies of a sedentary species of this kind. His study area is a permanent grid of 100 × 80 yd overall (see Figs. 5–7). For several years regular monthly trapping (excluding the winter months) has been carried out on the area, the traps being set for 4 days and examined in the evening and morning of each day. In this way information was obtained on the whereabouts of a large number of voles during the time they were resident on the area. From the known longevity of the vole, it can be assumed that, for many, their residency throughout life has been

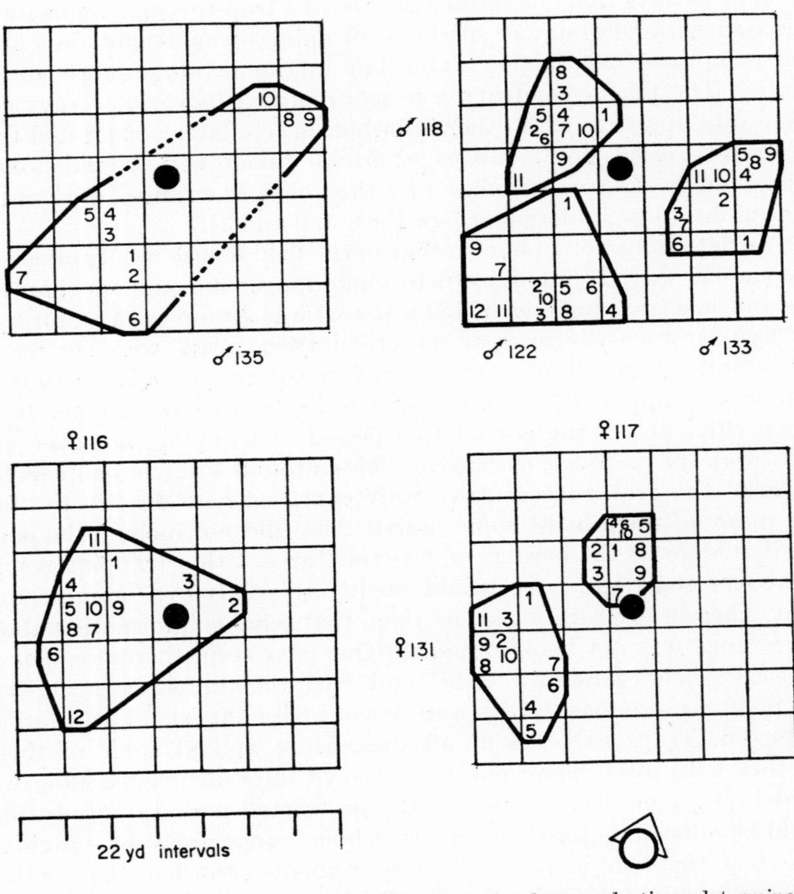

Fig. 3. The "home ranges" of seven field mice, *Apodemus sylvaticus*, determined by grid trapping on an open area on the southern side of Skomer Island in October, 1962. The area was set with forty-nine traps for 12 nights, one trap in each square, the traps being moved to different quadrants of the squares on successive nights. The numerals indicate successive points of capture of each mouse. In addition, for four successive nights, no traps were set on the grid as a whole but ten traps were placed at the central point (large dot). All seven mice were captured at this point together with many others whose apparent home ranges had been on the outer borders of the area and had not included the central trapping point. (From Fullagar, 1965.)

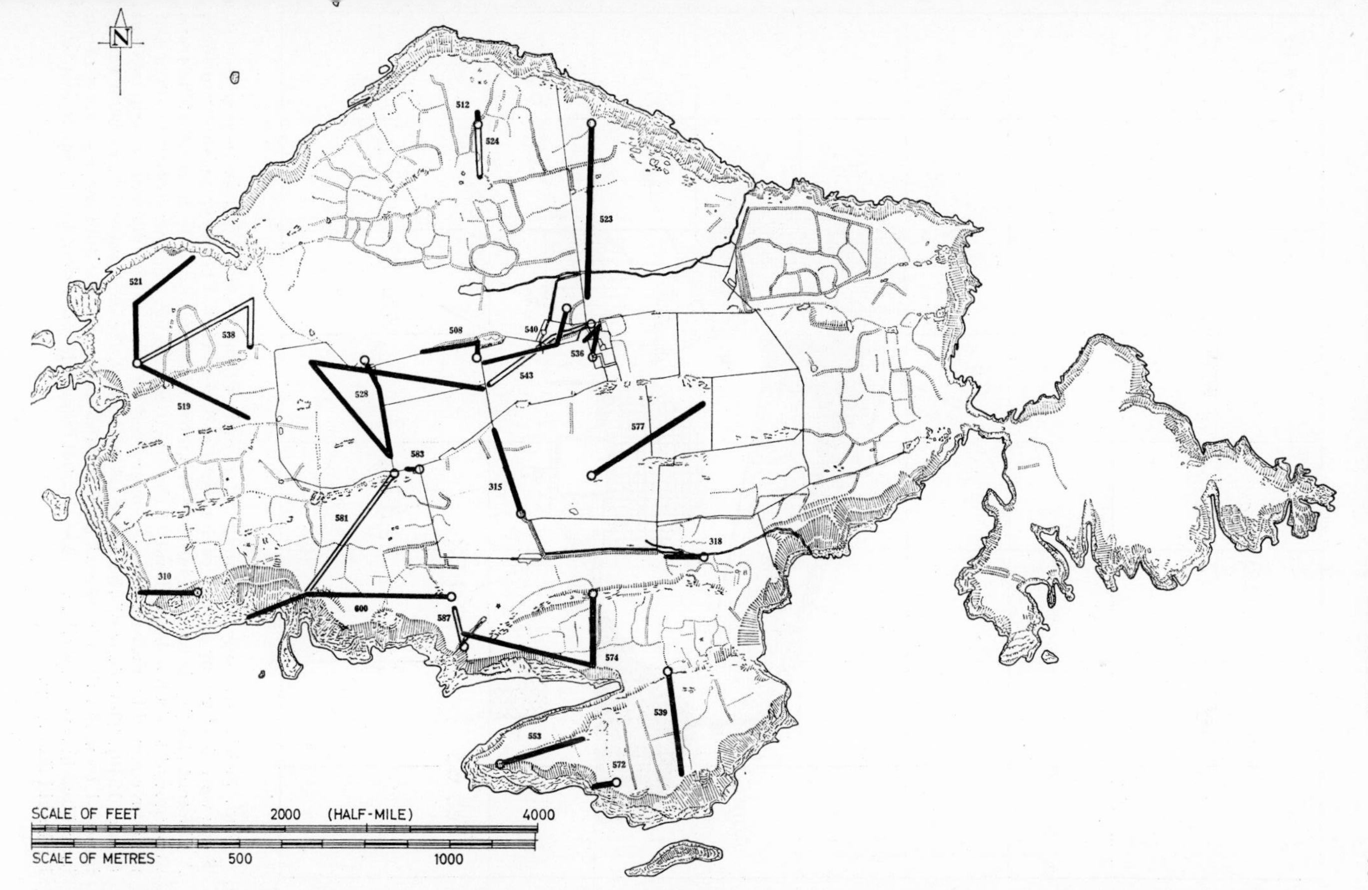

FIG. 4. The movements of twenty-three male field mice *Apodemus sylvaticus*, on Skomer Island in April 1963. The sites at which individuals were first captured, marked and released are indicated by open circles, and the identification number of each mouse is given. Lines (either solid or open) have been drawn to link up the successive recapture points for each mouse. (From Fullagar, 1965.)

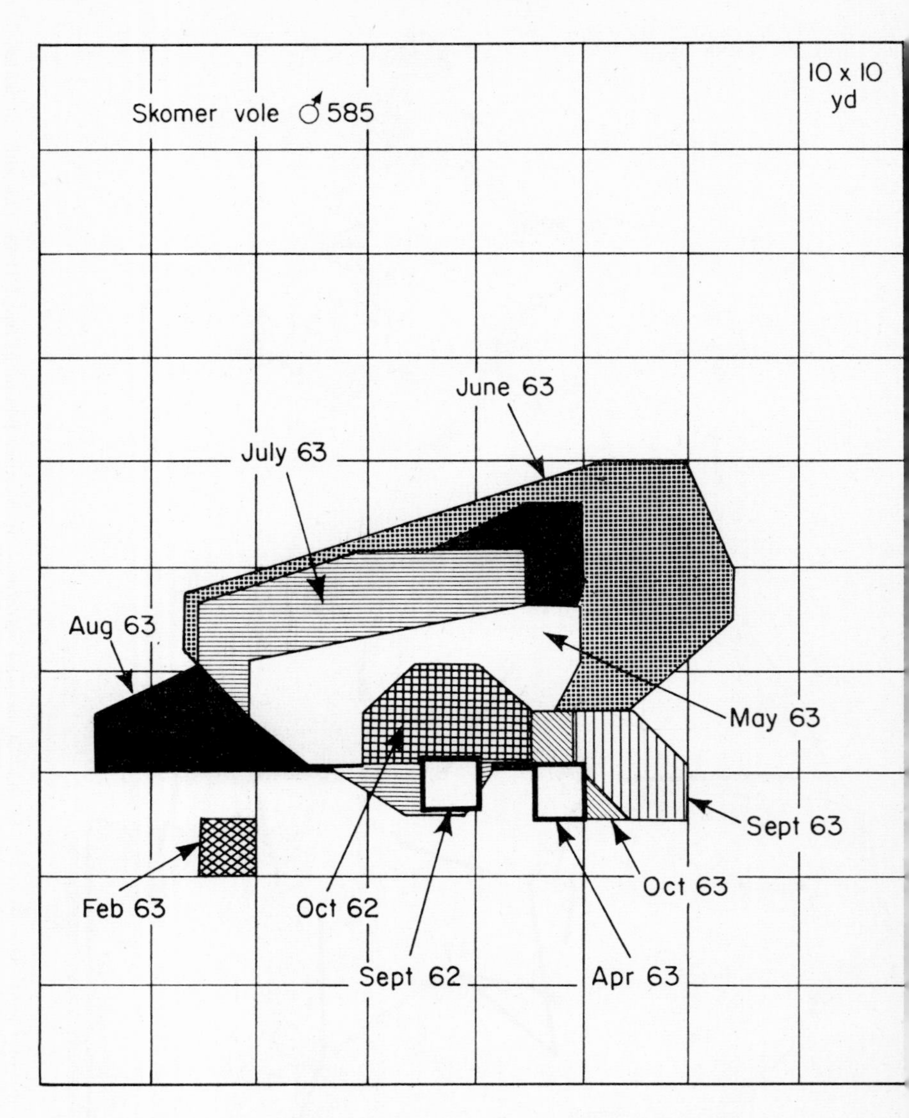

FIG. 5. The trap-revealed range of a male Skomer vole, *Clethrionomys glareolus*. Traps were set for four days in each month and were visited both evening and morning. A different shading is used to indicate the movements recorded each month. The traps were moved to each sub-quadrant of the 10 yd squares on the four successive days and the area covered by movement was constructed by the inclusive boundary strip method (Blair, 1940). The plans of the range of movement for each month have been superimposed to make the diagram. The results demonstrate the lifetime residency of an individual in a very small area. Constructed from field work data kindly made available by David Saunders.

recorded. Some examples of the results are shown in Figs. 5–7. Figures 5 and 6 show the ranges of a male and a female vole that appear to have remained in one small area throughout their life. Each was first caught as an immature animal in the autumn of 1962 and was recaptured in

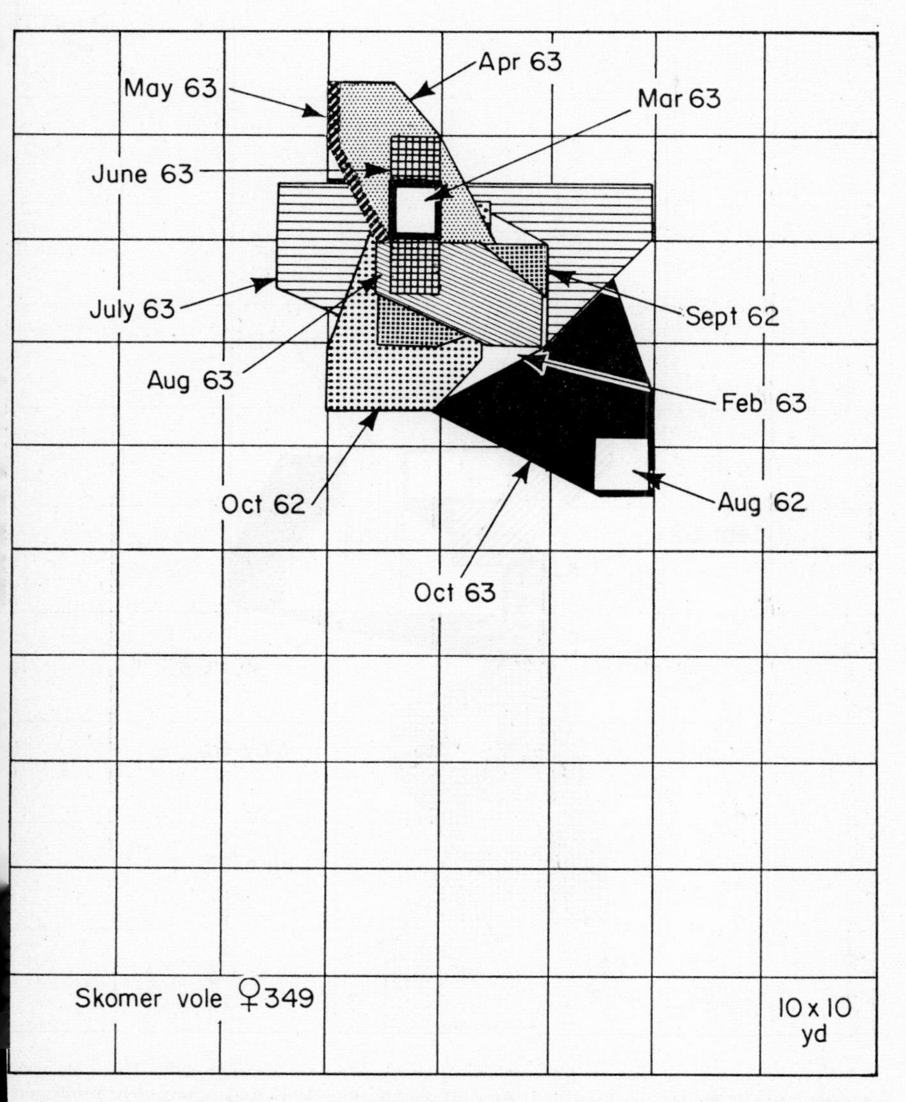

Fig. 6. As Fig. 5. The trap-revealed range of a female Skomer vole that was resident in a small area from August 1962 to October 1963.

the same area the following spring. The way in which more wide-ranging movements are made as summer, and the breeding season, advances, can be seen. The larger total area covered by the male is typical.

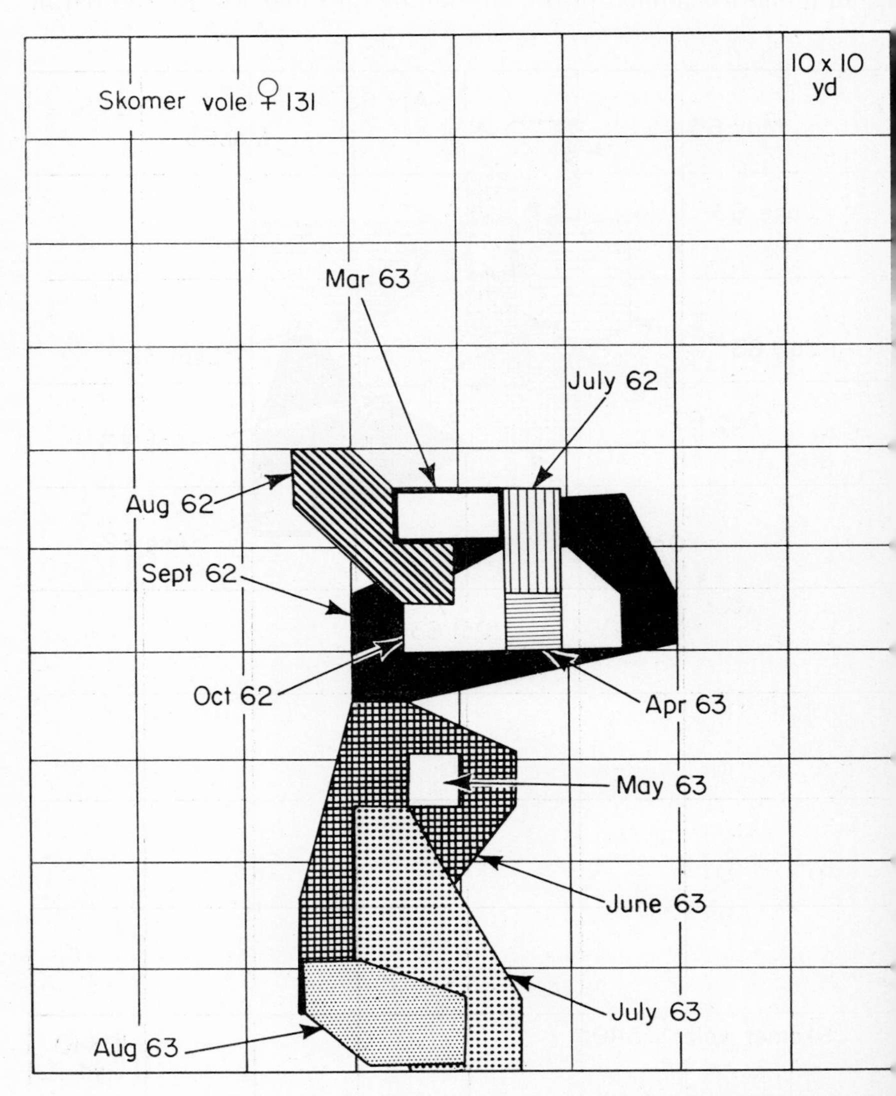

FIG. 7. As Fig. 5. The trap-revealed range of a female Skomer vole. The vole was resident in the centre of the grid from July to October 1962 and apparently remained there over winter being captured again in March and April 1963. With the advent of the breeding season in May, the animal shifted its range slightly to the south.

Figure 7 shows the whereabouts of a female that was first caught as a breeding adult in the summer of 1962 and that survived to breed again in the following year. It is interesting that she made a slight shift of range, but it is reasonable to assume that at least part of the new range was familiar to her. The particular value of this long-term study lies in the fact that although the trapping procedure itself is restrictive, and not very informative on the extent of range, the animals are free to move in the intervals between trapping. The adherence by individuals that have successfully established themselves to a very small area is, therefore, a real phenomenon, and the lifetime range of these individuals is indicated.

New methods of following the movements of small mammals are needed, and those that employ foot-impressions on marker-boards (see Brown, pp. 124–129) have an obvious potential. For larger mammals, small radio-transmitters attached to the animal are clearly destined to provide new information of an extremely valuable kind. Even so, it is of interest that established methods of analysing data on home range can be applied usefully to information derived from this new technique (see for example, Storm, 1965).

Some home range areas for a number of species are gathered together in Table I. The figures should be taken to indicate no more than orders of magnitude. Densities may be calculated in a different way, for example either based on the whole area surveyed or only on that part of it actually used by the animals. Home ranges may differ widely between the sexes, and there are many other obstacles to comparison.

THE CONCEPT AND FUNCTION OF HOME RANGE, AND DEFINITION OF TERMS

Many naturalists have recognized that the majority of mammals keep to a particular tract of ground for the greater part of their lives. Seton (1910) is often quoted for his descriptions of the "home region" or "home ground" possessed by mammals, whilst others, for example Darling (1937), wrote of these areas as an animal's territory. It remained for Burt (1943) to advocate separate uses for these terms and to distinguish the concepts of home range and territoriality. He did not attempt a rigorous statement, however, and he gave two different definitions of home range in his paper: (1) "that area traversed by the individual in its normal activities of food gathering, mating and caring for young" and (2) "the area, usually around a home site, over which the animal normally travels in search of food". Burt considered that an animal could be said to have a home range only after it had established

TABLE I

Species	Group size extremes: and/or mean	Population: Total numbers	Population: Total study area	Population: Density	Size of home range	Geographical site	Reference
Opossum *Didelphis marsupialis*				1 to 20–40 acres	0·5 acres		Fitch (1958)
Howler monkey *Alouatta palliata*	4–35 : 17	489	6 sq. miles	82/sq. mile	0·5 acres	Barra Colorado	Carpenter (1934)
Bonnet macaque *Macaca radiata*	6–58				2·0 sq. miles	South India	Simonds (1965)
Baboon *Papio* spp.							
Olive baboon	12–87 : 42	374	40+ sq. miles	10/sq. mile	3–16 sq. miles	Nairobi Kenya	De Vore and Washburn (1963) De Vore and Hall (1965)
Yellow baboon	13–185 : 80	1 203		25/sq. mile		Amoseli Kenya	
Chacma baboon	8–109 : 34	1 800		6/sq. mile	3·5–13 sq. miles	Southern Africa	
Langur *Presbytis entellus*	5–120+ : some lone males 25	(1 000)		12/sq. mile	0·5–5·0 sq. miles	North India	Jay (1965)
Gibbon *Hylobates lar*	2–6 : 4	(93)		11/sq. mile	30–100 acres	North Siam	Carpenter (1940)
Chimpanzee *Pan satyrus*	2–25 (3–5 most frequent)	60–80	30 sq. miles	2–3/sq. mile	6–20 sq. miles	Gombe Tanzania	Goodall (1965)
Mountain gorilla *Gorilla gorilla beringei*	2–30	450	155 sq. miles	2·9/sq. mile	8–15 sq. miles	Congo-Uganda border	Schaller (1963)
		150	96 sq. miles	1·5/sq. mile			

Table I—*continued*

Species	Group size extremes: and/or mean	Population: Total numbers	Population: Total study area	Population: Density	Size of home range	Geographical site	Reference
Man *Homo sapiens*							
Bushman	20			1/33 sq. mile	440–1 1250 sq. miles		Sources in De Vore (1963)
Aborigine	30			1/12 sq. mile	100–750 sq. miles		
Snowshoe hare *Lepus americanus*					14·5 acres		O'Farrell (1965)
Rabbit *Oryctolagus cuniculus*	150 (fluctuating) in warren				2 acres	Berkshire parkland	Southern (1940)
Wolf *Canis lupus*		4		1/40–50 sq. miles	150 sq. miles	Wisconsin	Thompson (1952)
		10		1/150 sq. miles	1 500 sq. miles	Alaska	Burkholder (1959)
	1–8	8		1/240 sq. miles	900 sq. miles	Canada	Rowan (1950)
	1–14	33–55	4 200 sq. miles	1/100 potential range 1/10 sq. miles actual range	Summer and winter ranges can be 60–70 miles apart	Rocky Mt. Parks in Canada	Cowan (1947)
Red fox *Vulpes vulpes*		2 adult males			910 and 1 040 acres	N.W. Illinois	Storm (1965)

Table I—*continued*

Species	Group size extremes: and/or mean	Population: Total numbers	Population: Total study area	Population: Density	Size of home range	Geographical site	Reference
Kodiak bear *Ursus middendorffi*		160	96 sq. miles	1/0·6 sq. miles; locally 10/sq. mile	A few sq. miles	Kaluk Alaska	Troyer and Hensel (1964)
Raccoon *Procyon lotor*				1/50 acres	111–503 acres		Fitch (1958)
Coati *Nasua narica*	2–15	400–600	6 sq. miles	4/25 acres	100 acres	Barra Colorado	Kaufmann (1962)
Marten *Martes caurina*		14–23	6 sq. miles	2–4/ sq. mile	Males 0·92 sq. miles; females 0·27 sq. miles	Montana	Hawley and Newby (1957)
Whitetail deer *Odocoileus virginianus*	1 buck and 1 doe				Usually in 160 acres max. 480 acres		Schoonmaker (1938)
Columbian black-tailed deer *Odocoileus hemionus*	Family group doe and fawns		400 acres (intensive study area)	90–144/ sq. mile (summer)	50–500 acres	California	Dasmann and Taber (1956)
Vicuna *Vicugna vicugna*	2–26 : 8			1/10 acres (good range)	20–115 acres	Central Andes	Koford (1957)
Lechwe *Kobus leche*		17 550	158 sq. miles	111/sq. miles 175/sq. miles intensively used area			Robinette and Child (1964)

itself, and that the wanderings of young animals were in a different category of movement. He recognized that an established animal could shift its home range but that "occasional sallies outside the area, perhaps exploratory in nature, should not be considered as a part of the home range". A migratory animal might have a winter home range and a summer home range but "the migratory route is not considered part of the home range of the animal". Dice (1952), and other authors, in defining home range have emphasized its habitual use in daily activities, but these definitions, which may have arisen from considerations of the behaviour of small mammals, are too restrictive when applied to large mammals in that they imply regular and frequent use of the area. These attributes are appropriate to the "core area" of a home range, to be mentioned shortly. Burt (1943) avoided the implication of daily use, but his specification of particular activities would now seem unnecessary. He usefully excluded the dispersal movements of young animals, but "exploratory sallies" may be an important way in which an animal extends and maintains its home range. His definitions can be restated in the form that "*home range is the area over which an animal normally travels in pursuit of its routine activities*".

It would be useful to have a term that does include the total area used by an animal, covering for example, both summer and winter grounds and the migration route, or the wandering shown by the males of many species at mating time. These movements may be over familiar ground, and a shift of home range may serve to give an animal experience of a more extensive, but continuous, total area. The word *range* itself can have this meaning but has other connotations, as when used to mean the geographical range or distribution of a species. Perhaps *lifetime range* would be a useful term to mean *the total area with which an animal has become familiar, including seasonal home ranges, excursions for mating, and routes of movement*. Jay (1965) has found *annual home range* a useful term to indicate the whole area used by langurs (*Presbytis entellus*) including the shifts from dry to wet season.

In many species a particular part of the home range is used more frequently, and with greater regularity, than other parts, and this zone has been given a useful description in the *core area* of Kaufmann (1962). The term is most appropriate where there are one or two such areas in the home range as amongst coatis (Kaufmann, 1962) or baboons (De Vore and Washburn, 1963), but where there are several such areas, small in size, scattered throughout a home range, Carpenter's (1940) description of *foci of activity* could be more appropriate. (It may be noted that the expression "core areas" has also been used in relation to the distribution of a species to mean regions in which the species is most abundant, and where it breeds most successfully (Harrington, 1965).) It would seem that further attempts to define the qualities of home range in a formal way are not very useful at the present time, when so little is known about home range behaviour. What is required is an understanding of the ways in which an animal makes use of the terrain in which it has established itself.

Apart from a few outstanding, and pioneering studies on the larger mammals, most investigations of home range have been developed in relation to small mammals. The majority of such studies have used trapping techniques and the analysis of results has given rise to statistical concepts of home range and expressions of the likelihood of an animal being at a certain place within its range (for example, Hayne, 1949; Calhoun and Casby, 1958). These approaches are extremely valuable because they provoke the observer to think of home range in ways other than as an area with a boundary. A fresh approach to these aspects of animal behaviour has followed the current renewal of interest in field studies. Examples are seen in the intensive work on primates (see the seven single-species studies under the editorship of De Vore, 1965), including that just completed on the Gelada baboon (Crook, pp. 237–258), the study on coatis (Kaufmann, 1962), and that on Soay sheep (Grubb and Jewell, pp. 179–210).

From these studies there emerges an impression of the manner in which animals use their living space and De Vore (1963) has discussed some of the earlier findings. Regular routes and pathways are a reality and recall Hediger's (1950) early observations. Amongst feral sheep, the existence and use of traditional sheep tracks (Grubb and Jewell, pp. 193–194) is as marked as if a shepherd were present. Snowshoe hares exhibit a striking example of the fixity of routes of movement. They use regular runways and when deep snow lies on the ground, giving potential freedom of movement on the snow surface, the hares still use routes that lie exactly over the summer runways on the ground (O'Farrell, 1965). Amongst forest-living animals, fruit-bearing trees form focal points in the range, whilst other trees form places for resting and for night roosts. Many observations suggest that a home range can have a boundary that is real for the occupants. A baboon troop at the edge of its range is nervous and ill-at-ease. Coatis that, on one occasion, had wandered outside their previously accepted boundary, suddenly panicked and rushed back to a familiar area. Again seen in coatis, the special attachment of a female at parturition, and of juveniles, to the central part of the home range expresses an animal's confidence in familiar areas.

It remains to consider the special function of home range as an ecological phenomenon that effectively disperses the members of a population, and the ways in which the maintenance of home range expresses an element of territoriality in the behaviour of mammals.

The concept of *territory* has been developed particularly in studies on birds. Territoriality in mammals was discussed by Burt (1943, 1949) and he accepted Noble's (1939) definition as holding the essence of the concept, namely "*any defended area*". Carpenter (1958) reviewed the subject and accepted the central idea of defence in stating that "attack, encroachment and defense constitute important aspects of territoriality, and so do challenge, vocalization, song, and other display or signalling activities." Mammals of many species do maintain territory of this kind. The vicuna is a good example (Koford, 1957). A male is attendant upon a band of females and juveniles and he defends their territory. The boundaries of the defended area are strict, the male will display to others that approach and chase off intruding males often far beyond the boundary. The Uganda kob exhibits a remarkable form of territoriality in which the males, when occupying positions on the traditional mating grounds, defend a very small, and rigidly defined area (Buechner, 1963). Amongst carnivores, lions and wolves will attack intruding members of their species, clearly displaying territoriality, although the relation of a defended area to total range has not been determined. Many species, it seems, may have a territory within their home range, indeed in the instance of the vicuna, a band will often graze outside its territory, on neutral ground, or in another territory if the occupants are out of sight. At the opposite extreme to strongly territorial species are those, like the gorilla (Schaller, 1963), that exhibit a high tolerance to one another and in which several groups have almost coincident home ranges. Between these extremes, however, are those species that must be recognized as possessing home ranges with some of the qualities of territories, yet that frequently lack the behavioural attributes usually understood as "defence".

Close examination of records of home range in many species will often reveal that there is, within each home range, an area that is used exclusively by the occupants, whilst other, peripheral areas, are shared with neighbouring groups. Sometimes a core area will also be an exclusive area but this is not necessarily so. Further, species that do not exhibit core areas, for example a grazing animal like the Soay sheep, may still show a distribution of neighbouring home ranges such that certain zones of each home range are exclusive to the occupants. Such an area can be usefully termed a *monopolized zone*. Pitelka (1959), on encountering the phenomenon in birds, asserted that "territory should be defined as an exclusive area, not merely a 'defended' one" and he argued the importance, in ecology, of recognizing the functional role of these exclusive areas.

The exact manner in which a monopolized zone is maintained by a home range group is not apparent. Soay sheep have not been observed to give any demonstration of possession, and in a great many species that maintain well-defined home ranges there is no obvious intergroup aggression. Sometimes display is present, but amongst primates De Vore (1963) has concluded: "Different groups are kept apart, however, not so much by overt aggression and fighting at territorial boundaries, as by the daily routine of a monkey group in its own range, by the rigid social boundaries of organized groups in many monkey species, and, in some species, by loud vocalizations."

It is evident that neighbouring groups in a population exert a restrictive effect on one another. Sale (1965) has observed in hyrax (*Procavia* and *Heterohyrax*) that isolated groups have larger home ranges than groups near together, so that although the home ranges of the latter overlap they do appear to exercise some limiting effect on one another. Another result of this influence of neighbours is the spacing out of individuals (in the case of species whose members lead a solitary or family-group life) so that they are dispersed through the habitat, as recorded, for example, in Columbian black-tailed deer (Dasmann and Taber, 1956). Similar effects are well known amongst small mammals. The qualities that near-neighbours possess may not all be antipathetic, however, and Calhoun and Webb (1953) have made the attractive suggestion that animals move into an area cleared of their own species "as if in an attempt to encounter again the stimuli produced by neighbours."

These observations and speculations bear directly on problems of population control. But just as our knowledge of the densities at which species thrive is meagre, so is there a singular paucity of information on the manner in which animals in natural habitats apprehend the space they live in. Unfortunately for us many unusual species, particularly the spectacular large mammals, are threatened with extinction or severe restriction of their range, and the time is getting short in which observation and experiment can elucidate this fundamental aspect of their ecology.

Acknowledgements

Field work on the Soay sheep has been supported by research grants from the Agricultural Research Council and the Nature Conservancy. The West Wales Naturalists' Trust gave permission for work on Skomer Island; their Warden, Mr. David Saunders, has kindly allowed me to use some of his own unpublished observations, and the Nature Conservancy provided a number of facilities. The map of Skomer (Fig. 4) is taken from a complete survey of the island carried out by Professor W. F. Grimes, that he generously made available for copying.

References

Baker, J. R. and Ranson, R. M. (1933). Factors affecting the breeding of the field mouse (*Microtus agrestis*). Part III. Locality. *Proc. R. Soc.* B, **113**, 486–495.

Blair, W. F. (1940). Home ranges and populations of the meadow vole in southern Michigan. *J. Wildl. Mgmt* **4**, 149–161.

Boyd, J. M., Doney, J. M., Gunn, R. G. and Jewell, P. A. (1964). The Soay sheep of the island of Hirta, St. Kilda. A study of a feral population. *Proc. zool. Soc. Lond.* **142**, 129–163.

Brown, L. E. (1962). Home range in small mammal communities. *Surv. biol. Prog.* **4**, 131–179.

Buechner, H. K. (1963). Territoriality as a behavioral adaptation to environment in Uganda Kob. *Proc. XVI int. Congr. Zool.* **3,** 59–63.

Burkholder, B. L. (1959). Movements and behaviour of a wolf pack in Alaska. *J. Wildl. Mgmt* **23**, 1–11.

Burt, W. H. (1943). Territoriality and home range concepts as applied to mammals. *J. Mammal.* **24**, 364–352.

Burt, W. H. (1949). Territoriality. *J. Mammal.* **30**, 25–27.

Calhoun, J. B. and Casby, J. U. (1958). Calculation of home range and density of small mammals. *Publ. Hlth Monogr.* No. 55 (Public Health Service Publication No. 592).

Calhoun, J. B. and Webb, W. L. (1953). Induced emigrations among small mammals. *Science, N.Y.* **117**, 385–390.

Carpenter, C. R. (1934). A field study of the behaviour and social relations of howling monkeys *Alouatta palliata*. *Comp. Psychol. Monogr.* **10**, No. 48, 1–168.

Carpenter, C. R. (1940). A field study in Siam of the behaviour and social relations of the gibbon (*Hylobates lar*). *Comp. Psychol. Monogr.* **16**(84), 1–212.

Carpenter, C. R. (1958). Territoriality: a review of concepts and problems. *In* "Behaviour and Evolution" (A. Roe and G. G. Simpson, eds.). Yale University Press, New Haven.

Cowan, P. M. (1947). The timber wolf in the rocky mountain National Parks of Canada. *Can. J. Res.* **25**, 139–174.

Darling, F. F. (1937). "A Herd of Red Deer". Oxford University Press, London.

Dasmann, R. F. and Taber, R. D. (1956). Behaviour of Columbian black-tailed deer with reference to population ecology. *J. Mammal.* **37**, 143–164.

De Vore, I. (1963). A comparison of the ecology and behaviour of monkeys and apes. *In* "Classification and Human Evolution" (S. L. Washburn, ed.), pp. 301–319. Methuen, London.

De Vore, I. (Ed.) (1965). "Primate Behavior". Holt, Rinehart and Winston, New York.

De Vore, I. and Hall, K. R. L. (1965). Baboon ecology. *In* "Primate Behavior" (I. De Vore, ed.), pp. 20–52. Holt, Rinehart and Winston, New York.

De Vore, I. and Washburn, S. L. (1963). Baboon ecology and human evolution. *In* "African Ecology and Human Evolution" (F. C. Howell and F. Bourliere, eds.), pp. 335–367. Methuen, London.

Dice, L. R. (1952). "Natural Communities". University of Michigan Press, Ann Arbor.

Fitch, H. S. (1958). Home ranges, territories, and seasonal movements of vertebrates on the natural history reservation. *Univ. Kans. Publ. nat. Hist.* **11**, 63–326.

Fullagar, P. J. (1964). The population structure and breeding biology of mainland and island varieties of the field mouse *Apodemus sylvaticus* and of *A. flavicollis*. Ph.D. Thesis, University of London.

Godfrey, G. K. (1954). Tracing field voles (*Microtus agrestis*) with a Geiger–Müller counter. *Ecology* **35**, 5–10.

Goodall, J. (1965). Chimpanzees of the Gombe Stream Reserve. *In* "Primate Behavior" (I. De Vore, ed.), pp. 425–473. Holt, Rinehart and Winston, New York.

Harrington, C. R. (1965). The life and status of the Polar bear. *Oryx* **8**, 169–176.

Hawley, V. D. and Newby, F. E. (1957). Marten home ranges and population fluctuations. *J. Mammal.* **38**, 174–184.

Hayne, D. W. (1949). Calculation of size of home range. *J. Mammal.* **30**, 1–18.

Hediger, H. (1950). "Wild Animals in Captivity." Butterworth, London.

Jay, P. (1965). The common langur of north India. *In* "Primate Behavior" (I. De Vore, ed.), pp. 197–249. Holt, Rinehart and Winston, New York.

Jewell, P. A. (1966). Breeding season and recruitment in some British mammals confined on small islands. *In* "Comparative Biology of Reproduction in Mammals" (I. W. Rowlands, ed.). *Symp. zool. Soc. Lond.* No. 15, 89–116. Academic Press, London and New York.

Kaufmann, J. H. (1962). Ecology and social behaviour of the coati, *Nasua narica*, on Barro Colorado Island, Panama. *Univ. Calif. Publ. Zool.* **60** (3), 95–222.

Koford, C. B. (1957). The vicuna and the puna. *Ecol. Monogr.* **27**, 153–219.

Lamprey, H. F. (1964). Estimation of the large mammal densities, biomass and energy exchange in the Tarangire Game Reserve and the Masai Steppe in Tanganyika. *E. Afr. Wildl. J.* **2**, 1–46.

Lee, R. B. (1963). The population ecology of man in the early Upper Pleistocene of Southern Africa. *Proc. prehist. Soc.* **29**, 235–257.

McNab, B. K. (1963). Bioenergetics and the determination of home range size. *Am. Nat.* **97** (894), 133–140.

Noble, G. K. (1939). The role of dominance in the social life of birds. *Auk* **56**, 263–273.

O'Farrell, T. P. (1965). Home range and ecology of snowshoe hares in interior Alaska. *J. Mammal.* **46**, 406–418.

Pitelka, F. A. (1959). Numbers, breeding schedule, and territoriality in pectoral sandpipers in Northern Alaska. *Condor* **61**, 233–264.

Robinette, W. L. and Child, G. F. T. (1964). Notes on biology of the lechwe (*Kobus leche*). *Puku* No. 2, 84–117.

Rowan, W. (1950). Winter habits and numbers of timber wolves. *J. Mammal.* **31**, 167–169.

Sale, J. B. (1965). Some aspects of the behaviour and ecology of the rock hyraces (*Provacia* and *Heterohyrax*). Ph.D. Thesis, University of London.

Schaller, G. B. (1963). "The Mountain Gorilla." University of Chicago Press.

Schoonmaker, W. J. (1938). Notes on the whitetail deer in New York State. *J. Mammal.* **19**, 503–505.

Seton, E. H. (1910). "Life Histories of Northern Animals", 2 vols. Constable, London.

Severinghaus, C. W. and Cheatum, E. L. (1956). Life and times of the white-tailed deer. *In* "The Deer of North America" (W. P. Taylor, ed.). Stackpole, Pennsylvania and Wildl. Mgmnt. Inst., Washington.

Simonds, P. E. (1965). The bonnet macaque in South India. *In* "Primate Behavior" (I. De Vore, ed.), pp. 175–196. Holt, Rinehart and Winston, New York.

Southern, H. N. (1940). The ecology and population dynamics of the wild rabbit, *Oryctolagus cuniculus*. *Ann. appl. Biol.* **27**, 509–26.

Storm, G. L. (1965). Movements and activities of foxes as determined by radio-tracking. *J. Wildl. Mgmt* **29**, 1–13.

Talbot, L. M. and Stewart, D. R. M. (1964). First wildlife census of the entire Serengeti-Mara region, East Africa. *J. Wildl. Mgmt* **28**, 815–827.

Thompson, D. Q. (1952). Travel, range, and food habits of timber wolves in Wisconsin. *J. Mammal.* **33**, 429–442.

Troyer, W. A. and Hensel, R. J. (1964). Structure and distribution of a Kodiak bear population. *J. Wildl. Mgmt* **28** (4), 769–772.

Symp. zool. Soc. Lond. (1966) No. 18, 111–142.

HOME RANGE AND MOVEMENT OF SMALL MAMMALS

L. E. BROWN

Department of Zoology, Imperial College, London, England

SYNOPSIS

A social hierarchy exists in natural populations of *Apodemus* similar to that found in experimental populations of *Peromyscus* and *Mus*. A powerful dominant controls a stable society. He regularly patrols his territory of 4–6 acres, his position being maintained by aggressive and other factors.

The whole colony has use of the area marked out by the dominant male. Subordinates use common feeding areas, the sizes of their individual ranges varying with age, sex and social position. Some overlapping of ranges is fairly common. The females maintain their home sites regularly both for their own use and that of the "clan". Individual tolerance limits are discussed. Nosing and grooming replace aggression for the residents, but transients will only gradually, if ever, be accepted into the society. A short life span of a few months for the majority further complicates the family groups. Yet here intraspecific control plays a more significant role than does predation. Interspecific reactions, including habitat preferences and peripheral extensions, are discussed.

Intraspecific control by the adult males keeps mice population relatively stable during the spring breeding season, the young being forced to keep out of the way or disperse. Although numbers may be very low at the time of the summer "lull" mice avoid cycles with peak and crash numbers that are found among voles. Female small mammals defend breeding ranges and often challenge the movement of the males amongst these ranges.

Movements above ground are purposeful and include many exploratory activities as well as feeding. Activities are centred around the particular home site in use, the small mammal often returning by the route it used for the outward journey. A night's or even a week's activity may be centred in one particular sector of the range giving the impression that it is longer than broad. Certain areas within the range are favoured and are visited frequently. Home range estimates are discussed both in relation to range length and areas and in relation to tracking and trapping results.

Seasonal movements (migrations) are discussed for mice and lemmings, including possible controls of movements. Artificially induced mass migration would operate in areas where population pressures are low. The theory of lemming migration being a "death" urge acting as a safety valve for over-population is not now accepted.

Range of movement is, however, closely related to population density. The area a *Peromyscus* ranges may be fifty times as large as that of a *Microtus*, but annual population per acre at its maximum may be fifteen *Peromyscus* as compared with 250 *Microtus*. Competition for space will only give a balanced equilibrium when the total combination of the operating forces are ideal for the particular species. Social hierarchies, nocturnal and diurnal rhythms, specialized habitats, seasonal changes of temperature, food, moisture, light and parasitic infections with the resultant physiological, psychological and pathological reactions, all play their part.

Interrelationships of home range, territory and the whole space needed for the animal to achieve its annual cycle (vital space) cannot be fully understood, or assessed, until more is known of the behaviour of each species of small mammals.

INTRODUCTION

In most cases the early estimates of the home range of small mammals were "by-products" of population studies. The worker had records of a number of points at which a small mammal had been captured and by examining these was able to report on the known area in which the animal was active. Obviously there were limitations when the animal's movements were restricted by trapping and to overcome these certain problems were considered: ought an additional peripheral area to be added to the known trapped area; would it be best to use the two most distant points of capture as a basis for calculation or would it be better to establish the geographical centre of all the points at which the animal was trapped and consider the likelihood of capture from this point (Hayne, 1949)?

Since this early work many people have continued to study the activities of small mammals, both in the laboratory and in the field, and we are gradually piecing together a more detailed understanding of their behaviour. It is this later work I wish to consider in relation to the movement of small mammals in their natural habitats.

Throughout all the work certain basic points are apparent. The small mammal cannot survive long as a wanderer, a "home" is vital to its existence. It will maintain it and return to it quickly. The most critical stage in the life of the young animal is the time when it is trying to establish a home, especially since it must be able to survive the residents' aggression.

Burt's (1943) description of home range was for a long time used as a convenient general statement defining this type of behaviour, and can be summarized as "that area around the established home which is traversed by the animal in its normal activities of food gathering, mating and caring for the young. It excludes occasional sallies outside the area". It has actually been found necessary to adjust this concept considerably.

THE SOCIAL HIERARCHY

One of the most important of these adjustments, I believe, is that one must appreciate that the majority of small mammals are part of an organized community. Their position in its social hierarchy will affect their behaviour, including the area over which they move. I have been studying the movements of some of the field mice *Apodemus sylvaticus* (L.) and bank voles *Clethrionomys glareolus britannicus* (Mill.) in a large pine wood at Middlemarsh, Dorset, using a tracking system that has allowed me to trace the movements of a number of small mammals within the same area, see Appendix. This work has continued for several years and each set of results shows certain points of similarity, especially for *A. sylvaticus*. Within a specific area there is one male, the *dominant*, who ranges far more widely than do any of the others, the *subordinants*. The dominant male patrols his range section by section. He explores very thoroughly the area in which he is working, leaving many tracks. He is often accompanied by one or two females, usually different ones in different sections (Figs. 1 and 2).

FIG. 1. Main areas of activity of a dominant male *Apodemus* (D4) from April to September 1963. A. General tracking area. B. General trapping area. Areas A and B were used in all months from April to September, except July. C. Observed or estimated position of home sites.

Areas	In use 1963
1–4	April
5–9	May and June
10–11	August
12–13	September

There was no record of this animal in the area in July. Estimated home range (Minimum Area method), 6·4 acres.

The dominant male and the organized community

Direct observations of some of these dominant males in the field showed they move confidently and without hesitation. The other mice

keep out of the dominant's way. The subordinate appeared to have
regular though brief time for visiting an object but this was postpone
if the dominant was around. Kikkawa (1964) reported similar behaviou
at his observation trap. Sadleir (1965) was able to demonstrate fo
Peromyscus maniculatus a dominance hierarchy which persisted fo
longer than 1 month. Similarly, laboratory experiments with the wil
house mouse, *Mus musculus* showed the importance of the dominan
male. In a relatively short time a single male would control a population
establishing himself by fighting (Crowcroft and Rowe, 1963).

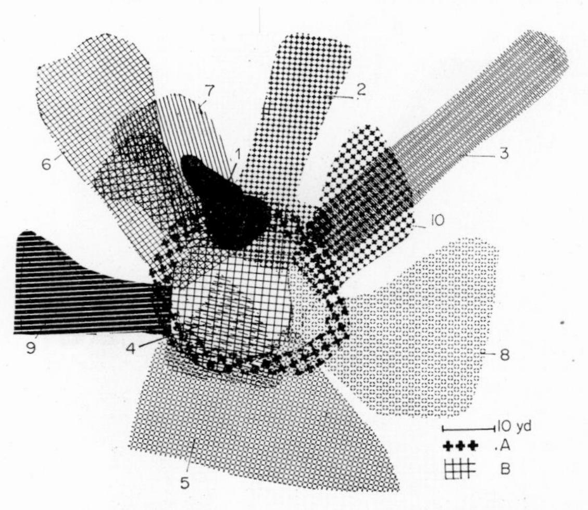

FIG. 2. Area of activity of a dominant male *Apodemus* (D6) from 11 July to 4 Sep-tember 1963. A. General tracking area. 6 August–4 September. B. General trappin area. 11–31 July.

Position of D6 each 3-day period of tracking

Position	Aug.	Position	Aug.	Position	Aug./Sep
1	6–8	5	18–20	9	30–1
2	9–11	6	21–23	10	2–4
3	12–14	7	24–26		
4	15–17	8	27–29		

Whilst at certain times the dominant male concentrates its main activity in sectors of the range (e.g. D4 in Fig. 1), at other times it moves around more freely as shown he for D6. D4 and D6 had adjacent ranges. Estimated home range (Minimum Area method 2·06 acres.

I suggest that one must replace any idea of every mouse with it individual home range in the field with the concept of each individua fitting, or seeking to fit, into a social pattern. As a member of the societ the mouse will move freely within it, accepting its position, especiall during the breeding season. A stable society is important; a stron powerful dominant will control a population where there will be a minimum of social strife (Crowcroft and Rowe, 1957). Bronson (1963) has shown with woodchucks (*Marmota monax*) that once a stable dominance hierarchy was established the individuals knew their relative status one to the other.

Whilst studying an area where a dominant had controlled a population since the early spring I found him dead in one of the traps in early July. During the next 3 months two males increased their range in a population containing many new immigrants (Fig. 3). They appeared to be co-dominant, but by the following spring a new dominant

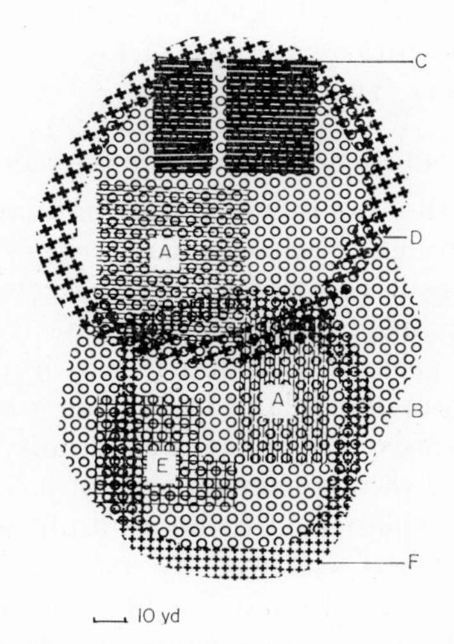

FIG. 3. From 6 April to 6 July 1963 a dominant male (D1) occupied the whole area B. When it died D2 and D3 became co-dominants until September 1963. A. Trapping areas of D1. B. Tracking area of D1. C. Trapping area of D2. D. Tracking area of D2 (outer limits). E. Trapping area of D3. F. Tracking area of D3 (outer limits). Estimated home ranges (Minimum Area method): D1, 3·5 acres; D2, 2·5 acres; D3, 1·7 acres.

male was patrolling the whole area. One factor that tends to complicate studies of this kind is that the life span of any mouse in the wild is short. Usually it is much less than 10 months, for many it is less than 10 weeks. Howard (1949) in fact found that more than half his *Peromyscus maniculatus bairdii* (prairie deer mice) disappeared during the first 5 weeks after birth.

Intraspecific control

The main explanation for continued reduced numbers, especially during the early summer, is that of an intraspecific control (Nicholson,

1933, 1957; Chitty, 1952, 1955, 1960; Christian, 1956, 1957; Louch, 1958; Sadleir, 1965). At the height of the main breeding season the adult males drive away or kill the young males, aggression being linked with the sex hormone level (Sadleir, 1965). It is interesting that in spite of all the outside forces operating upon the small mammal the vital control of its population and movement is apparently an intraspecific one. At all times this community relationship affects the individual, but so far the major interest in its study has been to investigate the situation when the tensions exerted become too great and the small mammals exhibit forms of mental illness. The literature is extensive. Vole populations especially have been studied in relation to these pathological states (Chitty, 1961; Clarke, 1953; Christian, 1957; Hoffman, 1958; Tanaka, 1960, 1962, 1964).

Signalling and agonistic behaviour

Little is known of the way in which the dominant labels its territory. The fact that he thoroughly inspects his territory influences my belief that he lays a scent trail. The water vole, *Arvicola,* marks his range by transferring secretions from his flank glands to his hind feet and then stamps these on the ground. Calhoun (1962) hypothesises that there may be calls across from one "clan" to another which would be outside the human auditory range. He believes each individual small mammal has some knowledge of others over an area of 6–10 acres. Such a large area allows the only explanation to be an auditory signalling system. Waves of calls are implied, followed by quiet periods. One individual would begin a burst of signals that would sweep through the environment. We await, with interest, experimental proof of this theory. We know calls are used by many mammals, birds and insects to mark out their territories or to notify their presence. How silent are the woods? An *Apodemus* is certainly alert to sounds around him.

Whatever means the dominant uses to label his territory certain facts are well known. Firstly, aggression plays a vital part in the dominant's behaviour. Secondly, the other mice know when he is around and mostly keep out of the way. Thirdly, when active above ground the small mammal is never "off guard". All its senses are keenly alerted. Aggression is not confined, however, to the dominant male. Some degree is found in all the adult males, according to their status, and in pregnant females (Crowcroft and Rowe, 1963, for *Mus*; for *Peromyscus* McCabe and Blanchard, 1950; Eisenberg, 1962; Sadleir, 1965). During the main breeding season the adult male *Apodemus* or *Peromyscus* will kill or drive away all who might interfere with his activities.

Early in the breeding season the adult males who have survived the winter have overwhelming control. They are so aggressive to the developing juveniles that very few of the latter are recruited into the population compared with the numbers carried by the pregnant females (Sadleir, 1965, for *Peromyscus*). My studies suggest the behaviour of the male *Apodemus* is similar; contributing to the very low June numbers (Brown, 1954; Miller, 1957; Tanton, 1965). The plight of the young male is desperate. Either he must oust out a low aggressive resident, find an empty space, or die (Andrewarthra and Birch, 1954). He may be more successful if he just manages to keep out of the way. In the field this "keeping out of trouble" can account for many examples of low home ranges. Sadleir (1965) in his maze experiments found that the juveniles who ranged too freely into territory occupied by dominant males were found dead. Those who kept themselves out of trouble survived by keeping to very small movements from base.

By the late summer few of the older males are still alive. The young males are now able to establish themselves and a second breeding peak occurs (Bishop and Delany, 1963).

Records of movements of small mammals need to be considered in relationship to the animal's age and to the season. In many instances the movements of what were probably dominant males, or their associating females were regarded as atypical and ignored (Hacker and Pearson, 1951; Allred and Beck, 1963; Tanton, 1965).

To regard all longer movements of the dominants as "occasional sallies" is not in accordance with the normal behaviour of the more aggressive males.

THE RANGE OF THE COMMUNITY

Areas of general use

I found for *Apodemus* that some parts of the woodland were in general use by the "clan" and that their holes were often more or less concentrated into groups. A number of resident mice would use these holes. The residents know their environment well (Blair, 1940; Caldwell, 1964). It is the transient that is at the grave disadvantage. We introduced a young male *Apodemus* into a woodland at Silwood. It repeatedly returned back to the trap from which we released it (Brown, 1956b), rather than escaping down the residents' runways. A strange *Apodemus* is more likely to be accepted into the collective feeding area—so long as it ventures no further, although gradually it may be absorbed into the "clan" (Curry-Lindahl, 1959).

The home site

My own observations confirm that for *Apodemus* and *Clethrionomys* several home sites, usually four or five, are used at one time for each individual. They are regularly visited and cleaned out. Similar results have been reported by Blair (1951) for beach mice and by Terman (1962) for prairie deermice. Home sites under trees that appear fairly permanent are not, however, always in use. Some new ones are made and old ones neglected for a time, to be re-opened perhaps by another generation the following year. In the autumn several of the holes will be used as foodstores and will be visited regularly. Whilst the dominant male patrols the whole area sector by sector, each member of the group, particularly the female, regularly inspects her section both for her own use or for escape tunnels for any other resident (Fig. 4).

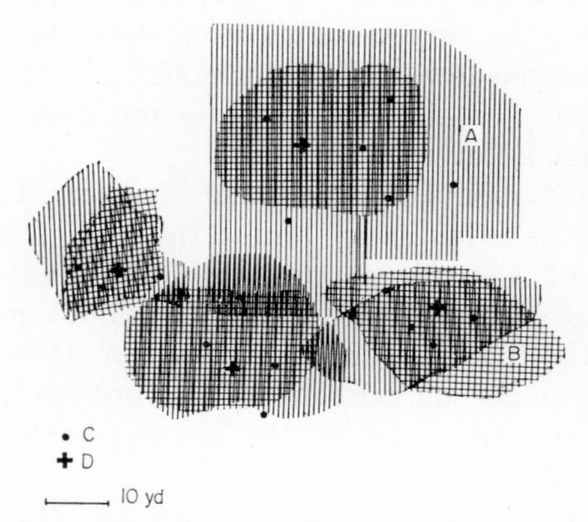

FIG. 4. Areas of activity of four female *Apodemus* from 24 May to 10 June 1963. A. Tracking area. B. Trapping area. C. Position of home sites that were in use. D. Centre of activity (Hayne, 1949). Little overlap of ranges occurred. Each female regularly maintained a number of home sites (direct observation). The four home ranges were 0·16, 0·18, 0·19 and 0·39 acres (Minimum Area method).

The well-established fact that the small mammal usually moves its home site to a greater or less extent is often not detected by trapping. Kikkawa (1964) describes how a female *Clethrionomys* moved to a new site three times between July and October—a fact he found with his radioactive tracking technique that trapping had not revealed.

Individual tolerance limits

Whilst the idea of each small mammal operating all its life from its own single hole is probably incorrect for the majority, yet there is another factor controlling the area over which many of these animals move. An individual tolerance limit may exist which in certain cases is so low that association within a group is impossible (Davis, 1958). Terman (1963) found that when he bred prairie deermice in isolation they remained unsociable throughout life and homed significantly more quickly than did the mouse born under natural conditions. Intra-specifically this behaviour will tend to spread the community. Within a quiet stabilized community, controlled by a strong dominant, "individual" or "safety" distances exist. Lockley (1961) found that for the wild rabbit, *Oryctolagus cuniculus*, these were 3 ft between dominant and secondary males and 1 ft, or a body's length, between other males and females.

Interspecifically a mutual avoidance will allow the co-existence of two species, even though one is dominant. Caldwell (1964) experimentally demonstrated this when he kept four *Peromyscus* and four *Mus* in an enclosed area. At first the two species kept at opposite ends, with some overlap, but eventually the *Mus* died, having a disadvantage over competition for food. *Peromyscus* then extended its range to cover the whole area. This type of behaviour which may in the field be dismissed as habitat preference is not always detected. The loss of dominance of the rabbit showed how it had subordinated the hare (Rothschild, 1958; Rothschild and Marsh, 1956).

Interspecific reactions

Restriction of movement of this type is also found at the periphery of two areas, each judged to be the typical habitat of one of the species. *Apodemus sylvaticus* and *Apodemus flavicollis* will both move temporarily into denuded *Microtus* areas, although they retreat to the woodlands when the *Microtus* population increases (Brown, 1954, 1956a; Curry-Lindahl, 1959). After over-wintering in barns it is easier for *Apodemus* to establish itself with the more tolerant vole. *Microtus* with its relatively small home range will provide more living space for the transient mouse during these early months. In the woodlands the resident male *Apodemus* are highly aggressive to all intruders at this time. The situation changes from July onwards. The transient mice will meet less antagonism in the wood and more aggression from the increasing *Microtus* population in the fields. Vigorous rejection of juveniles and transients early in the year keeps the numbers of *Apodemus* diluted and avoids the strains of overpopulation. In Japan, a colony of Smith's red bank voles, *Eothenomys*, showed peak levels in 1955 followed by a crash. Tanaka (1956, 1957, 1960, 1963b, 1964) has found that during this last decade they have fluctuated in phase. Yet the associating *Apodemus argenteus* has shown no such violent changes.

Habitat preferences

Habitat preferences and the dominance of one species over another are often easier to detect in the field than to explain. Good ground cover gave the Skomer vole (*Clethrionomys glareolus skomerensis*) areas of advantage over *Apodemus* (Fullager *et al.*, 1963). Often two habitats which appear to have the same vegetation have just that difference of microtopography (nest site, cover, food, etc.) to allow one species a greater advantage (Curry-Lindahl, 1959). All these factors affect the size of the small mammal's range. Boyd (1963) showed how the St. Kilda field mouse, *Apodemus sylvaticus hirtensis*, had its movements affected by the distribution of cleitans (man-made stone shelters). Behavioural differences of the species, on the other hand, may largely contribute to their choice of habitat. In laboratory experiments Brown (1964) found *Peromyscus boylii* and *Peromyscus leucopus* to be socially incompatible. Their fighting would explain the sharpness of the ecological distribution of the two species. *Peromyscus leucopus* lives in cedar glades whilst *Peromyscus boylii* is found at their periphery.

NORMAL PATTERNS OF BEHAVIOUR

Homing, wandering and dispersal

There is a spatial framework to each population, affected by all neighbouring forces and delicately in balance. Harrison (1958) tried to increase the numbers of Malayan rats by adding others to a natural population. He did not succeed. The new rats left the area and where possible returned to their original home. The impressive speed at which homing occurs is the best evidence of the spatial framework of the population. Evans (1942) and Hacker and Pearson (1944) found *Apodemus sylvaticus* moved back half-a-mile in a day. Boyd (1963) reported the St. Kilda field mice back, even from as far as 2 800 ft in a few hours. I have found in the pine woods in Dorset that *Apodemus* is back home from similar distances before my next visit to the traps (about 6 h). They will move, if necessary, during the daylight. Wandering in foreign territory is hazardous and the need to defend their own home is great.

Lockley's (1961) experiments with wild rabbits in large enclosures illustrate this fate of a displaced dominant. A buck, designated M_7, patrolled his warren every evening and from time to time made excursions which covered the whole of his territory. He was not satisfied until every rabbit had retreated before him, any failure to submit was followed by an attack by M_7 to convince the underling of his status.

In October M_7 was removed and kept away from his territory for 3 weeks. During this time he made desperate efforts to return, he pined and stopped feeding. M_{21}, the second dominant male, took over in M_7's absence and fierce fighting followed when M_7 returned. M_{21}, the victor, remained in the best warren and maintained this position for the whole of the breeding season. Not until the following July did M_7 become first dominant again. The life span of a male *Apodemus* is not long enough to allow for "second chances".

In spite of this strong urge to return to its home it is important to realize that wandering and dispersal movements are as much a part of the life of a mouse, especially a male, as are the restricted movements around its home site. As Kikkawa (1964) has pointed out in relation to an understanding of population dynamics: it is more important to know the proportion of animals in the population which show wandering and dispersal movements and how these vary with age, sex, season, habitat and density than to obtain a calculated size of the average of its range.

Exploration

In its natural habitat the small mammal spends a great deal of its time, when above ground, exploring, learning about its environment and keeping a check on its own home range. Details of this behaviour are known for *Microtus* (Shillito, 1963a). When actively exploring the vole, with all senses alerted, follows a series of jerky movements, and if alarmed will dash back for cover. Smell is highly important. First the *Microtus* "noses" and then with jerky gait approaches the object. The jerkiness is due to a mixture of fear and curiosity, it is the consequence of immobility followed by quick movements and is typical of many camouflaged animals. The body when rigid is low to the ground and maximally extended. The object when reached is smelt and touched with the front feet. I have watched similar behaviour with *Clethrionomys* and *Apodemus* when they approach my tracking cartons. Personally, I always wear gloves to keep human smells to a minimum. Were it not for this drive to explore, tracking results would be more difficult to obtain; in fact regular visits are made to objects, even familiar ones. Laboratory experiments demonstrating this have been performed with wild house mice (Crowcroft, 1955; Crowcroft and Jeffers, 1961).

The small mammal is an active animal, with much to explore and its period above ground is spent in many pursuits other than feeding. It is not confined, as is a laboratory animal, to a small enclosure. Recording absences from the home site for more than 15 min, Kikkawa

(1964) studied (during the winter) the periods of activity of a male *Apodemus*. It had two long outings around dusk and one from 2.00–4.45 h, followed by another short one at dawn. Similarly for a male *Clethrionomys* there were four active periods of roughly 1–2 h durations, mainly at dusk and dawn. These were longer periods than those animals had ever spent at the observation trap and during these active periods they were recorded by a Geiger–Müller counter at several points. Extended trips of exploration are considered to be typical of the majority of mice. Experimental evidence of such movement is very difficult to obtain.

Peripheral extensions

Either by its own exploration, or from the lack of auditory signals, the small mammal appears to know when an area is unused. In 1950 existing populations at Silwood of both *Apodemus* and *Clethrionomys* were considerably reduced by "Cimex" treatment for rabbits (Brown, 1954). Yet new *Apodemus*, in particular, soon occupied the empty areas. *Clethrionomys* took longer to recover. Its more restricted movements, concentrated around areas of dense cover and deterred by more open ground, meant that rapid re-establishments were not to be expected. There is much similar evidence showing that if an area loses a proportion of its population others will enter after a short time (Blair, 1940; Stickel, 1946; Calhoun and Webb, 1953).

The influence of predation

As well as range extension there is usually a surplus of young animals needing "living room". This is why predation is regarded as having only a temporary effect on small mammal numbers (Blair, 1940; Calhoun and Webb, 1953; Chitty, 1957; Frank, 1957, Darling, 1959). The predators, once they have reduced the numbers of a population must look to new feeding areas. They will always be drawn to areas where foraging is easiest. There are, however, several studies that have illustrated the temporary power of their control. Brant (1962) gives an example of the complete destruction of a *Microtus* population. Roughly twenty-four mice a day were eaten by cats that would sit by the *Microtus* runways. Pearson (1964) studied a 35 acre area in California and found that in one winter predators consumed 4 000 *Microtus*, 400 harvest mice, and 500 wild house mice. Cats were the dominant predator, but there were also foxes, raccoons and skunks.

Several cats from nearby houses were seen at Middlemarsh, in the early morning, as well as a barn owl and weasels. I would consider one of the heaviest attacks on the spring and summer populations came from the grass snake, *Tropidonotus natrix*, judging by their numbers and their size.

One wonders how much warning can be given to any small mammal of the predator's presence. Do auditory calls play any part? The greatest defence need is in fact to maintain the colony against individuals of the same species, i.e. in the establishment of either a home range or a territory. The retention of a sufficiently large area for feeding, the protection of the young by the female, the sexual satisfaction of the male—these, not a safeguarding against predation, control behaviour.

The control of territories and breeding ranges

Burt (1943) defined territory as "that part of the home range which is protected from individuals of the same species either by fighting or by aggressive gestures". This term must be considered collectively; for example, a territory may be a feeding ground used by an entire population that may be settled elsewhere (Curry-Lindahl, 1959). A socially organized pattern restricts the maintenance of individual territories to the dominants, e.g. where there is an infestation of wild house mice in a corn rick (Crowcroft and Rowe, 1963). In the field I found the dominant *Apodemus* had prime control of his wide territory only sector by sector. In his absence others were moving freely around. However, once the hierarchy is accepted, nosing and grooming replace aggression, as was shown by King (1957) in laboratory tests with male *Peromyscus maniculatus bairdii*.

Breeding ranges set up by the females are the most fiercely defended. Male *Microtus* are only allowed near breeding territories when the females are in oestrus (Frank, 1957). Breeding ranges are established by female shrews (*Sorex araneus*) and the males move freely among them. This ensures not only the best chance of rearing the young, but allows the males to find the females for the short time they are in oestrus (Shillito, 1963b).

In searching for the females the range of the male is often rectangular. Studying meadow mice, Mohr and Stumpf (1964) found that the home range of the males was of the order of two to eight times as long as wide. Contact with more females will be made on such a strip than in a compact circular area. Escape from predators would be easier. A further advantage they considered was that such a strip would sample more types of habitat, favourable under all weather conditions, and at different times of the year. Godfrey's (1954) ranges for *Microtus* were mostly rectangular.

Tracking *Apodemus* males I found they tended to move out along a single radius which made any particular part of their range appear to be rectangular.

HOME RANGE ESTIMATES

Telemetry and radioactive tracers

The calculation of the actual area over which the small mammal moves is almost always confined to its activities above ground. A further refinement of radiotracking devices will probably allow us to track its underground movements which are usually extensive. They not only consist of subterranean runs connecting one sheltered area to another, as for *Clethrionomys*, but do in fact represent the main activity of the small mammal, even to some extent for their feeding. Shillito (1963b) pointed out that the shrews remain below soil level in the winter, mainly because their food is there; the soil invertebrates migrating to this level.

Telemetry opens up the possibility of a far more extensive study, especially for the secretive animal or one that lives in dense cover or underground. Radio signals are received from rotating antennae supported on two towers spaced half a mile apart (Tester, 1963). After amplification and conversion these are fed to a fifty-two channel receiving and recording system in a laboratory between the two towers. Data can be continuously recorded on 16 mm film and a computer does the automatic map construction showing the time and range of activity. Rapid calculations of the centre of activity and the distance of all points from this centre can be made (Siniff and Tester, 1965).

So far the animals used have been larger than small mammals. An automatic record to replace the human handling of every piece of data is for most of us, as yet, only a dream. Tester and Siniff's (1965) results with the male raccoon, *Procyon lotor*, show interesting points of similarity with my work with male *Apodemus*. The animals worked sectionally, the length of their activity radii were considerably influenced by such environmental factors as weather and season and whilst the whole range was fairly regularly visited there were areas of intensive use within the home range. The centre of activity was not a place of any biological significance. As yet the radio-ecologist usually finds it best to work with only one animal in an area, therefore not allowing a study of a community.

Whilst tracking methods give us more possibility of understanding movements, direct observations will always be needed for a full appreciation of the animal's activities. Methods of study used for estimating movements based on trap-release data have been reviewed (Brown,

1962). They either assume there is a fixed boundary to the home range, or they estimate from the basis of the probability of capture at certain distances from a definite point.

Table I shows how wide a range of movement will be found, many of the factors involved have been discussed. In Table I no distinction is made between ages, sexes, seasons, shifts of home site, population density or methods employed. I suggest that any range size above 2 acres for *Apodemus* or *Peromyscus* represents the behaviour of the

TABLE I

Variation in range size within selected communities

Species	Range size (acres)	Reference
Mice and deermice		
Apodemus sylvaticus	0·004–5·67	Miller, 1958
	0·23–2·87	Brown, 1956a
	0·20–6·00	Brown*
	0·065–1·06	Kikkawa, 1964
agrarius	0·54–1·06	Youngman, 1956
	0·80–3·73	Howell, 1954
Peromyscus polionotus	0·97–10·66	Blair, 1951
gossypinus	0·45–4·36	Griffo, 1961
maniculatus	0·74–1·67	Morris, 1955
boylii	0·22–0·87	Brown, 1964
Mus musculus	0·42–1·65	Howell, 1954
Voles		
Clethrionomys glareolus	0·17–1·8	Brown, 1956a
	0·20–1·34	Brown*
	0·13–0·94	Kikkawa, 1964
rufocanus	0·08–0·23	Ueda, 1949
	0·19–0·54	Tanaka, 1953
gapperi	0·49–3·56	Blair, 1941a
	0·37–0·98	Morris, 1955
Microtus pennsylvanicus	0·19–0·50	Blair, 1940
	0·02–0·58	Blair, 1941b
	0·07–0·58	Hayne, 1950
montebelli	0·06–0·28	Tanaka and Teramura, 1953
arvalis	0·07–0·37	Reichstein, 1960
agrestis	0·06–0·70	Brown, 1956a
ochrogaster	0·05–0·18	Harvey and Barbour, 1965

* Results from Middlemarsh, 1963.

dominant as did such ranges at Middlemarsh. Miller (1958) had two male *Apodemus* with large ranges during the breeding season. He suggested they were unmated animals searching for females, they could have been two dominant males. In Table I results are shown of Harvey and Barbour's (1965) radioisotopic tagging of *Microtus ochrogaster*. The tags were inserted subcutaneously and with each 10 ft movement of the scintillation pole they were able to check over an area 40 ft wide, including some subterranean activity. Four males tracked in the same area showed there was some overlapping of ranges for them (and probably for others in the same area). Records of roughly twice the size shown in Table I were obtained using the Minimum Area method (Brown, 1962). Table I gives results from their modified Minimum Area method where a quarter range length was used as a standard to fix the outer limits of the range.

Table I shows the extremes of the range size from the small juvenile to the most adventurous male. The movements of the majority are, however, much more limited, as will be seen in Table II. The greater average range of the male compared with the female is also shown.

Range lengths and range sizes

Linear measurements from which home ranges are calculated are usually either the straight line distance between the two most widely separated points of capture (range length) or measurements from a calculated centre of activity. Range length may be used to discuss home range, without conversion to areas (Stickel, 1954). In these terms the average range length for *Peromyscus leucopus* lies between 67 and 133 yd for males and 50 and 100 yd for females (Stickel and Warbach, 1960). Similarly figures for *Apodemus sylvaticus* are 40–80 yd for males and 20–60 yd for females (Evans, 1942; Brown, 1956a; Miller, 1958; Kikkawa, 1964; Tanton, 1965). In Table III, which gives other examples, the two sets of figures (a) and (b) represent results from the same data of more than fourteen captures (a) and from four to seven captures (b). The authors believed a true home range lay between these two sets of figures: an illustration of the type of variation experienced according to experimental and other factors (age, sex, season and size of habitat).

Recent work with the common shrew, *Sorex araneus* (Shillito, 1963c), illustrates a more realistic use of range length. Whilst one could make an overall average range length for this species of 28–39 m this was best analysed as an average of 37 m for juveniles, 39·6 m for short range females but up to 112 m for long range females, who moved to a new range before breeding. Whilst some short range males moved between 22 and 66 m other males showed prolonged wanderings. Those remaining within the wood recorded distances between 79 and 144 m, but others left the wood temporarily or permanently. In general the shrew adjusted its range length to its particular habitat and the focus of activity was always from the particular hole in which it was living.

Dice and Howard (1951), studying snow tracks of prairie deermice, found that each animal returned by exactly the same route as it used when it set out. My track results with *Apodemus* always suggest this but cannot prove it. Similarly, only natural tracks in snow or sand will determine the exact point from which the animal is operating. Before these tracks have melted or been blown away one can measure linear distances. Blair (1951) found for *Peromyscus polionotus* (beach mice) that these varied from 5 to 293 yd, the mice always making purposeful

TABLE II

Average range sizes

Species	Average range size (acres) Male	Female		Reference
Mice and deermice				
Apodemus sylvaticus	0·72	0·24		Miller, 1958
	0·53	0·43		Brown, 1956a
	0·77	0·39		Brown*
	0·45	0·27		Kikkawa, 1964
Peromyscus gossypinus	1·82	1·44		Griffo, 1961
maniculatus	0·63	0·61		Blair, 1940
	2·31	1·39		Blair, 1942
boylii	0·64	0·38		Brown, 1964
Voles				
Clethrionomys glareolus	0·40	0·31		Brown, 1956a
	0·38	0·29		Brown*
	0·55	0·27		Kikkawa, 1964
rufocanus	0·47	0·21		Tanaka, 1953
Microtus pennsylvanicus	0·31	0·19	Moist grassland	Blair, 1940
	0·50	0·28	Dry grassland	Blair, 1940
	0·43	0·19		Hayne, 1949
agrestis	0·24	0·16		Brown, 1956a

* Results from Middlemarsh, 1965.

trips away from and back to the hole. Tracking, unless each individual mouse is labelled, does not tell you the number of animals involved nor the actual number of trips made. It is because of these difficulties that, with trapping data, the centre of activity (Hayne, 1949; Dice and Clarke, 1953) is used. Obviously percentage movements from such a point are a general mathematical estimation, but they may be the best type of analysis that the particular data allows.

Comparisons of trap and track results

How far do the tracking results I have obtained for *Apodemus* compare with published trap records? Stickel and Warbach (1960) describe a 5-year trapping, at roughly 2-monthly intervals of the wood-mouse, *Peromyscus leucopus*. They group their results into four categories. Firstly, a limited number of mice had extensive ranges and showed changing areas of use. Within the period of study five males travelled extensively over the entire woodlot (4·4 acres), either sectorially or making an almost complete circuit within a particular trapping

TABLE III

Average range of movement

Species	Range length (m) Males	Range length (m) Females	Reference
Mice and deermice			
Apodemus sylvaticus	53	47	Brown, 1956a
	61	35	Miller, 1958
agrarius	119	83	Jones and Barber, 1957
Peromyscus maniculatus	160	102	Allred and Beck, 1963
leucopus (a)	115	85	Stickel and Warbach, 1960
(b)	57	42·5	
gossypinus	63	58	Shadowen, 1963
nutalli	79·5	62	Shadowen, 1963
Voles			
Microtus agrestis	36	27	Brown, 1956a
Clethrionomys glareolus	53	43	Brown, 1956a
rufocanus	61·1	25·7	Tanaka, 1953

Range of movement (or range length) is the straight line distance between the two most widely separated points of capture.

period. Very complete details are given for one male, no. 3348, who lived for a record 38 months and was captured more than any other mouse (118 times in nineteen trapping periods from December 1950 to January 1954; Table IV). Its home site was in the east quarter of the

TABLE IV

Trapping history of a male Peromyscus leucopus (No. 3348)

Year	Month	Position of captures in each period (4·4 acre woodlot)
1950	December	South corner
1951	February and April	East quarter
	June	Diagonal route across woodlot
	August, September and November	East quarter
1952	January	East quarter
	March	East quarter to south corner
	May	Diagonal route across woodlot
	July	East quarter
	September	East quarter to south corner
	December	West quarter
1953	February	West quarter
	April	Almost complete circuit
	June	East quarter to central area
	October	East quarter
1954	January	Central area (not trapped here before)

P. leucopus No. 3348, was trapped 118 times from December 1950 to January 1954 (Stickel and Warbach, 1960).

woodlot, in a tangle of honeysuckle and dead branches; in one of the favourite positions. When no. 3348 was absent other mice were regularly trapped here. No. 3348 was first captured when about 2 months old and appears to have remained on the area during the whole of its long life. Since his first capture was as a sub-adult he probably invaded the woodlot from elsewhere. It is considered likely that on occasions he departed on trips of exploration (Stickel, 1965, personal communication). Such an animal corresponds with a dominant male *Apodemus*. Two females were reported in this category; for *Apodemus* this meant they were associating with a dominant male.

The second category includes the mice that occupy stable ranges: 79% of the mice (seventeen males and twenty females) had relatively stable ranges and stayed in the same general area from month to month. This is the general pattern of behaviour of the majority of subordinate female *Apodemus*. The third category include the mice for whom occasional records exist for long trips away from their normal home range, and the fourth category deals with the *Peromyscus* who shift their range perhaps gradually across an area.

SEASONAL MOVEMENTS

The movements of the male small mammals deserve further consideration. It is a well-established fact that they normally move over wider areas than do the females. Their increased range may coincide with the breeding condition of the female. Miller (1958) found the average range for male *Apodemus* from March to May was 88 yd compared with 20 yd in September and November. After the spring breeding season their behaviour will partly depend on their position in the social hierarchy. The dominants appear to remain located in their favourite positions even if they move around more freely with some extended trips of exploration. In the whole population there is, however, especially in June, a great reduction in trappable numbers (Evans, 1942; Brown, 1954; Miller, 1958; Kikkawa, 1964; Tanton, 1965), resulting in a "summer lull" in the population. The reasons for this include the fact that the death rate of over-wintered animals goes up in early summer (Chitty and Chitty, 1962, for *Microtus*; Shillito, 1963b, for *Sorex araneus*).

This is the time of dispersal of sub-adults and juveniles of both sexes, and there is much evidence that the adults, especially the males, are moving out of woodlands to cultivated fields, corresponding with local farming activities (Miller, 1958; Rowe *et al.*, 1963). Absence from an area, with subsequent reappearance is again common at this time (Blair, 1940; Miller, 1958; Shadowen, 1963; Kikkawa, 1964). More males than females wander and fewer return. Thus the calculated death and dilution rates for *Apodemus* are higher for males than for females and the majority of long-term recaptures are those of females (Kikkawa, 1964).

Tanton (1965) could find little evidence for migration from his data, and believed there was a twin population of *Apodemus* in the summer, of which the trapped animals were but a small percentage. Disinterest in entering a trap could be explained if "lying out" occurs in subordinate *Apodemus* as it does with those rabbits that are without warrens (Lockley, 1961). Feeding habits change seasonally (Miller, 1954) and abundant insect food could explain lack of interest in corn-baited traps. Food storage is unlikely to occur until later in the year.

Seasonal movements, or migrations, are a normal pattern of behaviour for many small mammals. In winter they congregate for warmth in dry habitats (cornricks, barns and houses) and in spring they return to breeding grounds and establish their homes (Curry-Lindahl, 1956, for *Apodemus* and *Microtus agrestis*; Tevis, 1956, for *Peromyscus*; DeCoursey, 1957, for *Microtus pennsylvanicus*). Lemming migrations are similarly connected with seasonal changes of habitat and are an effective mechanism of dispersal (Kalela, 1949, 1961). The concept of a "death" migration as a safety valve of overpopulation is not now accepted. Field observations dispel the old-fashioned concept of "foolhardiness". Autumn migration, usually in the darkest part of the night, is fairly directive and at about 3·6 km per h. Running paths, giving protection and ease of movement are preferred, and swimming is only attempted when the land is silhouetted on the other side of the lake. The nostrils are kept well out of the water, high mortality occurring in windy weather, as waves are dangerous. Lemming migration is much more solitary in its general nature than one concludes from many descriptions in the early literature (Myllymäki *et al.*, 1962).

To what extent do small mammals move during the spring and summer in such a manner that it could be regarded as migration: a dispersal mechanism connected with seasonal changes of habitat? Although other explanations exist there is always the possibility of migration having occurred when trappable numbers in an area can, but do not always, fall to nil as, for example, at the time of the summer lull (Brown, 1954, for *Microtus*; Stickel and Warbach, 1960, for *Peromyscus*; Tanton, 1965, for *Apodemus*). This is a normal time for juvenile and sub-adult dispersal due to agonistic behaviour of the adult males. If migratory movement of the adults is also occurring at this time it is operating when the population pressures are very low. Calhoun (1962) seeks to create artificially such depleted areas in order to examine induced mass migrations. He suggests that signals will tell the mouse directions where competition is least and the mouse will be seeking to keep a maximum distance from its nearest neighbour. With the absence of signals in a particular area the mouse will experience an urge to move in this direction. This urge is so great that at the limit the mouse will be moving to its death over unsuitable terrain (disproved for lemmings; Kalela, 1961). An urge that can overcome those controlling social behaviour, and breeding, is a very strong one indeed. Landmarks, retreats, signals, foodstores, and all other normal stimuli are sacrificed.

I believe these experiments are only feasible outside the main breeding season and forces that control a small mammal to settle would prevent the whole population from taking part. The "stay at homes" would remain. Does a wanderer continue to wander or does it stop when a suitable home is found? Calhoun's experiments are designed to investigate whether you can induce small mammals away from agricultural land. "Control densities in neighbouring reservoir habitats and the damage to adjoining agricultural land will diminish to a point of economic insignificance".

Migrations, at all seasons, are fundamentally associated with survival, and linked with availability of food. In the summer the small mammal can be selective in its choice of food, moving to favourite feeding areas (Miller, 1958; Curry-Lindahl, 1959, 1962.). A strong natural migration into agricultural land, when crops are attractive as food, will be very difficult to counterbalance. Calhoun's (1962) suggested experimental procedures deal with "a phenomenon of behavioural physics of population, in which many 'atoms' or units, the individual animals, are required for appropriate analysis". Six to twelve workers would daily handle several thousand animals for at least a 90-day continuous removal period. As Calhoun comments, biological studies of population seldom utilize such a mass effort.

DISCUSSION

Whether one is thinking in terms of behavioural physics of populations, of single communities or of single individuals, much has yet to be investigated concerning both the methods and causes of the movements of small mammals. These movements range from a miniature type of nomadism within a small area around the home to the long migrations in search of food and shelter for the winter or in search of a mate in the spring. The home is the base from which the small mammal will direct its normal activities, here then will be the maximum safety, security and social stability. The concept of home range embodies an important biological and psychological pattern of behaviour. It is our definitions that are limited because we are attempting to state in static terms (e.g. acres) the area of activity of a living mobile animal that may have its movements influenced by a great many factors in the physical and biological environment (Blair, 1951). Home range is best considered as "that area habitually traversed by the individual in its normal activities within a specific period of time" (Shillito, 1963c). Alternatively, one can consider the animal's "movement pattern"—

the actual movement in three-dimensional space that the animal makes during a specific period of time (Brant, 1962).

The composition of the community will affect the range of movement (Calhoun, 1962). Within the one species a social hierarchy exists. Between two species there may be a balanced relationship, of dominance and subordination, or of time (nocturnal and diurnal rhythm of activity) or of microhabitats within the same environment. Other, less common species, will restrict themselves to highly specialized localities.

General statements regarding the movements of all small mammals may be limited in value because the fundamental reasons for diversity in population densities may vary. Population size and range of movement are closely interrelated. Brant (1962) estimates that the area occupied by an individual *Peromyscus* may be fifty times as large as that occupied by a *Microtus*. Calhoun (1962) regards *Microtus* as an "extra-community" species, probably representing a late evolutionary stage in overcoming complexities of small mammal communities. Such species tend to be grass eaters. They tolerate excessively high densities, although the causes of their "crash" are still being investigated. *Microtus agrestis* at Lake Vyrnwy averaged in good habitats 120 voles per acre in the spring and 250–300 voles per acre in the autumn (Chitty and Chitty, 1962). A comparable average range of numbers for *Apodemus sylvaticus* is from three animals per acre in the late spring to seventeen animals per acre in the autumn (Brown, 1954; Miller, 1958; Kikkawa, 1964). Small movement pattern and high densities for *Microtus* were considered interdependent by Brant (1962). Similarly, he judged that seasonal changes in the mean distance between successive captures (average distances) of the deermice and harvestmice he studied were inversely density dependent. Comparative figures of average distances for *Peromyscus maniculatus gambeli* and *Microtus californicus californicus* were 172 ft for the former and 26 ft for the latter.

The living space needed by any individual small mammal varies, therefore, from one species to another. This space can be classified in three ways: as the animal's home range, its territory, or its vital space. Home range is the area used by the individual within a specific period of time, territory is that area defended intraspecifically and vital space is the whole space necessary for an animal to achieve its annual cycle (Saint Girons and Saint Girons, 1959).

Competition for this space by the individual, the "clan" or the species will cause constant reactions that only ideally will give a balanced equilibrium. Small mammals provide a great part of the food of larger carnivorous mammals (and birds of prey). Their success in survival is to an important extent due to their high rate of breeding. Yet the intraspecific control of numbers would appear to be more important than any other factor in the natural environment. Either high populations are tolerated or there is constant intraspecific strife and a dominance hierarchy. In the latter case, with *Apodemus*, the stronger and older males control the spring breeding and the family group. The territory of the clan is protected by the males and maintained by the females. Only the fittest young will survive an enforced dispersal. Social strife need not always involve aggressive behaviour, but its effects may be marked even in individuals not directly involved. Crowcroft and Jeffers (1961) found the attitude of the female *Mus* to entry into traps was influenced by the presence or absence of males.

Homing experiments have often assumed that a lake is a barrier to small mammal movements (Hacker and Pearson, 1944, 1951). Recent work by Sheppe (1965) has shown that *Peromyscus leucopus* behaves like the lemming when needing to cross open water. The swimming is towards visible goals and only when land is silhouetted on the other side. Both have the same inability to swim under water, and drown in choppy conditions. Where floating plant life is present in the lake the mouse runs over this as if it were on dry land. The longest swim of a *Peromyscus* was 765 ft when the animal was returning to its island home. All the emigrants from natural populations were young mice.

The life of the small mammal within its natural community is as yet only vaguely understood. The captive animal must modify its drives for exploration, for food seeking, for protection against enemies or seasonal hazards. In orientation, the diurnal *Clethrionomys* relies more on sight whilst the nocturnal agile *Apodemus* relies more on sounds and perhaps vibrations. Whitaker (1963) described how the meadow jumping mouse, *Zapus*, produces a drumming noise by vibrating its tail rapidly. Each time this behaviour was observed the animal was in a high state of excitement in its cage. In the wild, ground vibration will be as important a warning as sound to a burrowing animal. How important they are for any particular species has yet to be investigated. Vocalization, as part of the small mammal's behaviour similarly needs more study. Lemmings use sounds as part of their threat display (Myllimäki *et al.*, 1962). I have observed this behaviour more often with the voles *Clethrionomys* and *Microtus* than with the mice *Apodemus* and *Mus*.

Where a dominant controls a community his activity will limit the territory within which individual home ranges operate. The size of such territory for a dominant *Apodemus* is about 4–6 acres. Howard

(1949) and Redman and Sealander (1958) found *Peromyscus* regularly moved over 5–6 acres, with one example moving over 10 acres. Except for this territorial patrolling of the dominant male, ranges revealed by live trapping appear to be significantly related to natural ranges. Stickel (1954) found this true when making experimental comparisons. I am in agreement with Blair (1951) that this is broadly true when comparing them with tracking results. No method yet devised is without its limitations. There is a maximum length beyond which the majority of small mammals seldom extend their range (Tanaka, 1963a). The boundaries for a clan appear to be those established by the dominant. Only those small mammals without homes will disperse further and they may do this at any time (Brant, 1962). A social hierarchy may itself mean that more than half the population is crowded into a few areas whilst the favourite positions remain empty under the dominants' control (Crowcroft and Rowe, 1963, for *Mus*). Although there is more space in the natural environment than there is under experimental conditions order still prevails. Even when spring flooding put most of the range out of action *Peromyscus* moved to drier areas within its range. Enlargement of the range did not occur (Ruffer, 1961).

Mutual avoidance will often prevent aggression. Brown (1964) found that *P. leucopus*, *P. maniculatus* and *P. boylii* would not actively seek out each other but would exhibit aggressive behaviour if one went into the nest box of the other.

Random behaviour, so important for statistical calculation, is not typical of small mammals. Statistical calculation tends to sacrifice for the biologist the majority of the information gained in the field. It may be based on assumption known, or later proved, to be invalid (Blair, 1951). Statistical significance may demonstrate methodological rather than biological regularities (Brant, 1962). Yet awareness of inexactitudes may foster further fruitful investigation.

Control of the numbers of small mammals, where this is necessary, cannot be effective until their movements and behaviour are understood. The problem is not simply one of direct damage to trees, crops or stored products. *Apodemus agrarius* has been shown to be the host for bacteria which cause a serious disease—leptospirosis among cattle and pigs (Bang and Lund, 1964).

Climate, as a factor influencing both population and movement of small mammals, has been reviewed (Brown, 1962). Severe winter conditions may take a heavy toll of populations. Gottschang (1965) found that the severe winter of 1962–63 caused a great decline in all small mammal numbers in Ohio and brought *Blarina brevicauda* down to a "crash" level. On the other hand, a good summer may bring peak numbers, increasing the reproductive and survival rates enormously. Yet this is an oversimplification of rodent fluctuation which is "under control of the complex agency of the ecosystem" (Tanaka, 1957).

Acknowledgements

A grant from the Nature Conservancy provided assistance for the work from 1963 onwards.

I wish to thank the Forestry Commission for allowing me to work on their land in Dorset and for their kind assistance.

References

Allred, D. M. and Beck, D. E. (1963). Range of movement and dispersal of some rodents at the Nevada Atomic Test Site. *J. Mammal.* **44**, 190–200.

Andrewartha, H. G. and Birch, L. C. (1954). "The Distribution and Abundance of Animals," 782 pp. University of Chicago Press.

Bang, P. and Lund, M. (1964). Annual report. *Årsberetn. St. Skadedyrlab.*, 1964, 76.

Bishop, I. R. and Delaney, M. J. (1963). Life histories of small mammals in the Channel Islands in 1960–61. *Proc. zool. Soc. Lond.* **141**, 515–526.

Blair, W. F. (1940). A study of prairie deer-mouse populations in southern Michigan. *Am. Midl. Nat.* **24**, 273–305.

Blair, W. F. (1941a). Some data on the home ranges and general life history of the short-tailed shrews, red back vole and woodland jumping mouse in northern Michigan. *Am. Midl. Nat.* **25**, 681–685.

Blair, W. F. (1941b). Techniques for the study of mammal populations. *J. Mammal.* **22**, 148–157.

Blair, W. F. (1942). Size of home range and notes on the life history of the woodland deer-mouse and eastern chipmunk in northern Michigan. *J. Mammal.* **23**, 27–36.

Blair, W. F. (1951). Population structure, social behaviour, and environmental relations in a natural population of the beach mouse (*Peromyscus polionotus leucocephalus*). *Contr. Lab. vertebr. Biol. Univ. Mich.* No. 48, 1–47.

Boyd, J. M. (1963). Home range and homing experiments with the St. Kilda field-mouse. *Proc. zool. Soc. Lond.* **140**, 1–14.

Brant, D. H. (1962). Measure of the movements and population densities of small rodents. *Univ. Calif. Publs Zool.* **62**, 105–184.

Bronson, F. H. (1963). Some correlates of interaction rate in natural populations of woodchucks. *Ecology* **44**, 637–643.

Brown, L. E. (1954). Small mammal populations at Silwood Park Field Centre, Berkshire, England. *J. Mammal.* **35**, 161–176.

Brown, L. E. (1956a). Movements of some British small mammals. *J. Anim. Ecol.* **25**, 54–71.

Brown, L. E. (1956b). Field experiments on the activity of the small mammals, *Apodemus*, *Clethrionomys* and *Microtus*. *Proc. zool. Soc. Lond.* **126**, 549–564.

Brown, L. E. (1962). Home range in small mammal communities. *Surv. biol. Prog.* **4**, 131–177.

Brown, L. N. (1964). Ecology of three species of *Peromyscus* in southern Missouri. *J. Mammal.* **45**, 189–202.

Burt, W. H. (1943). Territoriality and home range concepts as applied to mammals. *J. Mammal.* **24**, 346–352.

Caldwell, L. D. (1964). An investigation of competition into natural populations of mice. *J. Mammal.* **45**, 12–30.

Calhoun, J. B. (1962). Induced mass movements of small mammals. *Publ. Hlth Monogr.* No. 59, 1–33.

Calhoun, J. B. and Webb, W. L. (1953). Induced emigrations of small mammals. *Science, N.Y.* **117**, 358–360.

Chitty, D. (1952). Mortality among voles (*Microtus agrestis*) at Lake Vyrnwy, Montgomeryshire in 1936–39. *Phil. Trans. R. Soc.* B, **236**, 505–552.

Chitty, D. (1955). Adverse effect of population density upon the viability of later generations. *In* "The Numbers of Man and Animals" (J. B. Cragg and N. W. Pirie, eds.), pp. 57–67. Oliver and Boyd, London.

Chitty, D. (1957). Self-regulation of numbers through changes in viability. *Cold Spring Harb. Symp. quant. Biol.* **22**, 277–280.

Chitty, D. (1960). Population processes in the vole and their relevance to general theory. *Can. J. Zool.* **38**, 99–113.

Chitty, D. and Chitty, H. (1962). Population trends among the voles of Lake Vyrnwy, 1932–60. Symposium Theriologica (Proc. int. Symp. Meth. Mamm. Invest. Brno, 1960), Praha, pp. 67–76.

Chitty, H. (1961). Variations in the weight of the adrenal glands of the field vole, *Microtus agrestis*. *J. Endocr.* **22**, 387–393.

Christian, J. J. (1956). Adrenal and reproductive response to population sizes in mice from freely growing populations. *Ecology* **37**, 258–273.

Christian, J. J. (1957). A review of the endocrine responses in rats and mice to increasing population size including delayed effects on offspring. *Nav. med. Res. Inst. Res. Rep.* **57**, 445–462.

Clarke, J. R. (1953). The effect of fighting on the adrenals, thymus and spleen of the vole (*Microtus agrestis*). *J. Endocr.* **9**, 114–126.

Crowcroft, P. (1955). Territoriality in wild house mice, *Mus musculus* L. *J. Mammal.* **36**, 299–301.

Crowcroft, P. and Jeffers, J. N. R. (1961). Variability in the behaviour of wild house mice (*Mus musculus* L.) towards traps. *Proc. zool. Soc. Lond.* **137**, 573–582.

Crowcroft, P. and Rowe, F. P. (1957). The growth of confined colonies of the wild house mouse (*Mus musculus* L.). *Proc. zool. Soc. Lond.* **129**, 359–370.

Crowcroft, P. and Rowe, F. P. (1963). Social organisation and territorial behaviour in the wild mouse (*Mus musculus* L.). *Proc. zool. Soc. Lond.* **140**, 517–531.

Curry-Lindahl, K. (1956). Habitats, home ranges, migrations and periodicity in some small mammals. *Fauna Flora, Upps.* **51**, 193–218 (Swedish with English summary).

Curry-Lindahl, K. (1959). Notes on the ecology and periodicity of some rodents and shrews in Sweden. *Mammalia* **23**, 389–422.

Curry-Lindahl, K. (1962). The irruption of the Norway lemming in Sweden during 1960. *J. Mammal.* **43**, 171–184.

Darling, F. F. (1959). The significance of predator-prey relationships in the regulation of animal population. *Int. Congr. Zool.* **15**, 62–63.

Davis, D. E. (1958). The role of density in aggressive behaviour in housemice. *Anim. Behav.* **6**, 207–211.

DeCoursey, G. E., Jr. (1957). Identification, ecology and reproduction of *Microtus* in Ohio. *J. Mammal.* **38**, 44–52.

Dice, L. R. and Clarke, P. J. (1953). The statistical concept of home range as applied to the recapture radius of the deermouse (*Peromyscus*). *Contr. Lab. vertebr. Biol. Univ. Mich.* No. 62, 1–15.

Dice, L. R. and Howard, W. E. (1951). Distance of dispersal in prairie deermice from birth places to breeding sites. *Contr. Lab. vertebr. Biol. Univ. Mich.* No. 50, 1–15.

Eisenberg, J. F. (1962). Studies in the behaviour of *Peromyscus maniculatus gambelli* and *Peromyscus californicus parasiticus*. *Behaviour* **19**, 177–207.

Evans, F. C. (1942). Studies of a small mammal population in Bagley Wood, Berkshire. *J. Anim. Ecol.* **11**, 182–197.

Frank, F. (1957). The causality of microtine cycles in Germany. *J. Wildl. Mgmt* **21**, 113–121.

Fullagar, P. J., Jewell, P. A., Lockley, R. M. and Rowlands, I. W. (1963). The Skomer vole (*Clethrionomys glareolus skomerensis*) and the long-tailed field mouse (*Apodemus sylvaticus*) on Skomer Island, Pembrokeshire in 1960. *Proc. zool. Soc. Lond.* **140**, 295–314.

Godfrey, G. K. (1954). Tracing field voles (*Microtus agrestis*) with a Geiger-Müller counter. *Ecology* **35**, 5–10.

Gottschang, J. L. (1965). Winter populations of small mammals in old fields of southwestern Ohio. *J. Mammal* **46**, 44–52.

Griffo, J. V. (1961). A study of homing in the cottonmouse, *Peromyscus gossypinus*. *Am. Midl. Nat.* **65**, 257–289.

Hacker, H. P. and Pearson, H. S. (1944). The growth, survival, wandering and variation of the longtailed field mouse, *Apodemus sylvaticus*. *Biometrika* **33**, 136–162.

Hacker, H. P. and Pearson, H. S. (1951). Distribution of the long-tailed field mouse, *Apodemus sylvaticus*, on South Haven Peninsula, Dorset, in 1937. *J. Linn. Soc.* (Zool.) **42**, 1–17.

Harrison, J. L. (1958). Range of movements of some Malayan rats. *J. Mammal.* **39**,190–206.

Harvey, M. J. and Barbour, R. W. (1965). Home range of *Microtus ochrogaster* as determined by a modified minimum area method. *J. Mammal.* **46**, 398–402.

Hayne, D. W. (1949). Calculation of size of home range. *J. Mammal.* **30**, 1–18.

Hayne, D. W. (1950). Apparent home range of *Microtus* in relation to distance between traps. *J. Mammal.* **31**, 26–39.

Hoffman, R. S. (1958). The role of reproduction and mortality in population fluctuations of voles (*Microtus*). *Ecol. Monogr.* **28**, 79–109.

Howard, W. E. (1949). Dispersal, amount of inbreeding and longevity in a local population of prairie deermice on the George Reserve, southern Michigan. *Contr. Lab. vertebr. Biol. Univ. Mich.* **43**, 1–50.

Howell, J. C. (1954). Populations and home ranges of small mammals on an overgrown field. *J. Mammal.* **35**, 177–186.

Jones, J. K. and Barber, A. A. (1957). Home ranges and populations of small mammals in central Korea. *J. Mammal.* **38**, 377–392.

Kalela, O. (1949). Über Fjeldlemming-invasionen und andere irreguliare Tierwanderungun. *Suomal. eläin-ja kasvit. Seur. van. eläin. Julk.* **13**, 1–90.

Kalela, O. (1961). Seasonal change in habitat of the Norwegian lemming. *Suomal. Tiedeakat. Toim.* A. IV. **55**, 1–72.

Kikkawa, J. (1964). Movement, activity and distribution of the small rodents *Clethrionomys glareolus* and *Apodemus sylvaticus* in woodland. *J. Anim. Ecol.* **33**, 259–299.

King, J. A. (1957). Intraspecific and interspecific conflict of *Mus* and *Peromyscus*. *Ecology* **38**, 355–357.

Lockley, R. M. (1961). Social structure and stress in the rabbit warren. *J. Anim. Ecol.* **30**, 385–423.

Louch, C. D. (1958). Adrenocortical activity in two meadow vole populations. *J. Mammal.* **39**, 109–116.

McCabe, T. T. and Blanchard, B. D. (1950). "Three Species of *Peromyscus*." 136 pp. Rood Associates, Santa Barbara, California.

Miller, L. S. (1957). Tracing vole movements by radioactive excretory products. *Ecology* **38**, 132–136.

Miller, R. S. (1954). Food habits of the wood mouse, *Apodemus sylvaticus* (Linnè, 1758) and the bank vole, *Clethrionomys glareolus* (Schreber, 1780) in Wytham Wood, Berkshire. *Säugetierk. Mitt.* **2**, 109–114.

Miller, R. S. (1958). A study of a wood mouse population in Wytham Woods, Berkshire. *J. Mammal.* **39**, 477–493.

Mohr, C. O. and Stumpf, W. A. (1964). Louse and chigger infestations as related to host size and home ranges of small mammals. *Trans. N. Am. Wildl. Conf.* 1964.

Morris, R. F. (1955). Population studies on small forest mammals in eastern Canada. *J. Mammal.* **36**, 21–35.

Myllymäki, A., Aho, J., Lind, E. O. and Tast, J. (1962). Behaviour and daily activity of the Norwegian lemming, *Lemmus lemmus* (L.), during autumn migration. *Suomal. eläin-ja kasvit. Seur. van. eläin. Julk.* **24**, 1–31.

Nicholson, A. J. (1933). The balance of animal population. *J. Anim. Ecol.* **2**, 132–178.

Nicholson, A. J. (1957). The self-adjustment of populations to change. *Cold Spring Harb. Symp. quant. Biol.* **22**, 153–173.

Pearson, O. P. (1964). Carnivore-mouse predation: an example of its intensity and bioenergetics. *J. Mammal.* **45**, 177–188.

Redman, J. P. and Sealander, J. A. (1958). Home range of deer mice in southern Arkansas. *J. Mammal.* **39**, 390–395.

Reichstein, H. (1960). Untersuchungen zum aktionsraum und zum re Vierverhalten des Feldmaus, *Microtus arvalis* (Pall). *Z. Säugetierk.* **25**, 150–169.

Rothschild, M. (1958). A further note on the increase of hares (*Lepus europacus*) in France. *Proc. zool. Soc. Lond.* **131**, 328–329.

Rothschild, M. and Marsh, H. (1956). Increase of hares (*Lepus europacus* Pallas) at Ashton Wold, with a note on the reduction in numbers of the brown rat (*Rattus norvegicus* Berkenhout). *Proc. zool. Soc. Lond.* **127**, 441–445.

Rowe, F. P., Taylor, E. J. and Chudley, A. H. J. (1963). The numbers and movements of house-mice (*Mus musculus* L.) in the vicinity of four corn-ricks. *J. Anim. Ecol.* **32**, 87–97.

Ruffer, D. G. (1961). Effect of flooding on a population of mice. *J. Mammal.* **42**, 494–502.

Sadleir, R. M. F. S. (1965). The relationship between agonistic behaviour and population changes in the deermouse, *Peromyscus maniculatus* (Wagner). *J. Anim. Ecol.* **34**, 331–352.

Saint Girons, H. and Saint Girons, M. C. (1959). Espace vital domaine et territoire chez les vertébrès terrestrès (Reptiles et Mammifères). *Mammalia* **23**, 448–476.

Shadowen, H. E. (1963). A live-trap study of small mammals in Louisiana. *J. Mammal.* **44**, 103–108.

Sheppe, W. (1965). Dispersal by swimming of *Peromyscus leucopus*. *J. Mammal.* **46**, 336–337.

Shillito, E. E. (1963a). Exploratory behaviour in the short-tailed vole *Microtus agrestis*. *Behaviour* **21**, 145–154.

Shillito, J. F. (1963b). Field observations on the growth, reproduction and activity of a woodland population of the common shrew, *Sorex araneus* L. *Proc. zool. Soc. Lond.* **140**, 99–114.

Shillito, J. F. (1963c). Observations on the range and movements of a woodland population of the common shrew, *Sorex araneus* L. *Proc. zool. Soc. Lond.* **140**, 533–546.

Siniff, O. B. and Tester, J. R. (1965). Computer analysis of animal movement data obtained by telemetry. *Bioscience* **15**, 104–108.

Stickel, L. F. (1946). The source of animals moving into a depopulated area. *J. Mammal.* **27**, 301–307.

Stickel, L. F. (1954). A comparison of certain methods of measuring ranges of small mammals. *J. Mammal.* **35**, 1–15.

Stickel, L. F. and Warbach, O. (1960). Small mammal populations of a Maryland woodlot, 1949–54. *Ecology* **41**, 269–286.

Tanaka, R. (1953). Home ranges and territories in the *Clethrionomys* population on a peat bog grassland in Hokkaido. *Bull. Kochi. Wom. Coll.* **2**, 10–20.

Tanaka, R. (1956). Fluctuations in vole populations following the widespread synchronous flowering of bamboo-grasses on Mt. Turngi. *Bull. Kochi. Wom. Coll.* **4**, 61–68.

Tanaka, R. (1957). An ecological review of small-mammal outbreaks with special reference to their association with the flowering of bamboo-grasses. *Bull. Kochi. Wom. Univ.* Ser. Nat. Sci. **5**, 20–30.

Tanaka, R. (1960). Some features in population dynamics of simultaneous vole-outbreaks over the wide range of Japan in 1959. *Bull. Kochi. Wom. Univ.* Ser. Nat. Sci. **8**, 11–17.

Tanaka, R. (1962). Adrenal analysis for critique of the social stress theory in natural populations of a montane vole. *Res. Popul. Ecol.* **44**, 8–16.

Tanaka, R. (1963a). Truthfulness of the delimited-area concept of home range in small mammals. *Bull. Kochi. Wom. Univ.* Ser. Nat. Sci. **11**, 6–11.

Tanaka, R. (1963b). Examination of the routine census equation by considering multiple collision with a single catch trap in small mammals. *Jap. J. Ecol.* **13**, 16–21.

Tanaka, R (1964). Population dynamics of the Smith's red backed vole in highlands of Shikoku. *Res. Popul. Ecol.* **46**, 54–66.

Tanaka, R. and Teramura, S. (1953). A population of the Japanese field vole infested with tsutsugamushi disease. *J. Mammal.* **34**, 345–350.

Tanton, M. T. (1965). Problems of live-trapping and population estimation for the wood mouse, *Apodemus sylvaticus* (L.). *J. Anim. Ecol.* **34**, 1–22.

Terman, C. R. (1962). Spatial and homing consequences of the introduction of aliens into semi-natural populations of prairie deermice. *Ecology* **43**, 216–223.

Terman, C. R. (1963). The influence of differential early social experience upon spatial distribution within population of prairie deermice. *Anim. Behav.* **11,** 246–262.

Tester, J. R. (1963). Techniques for studying movements of vertebrates in the field. *Proc. 1st. natn Symp. Radioecol.* 445–450.

Tester, J. R. and Siniff, O. B. (1965). Aspects of animal movement and home range data obtained by telemetry. *Trans. N. Am. Wildl. Conf.* **30,** 379–392.

Tevis, L. Jr. (1956). Behavior of a population of forest mice when subjected to poison. *J. Mammal.* **37,** 358–370.

Ueda, M. (1949). Ecological observations on the Bedford's vole. *Trans. Soc. Agric. For. Sapporo* **38,** 14–18.

Whitaker, J. O. (1963). A study of the meadow jumping mouse, *Zapus ludsonius* (Zimmerman), in Central New York. *Ecol. Monogr.* **33,** 215–254.

Youngman, P. M. (1956). A population of the striped field mouse, *Apodemus agrarius coreae,* in central Korea. *J. Mammal.* **37,** 1–10.

APPENDIX

I have studied the movements of small mammals in various habitats in Dorset since 1961. The data selected for this paper refers, with minor exceptions, to that obtained in 1963 in 18 acres of Poorstock Forest, in Middlemarsh, Dorset.

In 1963 the populations of *Apodemus* were studied in three adjacent areas, A (1·9 acres), B (2·1 acres) and C (3·0 acres), from April to October. A was an area of young pine trees in which *Apodemus* had only recently established itself. B was an area of well-developed pine and mixed woodland with much undergrowth, and C was a mixed area of newly planted and well-grown trees. Population estimates (Hayne, 1949) were obtained after 3 days pre-baiting followed by 4 days live-trapping. Selected *Apodemus* were then studied longer in relation to their movements, first by further trapping and then by tracking. They were toe-clipped to allow individual tracking recognition, having originally been marked with numbered monel rings. Tracking allowed a wider range of study of the free animals. The newly established area A had its own community and dominant, but areas B and C had cut into sections of several dominants. Only those animals that were toe-clipped could be individually tracked. The tracking plates were strips of paper-backed metal foil overlaid with a fine talc suspension held in a silicone water repellant medium. The plates were placed, for protection, in waxed cartons. Large numbers were used, especially in areas of particular interest. Tracking plates that had been visited were replaced, but the cartons were handled as little as possible and were destroyed after use. Scent marking by urination is typical and re-use would have complicated the results. The cartons were held in place by metal skewers and the entrance was protected by a plastic hood. It was not necessary to provide food: experiments showed the mice entered unbaited cartons as readily as baited ones. (Return along the same route as the outward journey—often found in small mammals—appears to be linked with the animal having scented its track or having followed the scent of another small mammal.)

Symp. zool. Soc. Lond. (1966) No. 18, 143–165.

TERRITORY IN SMALL CARNIVORES

J. D. LOCKIE

Department of Forestry and Natural Resources,
University of Edinburgh, Scotland

SYNOPSIS

1. Aspects of territory and home range in small carnivores are discussed with reference to the literature and to the author's previously unpublished work on weasels (*Mustela nivalis*) and stoats (*M. erminea*).

2. The evidence suggests that weasels and stoats can have a territorial system, with closely defended boundaries. Home range, that is a more loosely organized system, is claimed for most small mammals but the literature, so far as it goes, suggests a considerable element of defence in the social system of small carnivores.

3. Territorial defence by overt threat occurs in birds and may also occur in small carnivores. However, the use of "scent" including urine and faeces to mark boundaries is also a form of threat and most small carnivores are eminently equipped to threaten in this way.

4. Dominant territory-holding weasels all come into breeding condition in March and all remain so until August in Scotland. Subdominants are more variable in the extent to which they come into breeding condition, some remaining in a non-breeding condition throughout the year. It is argued that this is an effect of being subdominant.

5. Some small carnivores seem to patrol the boundary of their territory and spend most time where the pressure from adjacent animals is greatest.

6. Sex ratios show a variation from 1 : 1 (or very occasionally an excess of females) to, more commonly, an excess of males. It is argued that the territorial system, in which the female is subdominant to the male and lives on his territory at his pleasure, can lead, during periods of food shortage and/or high numbers, to a differential mortality. Males become more aggressive and tend to treat females as males with consequent poor breeding and high mortality of females.

7. Before a territorial system can be set up there must be more than a certain threshold number of males. The sizes of territories depend not only on the food supply but also on the number of animals competing at the time the territories are set up.

INTRODUCTION

The reviewer of territory and home range in small carnivores has a fairly easy task since the literature is meagre. The difficulty comes in trying to make sense of the various reports and to relate them to other aspects of the animals' lives. I have therefore had to lean heavily on my own work on weasel (*Mustela nivalis*) and stoat (*M. erminea*). But where data are few I have speculated freely because I feel that only thus will outstanding problems be defined so that means can be sought for their study.

In order to avoid disrupting the narrative, I have relegated all descriptions of technique and study areas to the Appendixes.

TERRITORY, HOME RANGE AND CLASSES OF ANIMAL

Some small carnivores, the solitary Mustelidae in particular, are often said to be great wanderers. In fact, like most animals, they stay put if they can hold a territory. If they cannot they may well travel long distances; for example, a tagged male long-tailed weasel (*Mustela frenata*) travelled at least 22 miles in 7 months (Burns, 1964); and there are other though somewhat less spectacular examples.

Figures 1 and 2 show the disposition of the territories of male weasels in a young forest plantation in the Carron Valley, Stirlingshire. The boundaries were formed by joining the outermost traps which were visited by each animal. Without exception, all the traps within the

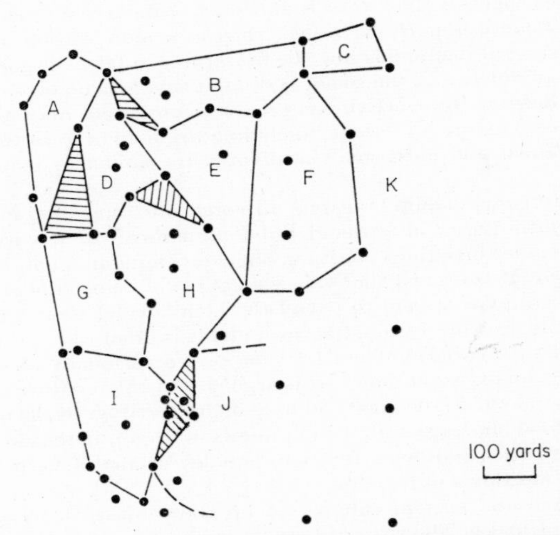

FIG. 1. Territories of male weasels in the Carron Valley, Stirlingshire. November–March. Dots indicate permanently sited trap; cross-hatching indicates areas of overlap between adjacent animals or areas where precise boundaries cannot be determined with the trap-spacing used. Each resident weasel is represented by a letter. The study area is about 80 acres (32 ha).

area so delimited were also visited by the owner of that ground. The cross-hatched areas show the points of overlap or apparent overlap between adjacent animals. Figure 1 refers to winter (November 1960 to March 1961) and Fig. 2 to summer (April to October 1961). Each territorial outline is based on at least twenty records.

In winter the degree of overlap was small whereas in summer, presumably owing to increased activity in the breeding season, overlap was greater. But, even in summer, it was remarkably small considering the ease with which these small animals cover the ground. Trapping in the way described is, of course, a crude technique for investigating range; nevertheless, if overlap had been substantial, I should have expected to detect it.

Not all weasels within the study area held territories. Transient animals passed through during most of the year with a peak in late summer and early spring. These animals were usually caught once only although some settled for varying periods within a territory. If they settled their movements were much restricted, often to one trap. Thus one might classify the population into residents, temporary residents, and transients as Weckworth and Hawley (1962) did with the pine marten (*Martes caurina*) they studied.

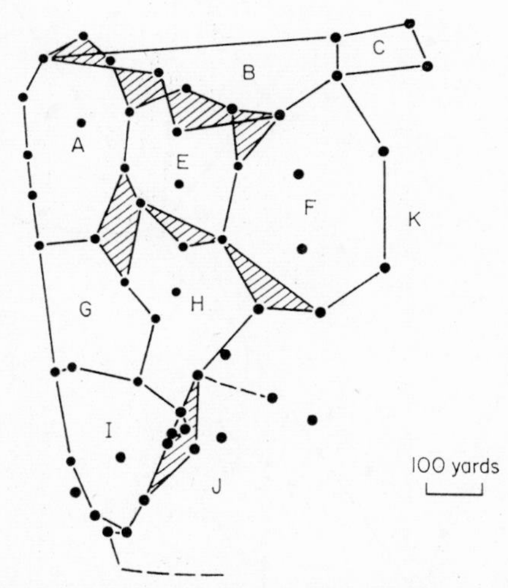

FIG. 2. Territories of male weasels in the Carron Valley. April–October. Key as in Fig. 1.

When a territory holder disappeared naturally or experimentally and a transient animal was in the vicinity, the transient immediately took over the vacant ground and established similar boundaries (five examples, Carron Valley; three examples, Midlothian). On one occasion (territory D in Fig. 1 and see Fig. 2), no transient male was present and, over a period of 6 weeks, three adjacent territory holders pushed out their boundaries and eventually shared the abandoned territory.

Stoats on the same ground also held territories similar to those of weasels but larger (Figs. 3 and 4). Whereas the territories of weasels were between 2·5 and 12 acres, that of one stoat was about 50 acres, and, as in weasels, transient stoats passed through the area but did not settle permanently except when a territory became vacant. Figure 3

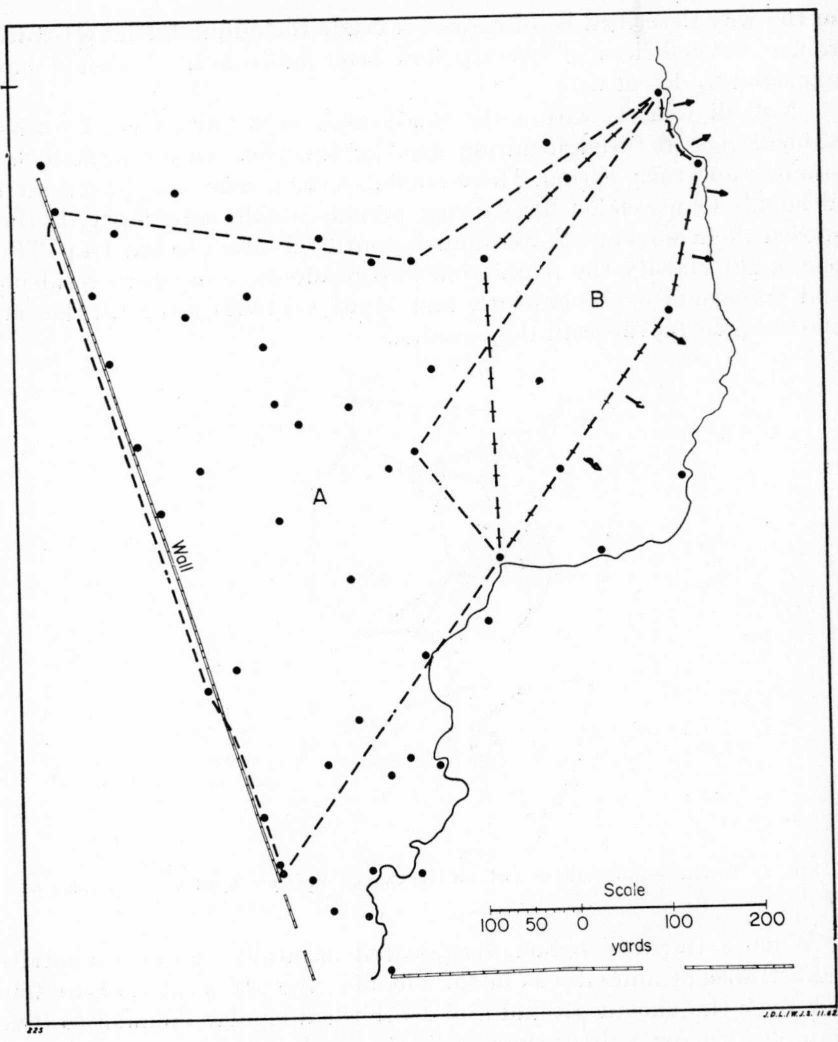

FIG. 3. Territories of stoats in the Carron Valley.

shows the territory of one male stoat (A) whose territory covered much of the study area and seemed to be wholly within it since this animal was caught on every occasion on which I trapped. Later, this stoat died in a trap during severe frost. The territory was then divided between one stoat known previously only on the edge of the study area (B) and two newcomers (C and D; Fig. 4).

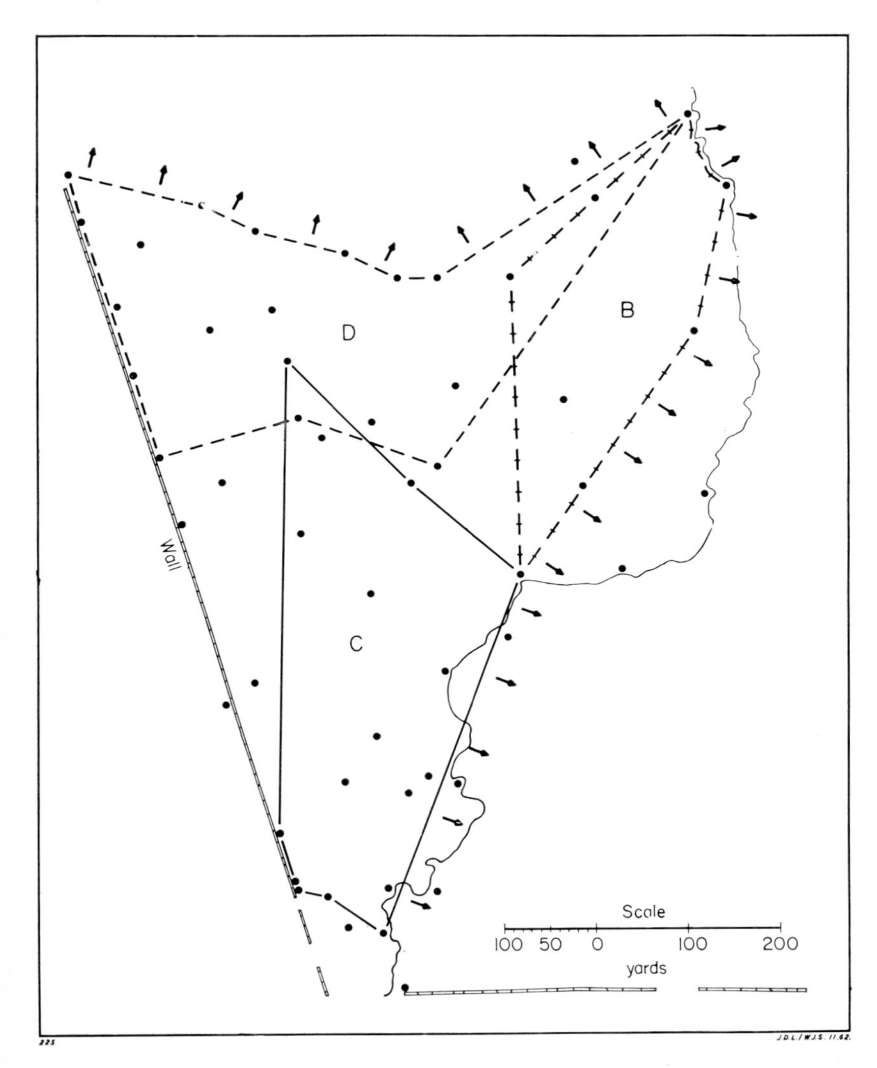

FIG. 4. Territories of stoats in the Carron Valley: reorganization after the death of a resident.

A territorial organization is implied since incomers settled and residents only extended their boundaries when a resident animal was removed. This implies a defence of boundaries. Most writers have referred to the area occupied by resident pine marten (*Martes caurina*) (Quick, 1956; Lensink, 1957; Hawley and Newby, 1957; Weckworth and Hawley, 1962) and weasel and stoat (Nyholm, 1959) as the home range. The term implies considerable overlap between adjacent animals but only Weckworth and Hawley (1962) mention how adjacent home ranges relate to one another. Apart from two males whose home ranges coincided, their description suggests defended boundaries.

Female weasels and stoats in the Carron Valley and in Midlothian did not show territorial behaviour as clearly as did the males. That is, their boundaries were not contiguous. Either they delimited an area smaller than that of males and were caught repeatedly in one trap only (3 examples) or they were caught only once (six examples). Thus among the females there were transients and residents, the latter occupying a smaller area than the male on whose territory they lived.

Nyholm (1959) followed the tracks of weasels and stoats in the snow. The home range of male stoats averaged 85 acres (34 ha) whereas those of females averaged 18 acres (7·4 ha). The range in male weasels was only slightly greater than that of females (4·2 acres as against 3 acres; 1·7 and 1·2 ha). But weasels spent much of their time below the surface of the snow where they could not be tracked and Nyholm also had difficulty in distinguishing the tracks of males and females. His figures for home range size in weasels, therefore, must be treated with caution. Hawley and Newby (1957) give the range covered by pine marten (*Martes caurina*) as 0·9 sq. miles (558 acres) for males and 0·3 sq. miles (186 acres) for females. But the number of residents on the ground could be much greater; for example, Weckworth and Hawley (1962) estimated that at a population peak there were eleven resident marten living within an area of 6·2 sq. miles (1 795 ha), but they did not say how far the ranges of these residents overlapped and how they compared with those after a decline to three marten in the same area. Ellis (1964) used radio transmitters mounted on collars to follow raccoons (*Procyon lotor*) and suggested that raccoons have smaller home ranges when the population is big than when the population is small.

It is sometimes difficult to avoid the conclusion that, in people's minds, the term "territory" refers to birds and "home range" to mammals without there necessarily being justification for the use of one or other term. I think that "territory" (that is, a defended area) more aptly describes the social set-up of the weasels and stoats I studied and, even if better means of study show that the overlap between adjacent animals is greater than I have found, the term is still applicable. The important point is that, once the territories have been set up, the residents prevent others from settling.

It is extremely difficult to make valid comparisons between territory size in the same species in different areas or between different species without knowing a great deal about the habitat and the food supplies. However, a valid comparison can be made between weasel and stoat in the Carron Valley since both species occupied the same ground and fed almost entirely upon voles (*Microtus agrestis*). The daily food requirements of stoat and weasel and the body size are both in a ratio of about 2 : 1. But the territory size is in the ratio of approximately 8 : 1. The discrepancy is in part due to the fact that weasels can exploit voles more efficiently than can stoats, since weasels can follow the voles below the ground whereas stoats hunt on the surface and have a curtain of grass between them and their prey. In order to get sufficient available voles stoats presumably need, in this particular situation, a disproportionately larger territory.

TERRITORIAL DEFENCE

Most small or medium-sized carnivores have scent glands. One presumes that these are used to mark territory and certainly the pine marten (*Martes martes*) sets scent (see photograph in Schmidt, 1943).

In addition to scent *per se*, most carnivores use urine and droppings in a seemingly organized way. For example, in the Beinn Eighe National Nature Reserve in west Scotland, pine marten use the partly overgrown timber extraction roads and deer tracks to move about the countryside. They deposit their droppings and urine along these tracks at varying intervals with one to three droppings at each point. Often, the droppings are of different ages suggesting a repeated use of the track and a renewal of the scent (Lockie, 1964). Quick (1951) found the same with *Mustela frenata* in Montana. At the dens of Mustelidae there are often very large lavatories (Quick, 1951; Lockie, 1964; Neal, 1948; Polderboer, 1942), although whether this is a concentrated effort at the defence of a den or a matter of sanitary convenience is uncertain. The wild cat (*Felis sylvestris*), unlike the domestic cat, does not bury its droppings but uses them and urine to mark its range (Lindemann, 1953). In addition to this, wild cats have claw sharpening trees distributed about their territory and these may likewise act as markers especially since a foot secretion is involved (de Leeuw, 1957). Domestic cats have claw sharpening loci—usually the best chair cover. In a house where several cats live, a hierarchy usually develops (Baron *et al.*, 1957) and it would be interesting to know if this decides which one may sharpen where.

The idea of defence by visual display which derives largely from studies of birds must be extended to include the laying of scent or other markers. For, although the potency of scent in defence is largely assumed, it seems a valid assumption since scent is used in an organized way and a boundary between adjacent animals is often maintained.

THE NATURE OF DOMINANT AND SUBDOMINANT ANIMALS

Rights of ownership confer assurance on a territory holder so that it immediately has an immense advantage over an intruder. This has been seen repeatedly in birds (e.g. Lack, 1943; Tinbergen, 1953). There is no reason to suppose that the same does not hold for small carnivores and, indeed, the fact that intruders or transients cannot usually establish a territory in the presence of an owner supports the view.

This being so one might reasonably expect that enforced relegation to subdominance might have a lasting physiological effect on the animal. One manifestation of such an effect might be a failure or delay in coming into breeding condition. Accordingly, I recorded the breeding condition of all male weasels by scoring the testes size "small," "medium," and "large." Hill (1939, p. 495) shows for weasels collected in England and Wales that when the average testes weight is 0·03–0·05 g (= "small"), the testes produce no sperms; when the average weight is 0·13–0·18 g (= "medium"), a varying proportion of testes produce sperms the remainder not; when the average weight is more than 0·18 g (= "large"), all the testes produce sperms.

Table I summarizes the proportion of each class of male weasel in each month which had "small" testes (that is, were producing no sperms and therefore were not in breeding condition). Clearly, the breeding season of resident weasels was precise, no animals being quiescent from March until July. In contrast, except in March, June and July (when some were recorded "medium"), a varying proportion of transients remained in a non-breeding condition.

Transients did not differ from residents in age or size; nor, presumably, did they differ in aggressiveness since once established on a territory they could hold it. Therefore the failure of some transients to come into breeding condition must have been due to their being "have-nots". Not all transients were quiescent, however, for some were distinguishable in their breeding condition from territory holders.

One male yearling weasel was followed fairly closely during its change of status. From November until January it was a subordinate animal living in the territory of another and much restricted in its movements, being caught repeatedly in one trap only. In early January it began

TABLE I

The proportion of resident and transient male weasels in non-breeding condition

Month	Residents		Transients	
	Percentage non-breeding*	No. examined	Percentage non-breeding	No. examined
January	30	10	100	2
February	11	9	17	6
March	0	11	0	7
April	0	9	6	18
May	0	8	33	9
June	0	8	0	3
July	0	12	0	4
August	33	15	—	—
September	17	6	33	6
October	100	9	100	1
November	100	10	100	3
December	100	10	100	2

* Note non-breeding = "small testes" (see text).

to move through the study area as indicated in Fig. 5. It reached territory C a few days later just after I had removed the owner. This transient settled and held territory C until its death 10 months later. It settled while its testes were "small" and subsequent development of the testes was slow; by the end of March they were classified as "medium" but not until the end of June as "large". Thus, with change of status, this transient's sexual development still lagged behind that of more long-standing residents. Furthermore, the territory held was the smallest on record (2·5 acres). I suggest that the physiological effect of being a transient lasted in this animal well into the period of being a full resident.

In contrast, another transient arrived in early February with testes already "medium". It immediately took over a vacant territory and held it until killed by a short-eared owl (*Asio flammeus*) 12 months later. By early April, the testes were "large" and remained so until late August when they regressed. Thus, this animal behaved like a full resident from the moment of its change of status. Both these animals were yearlings and both weighed 180 g (April).

Either not all transients reacted similarly to lack of territory or some were territory holders whose status had recently changed. The

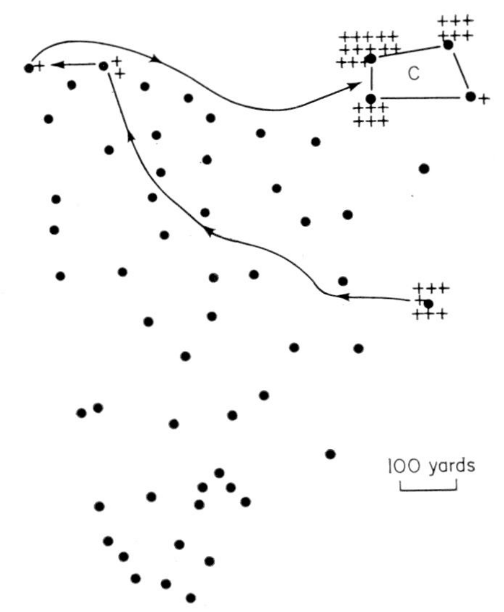

FIG. 5. Change of status of one male weasel from temporary resident to transient and to full resident. Dots represent traps in the Carron Valley study area, and crosses the number of captures of animal C.

second suggestion is possible, particularly in some agricultural areas where the condition of the habitat is continually changing. Indeed, since the age structure of resident and transient males was very similar (Table II) and since the territorial system did not break up annually

TABLE II

*Age structure of weasels**

Age in months from independence†	Males				Females	
	Resident territory holders		Transients			
	No.	%	No.	%	No.	%
6–12	7	(50)	69	(58)	14	(66)
13–24	6	(43)	22	(21)	3	(14)
25–36	1	(7)	21	(20)	3	(14)
Over 36	0		7	(1)	1	(6)
Total	14	(100)	119	(100)	21	(100)

* Information from study areas in Midlothian and the Carron Valley, Stirlingshire are pooled, there being no detectable difference between the age structures of the populations in the two areas.

† The first age category begins at 6 months to avoid confusing transients with dispersing young.

(see p. 159), I am led to the conclusion that territory holders must quite often be displaced by some means. However, in the small number of resident male weasels I studied in the Carron Valley and in Midlothian most vacancies were produced through predation by owls, by natural accidents and by my mistakes, and few, if any, by displacement of the owner of the territory. A further conclusion can be made: that age has no bearing on the ability to gain a territory. I suspect that the good fortune of being in the right place at the right time is a far more potent factor. Furthermore, the similarity of age distribution of residents and transients suggests that mortality factors act equally on all age groups after the first 6 months of age even if transients as a whole suffer greater losses than residents. In this respect, weasels are similar to many birds (Lack, 1954).

USE MADE OF TERRITORIES

Trapping as a means of learning how an animal moves about its territory or home range can only give a broad picture. If one traps intensively over a short time, the animal is disturbed unduly; if with lesser intensity over a long period, the information can only be general. Tracking in snow is useful but individuals cannot usually be distinguished and the study is limited to one part of the year.

The recent development of radio telemetry offers a wonderful field for the study of the movement of animals. Transmitters are small enough now to be incorporated into a collar for animals the size of pine marten, wild cat and raccoon; and a wide variety of animals is already being studied by radio telemetry in America (e.g. Storm, 1965; Ellis, 1964). But I doubt if radios on collars will be satisfactory for weasels and stoats and there is no other way of attaching the transmitter without inconveniencing the animal. I have therefore started trials in captivity and in the field on a system of mutilating the foot of weasels by cutting off one toe so that the animal leaves a distinctive footprint. In America the method has been used by Justice (1961) for small rodents. Scattered about the territory are tunnels, similar to traps, in heaps of stones. The tunnels contain paper and stamping ink. First trials look hopeful but the footprints of weasels and stoats are never as clear as those of small rodents which also use the tunnels.

These are techniques for the future. In the meantime we must make the best use we can of the standard techniques of trapping and tracking.

Figure 6 shows the territory of one male weasel in the Carron Valley and the use the animal made of the territory over a 6 month period as indicated by the number of trappings at each point. There are two main factors which could in principle affect the use of territory—food supply and adjacent animals. The food supply (*Microtus agrestis*) was measured by W. N. Charles during this study and was fairly uniformly distributed, the vegetation types being few and near randomly distributed. It is possible but unlikely that the availability of food was markedly different in the different parts of the territory. I believe in this instance that adjacent territory holders decided in some degree the activity of the owner about its territory. At trap *a* (Fig. 6), an intrusion into another territory, there is one record only. At trap *i*, where a neighbour intruded there are six records. This animal spent much time at traps *b*, *c* and *d*; *b* and *d* were traps at which three resident animals met;

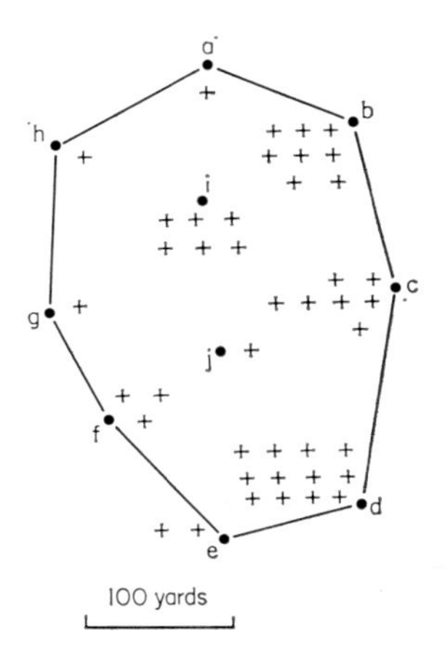

FIG. 6. The use made of a territory by a male weasel as shown by trapping results. Dots represent traps and the lines enclose one weasel territory. Crosses indicate the number of times the animal was caught in each trap.

and *b*, *c* and *d* were the common boundary with the resident holding the largest territory. The remaining traps at which only one neighbour was involved had few records. The inference is that the territory holder spent more time where pressure from adjacent animals was greatest. The apparent connexion occurs in other territories but is not entirely consistent. Clearly other factors also influence the use made of a territory.

In trapping both weasels and stoats I was repeatedly struck by the speed at which both species could move from end to end of their territories. Indeed, the impression I had was that weasels and stoats patrolled their boundaries. This is to be expected in a territory holding species which must renew scent and which may also deter intruders by direct confrontation.

I have only once seen a territory holder escort a transient from its territory. I had a clear view only because the chase was along a wide track which passed through the territory. Both animals suddenly appeared running towards me, the chaser shrieking now and again. They paid no attention to me and passed close by. At the known boundary of the territory the owner broke off and returned into his territory where he was shortly after trapped and examined. The other animal kept running and disappeared from view a quarter of a mile down the track. I was unable to catch and examine the chased weasel, but since none of the known residents were missing I presumed it to be transient.

On another occasion, I trapped a transient stoat which squealed as it came out of the anaesthetic (see Appendix). Immediately, the presumed owner of the territory appeared racing towards me apparently to see what was happening. Unfortunately, it broke off and disappeared when it saw me.

The pine marten (*Martes caurina*) and fisher (*Martes pennanti*) in America (Grinnel *et al.*, 1937) and pine marten (*Martes martes*) in the Lake District of England (Southern, 1964, p. 361) are alleged to move around the circumference of their range, American marten travelling around a circle of from 5 to 30 miles circumference with temporary residence at points along the circumference. This may well be a scenting expedition for even a circumference of 30 miles need take a marten no more than 3 days (Marshall, 1951).

Likewise, Hawley and Newby (1957) give forty minimum daily movements of one male pine marten ranging from no recorded movement to 1·6 miles. The maximum length of this animal's home range was 2 miles so that it could easily have supervised the whole boundary.

Most writers speak of home range in small carnivores. I have used the term territory for weasel and stoat. But the terms are not distinct and one might reasonably expect different species or the same species in different seasons to show both types of land tenure, that is, a loosely and a strictly held boundary. Whichever the animal uses, it must move around the limits of its range or it will lose ground since, as we have seen, the pressure by adjacent territory holders and transients is continuous. Thus, the statement by Nyholm (1959) that stoats and weasels use several hunting areas and switch from one area to another with a few days interval needs explanation since the boundary of these stoats' ranges would presumably remain undefended for possibly some weeks.

Criddle (1947) reported that the winter den of the least weasel (*M. rixosa*) was thickly lined with vole fur suggesting regular use. Likewise, Raievsky (1946) states that the sable (*Mustela zibellina*) is bound to a single winter den and this fact is used in making a census of these animals. In contrast, Nasimovich (1949) writes that dens of weasels are not used permanently.

It would seem that territory holding weasels and stoats move quickly and regularly around their territories and that some parts of the boundary get more attention than others; a fact that Hawley and Newby (1957) report for the pine marten in Montana. On the use of dens the evidence is contradictory but it may be that use varies with the season and with the severity of the winter.

RELATIONSHIP BETWEEN THE SEXES

The sex ratio in small carnivores poses some problems. Many workers lump the year's catch together and usually get a 2 : 1 or 3 : 1 ratio of males to females (Deanesly, 1935, for the stoat; Hill, 1939, for the weasel; Hall, 1957, for American weasels). This is usually explained by the greater activity and therefore proneness to trapping of males. In both weasels and stoats, males and females show a different proneness to capture at different seasons; this is partly a function of trapping and partly a function of the annual cycle of these species (Lockie, in progress). Added to this, however, is the undoubted fact that females can become genuinely scarce (Weckworth and Hawley (1962) and Lampio (1951) in the pine marten; stoat in the Carron Valley, Lockie unpublished) and, on one occasion, disappear altogether (e.g. weasels in the Carron Valley, see Appendix 1). The factors associated with such occurrences are high numbers, even when the food supply is abundant, and a declining food supply. Thus, Weckworth and Hawley (1962) show that even resident female marten were in poor condition during a population peak before their small rodent prey began to become scarce. Later, when the small rodent food supply crashed females suffered more than males. Likewise, in the Carron Valley, I had three male and two female resident stoats using part of the study area. As the food supply declined, first both females disappeared then two males. Finally when voles were about forty-five per acre (W.N. Charles, unpublished) only one male remained. Weasels in the same area had been very numerous prior to the start of this study. But during the study female weasels, at first in a ratio of one to every three males, became steadily scarcer until for 10 months in 1961 I could find none on the study area nor in the countryside around it. It would seem that under certain circumstances female mustelids do less well, sometimes markedly less well, than males. I believe the territorial organization may indicate how this may come about.

If the male's territories are contiguous, if there are as many females as males or fewer and if the females are not concentrated in the territories of a few males, it follows that the territories of females cannot be contiguous since they are smaller than those of males. Any defence of an area by females by setting scent or otherwise cannot be a signal between adjacent territory-holding females, although scent could well act as a sign to wandering females. I suggest that female weasels and stoats defend their small territory mainly against the male owner of the territory in which they live.

This view of male and female relationship has some support from observations on the relationship of male, female and young weasels in captivity (Lockie, in progress). The animals were housed in a cage $12 \times 2 \times 1{\cdot}5$ ft in the open. Outside the breeding season it is difficult in captivity to keep male and female weasels together since the male dominates the female, restricts her movements greatly and often kills her.

I put the male and female together in March with plenty of cover to allow the female refuge. The male chivvied her when she came near him but did not press home the attack; she always retreated before him. She must have been receptive during oestrus for, by 18 April the female was pregnant. At mid-pregnancy it became difficult to tell which animal was dominant, and as pregnancy advanced dominance gradually passed to the female and lasted until the young were several days old. At this point, the young met with an accident and the female reverted to a subdominant position. A month later she was again pregnant and again dominance passed to the female and remained with her until the young were about 12 weeks old and became independent, when the male resumed dominance over both the female and the young.

If we try to marry these observations with those, admittedly meagre, from the field, the picture I suggest is of a male territory and, within it, a female territory which expands and contracts with the breeding condition of the female. The point is that the female exists on the male's territory at his pleasure. It is advantageous for the male to be aggressive but not too agressive for, if the latter, he will tend to drive females as well as males out of his territory. The presence of the female is the resultant of a rather delicately balanced aggressiveness toward other males and toward the female within his territory.

There are, however, occasions when the delicate balance may well be upset—at high population density or when the food supply is in decline. In the red grouse (*Lagopus scoticus*) which has a similar territorial organization, Jenkins *et al.* (1963) have shown that in bad years for grouse the sex ratio is biased towards males because the hens are not so readily accepted by the territory-holding cocks. In good years, the sex ratio is near unity and some cocks may accept two hens.

Weasels and stoats apparently behave in a similar way, and I would postulate that under favourable circumstances some male mustelids might be bigamous or polygamous. Polygamy is indeed suggested for the pine marten in America (Marshall, 1951) and Nyholm wrote me of one area he studied in Finland where female stoats outnumbered males.

This might be claimed as another example of the importance of males in controlling population size and breeding rate (Wynne-Edwards, 1962). If so, one must explain why males who behave in an aggressive way towards females are not selected against since they leave no offspring, or one may invoke a group selection that benefits the species but for the evolutionary operation of which there is no explanation. I would prefer to look upon the pressure against females rather as the consequence of a social organization which, while it may be of immense advantage to the individual in other ways, can, on occasion, go wrong.

STABILITY OF THE TERRITORIAL SYSTEM

I did not witness the setting up of territories since the organization of Figs. 1 and 2 was already in being in November 1960 when the study began properly. The set-up described continued with minor changes of boundary and some change of individuals until November 1961. During this time, the food supply fluctuated between 45 and 220 voles per acre (Fig. 7). Transient animals were usually entering the area, but even when voles were numerous they could not settle. (The number of transients shown in Fig. 7 is a minimum, however, since trapping was done at monthly or half-monthly intervals for 3 days and so many transients probably came and went between trapping sessions.)

Thus, the resident weasels made no attempt to adjust their numbers to the fluctuating food supply. (The loss of one resident in March 1960 was by predation. No transients were caught at that time on that territory and the three adjacent residents shared the vacant ground.) This means that the number of weasels holding territories must have been decided previous to November 1960 and subsequently was unaffected by the considerable fluctuations in the food supply.

Likewise, in Midlothian, a similar territorial system involving three resident males and one female was stable from April 1964 until at least September 1965. There was no break-up of territories following the breeding season.

Moving on to November 1961 (Fig. 7) the number of resident weasels declined rapidly. This can be explained in the following way. During trapping in November 1961 one resident died of an injury, two by predation, another under the anaesthetic and two disappeared. These animals are indicated by letters set in a circle in Fig. 8. The losses left lacunae in the territorial set-up and immediately the remaining residents pushed out their boundaries but, meeting no opposition, continued to move as indicated in Fig. 8. Thus the whole cohesion of the system broke down and did not reform during 1962 or 1963

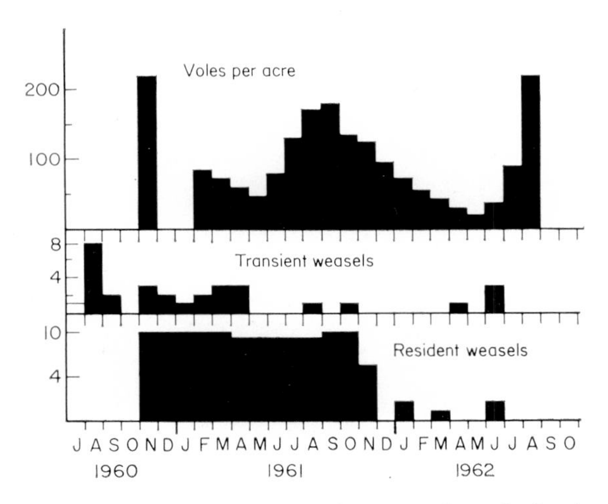

FIG. 7. The number of resident and transient weasels and of voles in the Carron Valley study area.

when the study ended in this area. But, during these years, sufficient male weasels entered the study area to populate it, as it had been in 1961, ten times over. At any one time, however, not more than two animals were present and thus they were not in contact with one another. I suggest, therefore, that for a territorial system to be set up in weasels requires at least enough animals to populate the area fully. After October 1961 when the population of residents had been reduced the remainder did not share the study area between them. Any considerable enlargement in one direction apparently meant a loss of contact in the other (Fig. 8). This suggests that the weasels were holding as much ground as they could.

Short-tailed voles fluctuate widely in number. It seems to me unreasonable to expect weasels to adjust their territories (assuming that territories are indeed primarily needed for a food supply) to such a rapidly changing prey population. Instead, I suggest that weasels hold as much ground as they can and this gives sufficient available food in all situations except the most extreme. Such extremely low prey numbers may come only once or twice or perhaps not at all in the early history of a forest plantation.

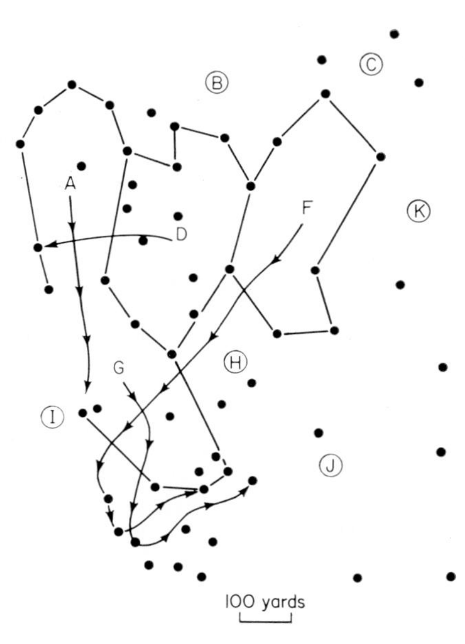

FIG. 8. The break-up of the territorial system of weasels in the Carron Valley, November 1961. Dots represent traps and encircled letters animals which died or disappeared. Arrows show the approximate route taken by weasels after the adjacent animal moved or died.

Thus, I suggest that the initial setting up of territories is not necessarily related to the food supply alone but also to the number of male weasels on the ground. If there are too few males, no territories result; if there are moderate numbers, a territorial system as shown in Figs. 1 and 2 results; if numbers are very high, aggressiveness by the males is probably high too in order to maintain a sizeable territory. This last situation may then explain why female weasels can come off badly even when the food supply is apparently adequate.

Suppose, however, that my interpretation of Figs. 7 and 8 is wrong. Could it be that the weasels can forecast in autumn the level to which the voles will fall in April of the following year? If so, the territories may have been maintained because the weasels "knew" that the prey in April 1960 would not drop below 45 per acre. But in autumn 1961 they "knew" that in May 1962 the prey would be down to 18 per acre and they acted accordingly. This is by no means impossible; but it perhaps requires that the weasels have a gauge not only of the numbers of the vole population but also its quality. W. N. Charles is at present working on the structure of the vole population in these years so that this possibility can be assessed before long.

Acknowledgements

I am grateful to the Nature Conservancy for allowing me to initiate and continue this work until 1964 when I left their employment; to Professor J. N. Black, Department of Forestry and Natural Resources, for his encouragement; to the Forestry Commission for permission to work on their land and for a grant to continue the work during 1965–66; to the National Coal Board for permission to work on one of their estates in Midlothian; to W. N. Charles for permission to quote some measurements he has made of the numbers of voles; to Ken East for his considerable help in the field and in the laboratory from 1961–64; to Duncan Ferguson for his assistance in the field and laboratory since October 1964; and to W. Buckie, John Shanks and Nita Spektarov who also helped.

References

Baron, A., Stewart, C. N. and Warren, J. M. (1957). Patterns of social interaction in cats. *Behaviour* **11**, 56–66.

Burns, J. J. (1964). Movements of a tagged weasel in Alaska. *Murrelet* **45** (1), 10.

Criddle, S. (1947). A nest of the least weasel. *Can. Fld Nat.* **61**, 69.

Deanesly, R. (1935). The reproductive processes of certain mammals. Part IX. Growth and reproduction in the stoat (*Mustela erminea*). *Phil. Trans. R. Soc.* B, **225**, 1–62.

Ellis, R. J. (1964). Tracking raccoons by radio. *J. Wildl. Mgmt* **28** (2), 363–68.

Grinnel, J., Dixon, J. S. and Linsdale, J. M. (1937). "Fur-bearing Mammals of California," Vol. 1. University of California Press, Berkeley.

Hall, E. R. (1957). American weasels. *Univ. Kans. Publs nat. Hist.* **4**, 1–466.

Hawley, V. D. and Newby, F. E. (1957). Marten home ranges and population fluctuations. *J. Mammal.* **38**, 174–84.

Hill, M. (1939). The reproductive cycle of the male weasel (*Mustela nivalis*). *Proc. zool. Soc. Lond.* **109** B, 481–512.

Jenkins, D., Watson, A. and Millar, G. R. (1963). Population studies on red grouse in north-east Scotland. *J. Anim. Ecol.* **32**, 317–376.

Justice, K. E. (1961). A new method of measuring home ranges of small mammals. *J. Mammal.* **42**, 462–470.

Lack, D. (1943). "The Life of the Robin." Witherby, London.

Lack, D. (1954). "The Natural Regulation of Animal Numbers." Clarendon Press, Oxford.

Lampio, T. (1951). On the sex ratio, sex differentiation and regional variation in the marten in Finland. *Riistat. Julk.* **7**, 20 pp.

Leeuw, A. de (1957). Die Wildkatze. *Merkbl. Niederwild. dt. Jagd-schutzverb.* No. 16.

Lensink, C. J. (1957). The home range of the marten and its significance in management. *Sci. Alaska,* 1954, 36–37.

Lindemann, W. (1953). Einiges über die Wildkatzes des Ostkarpathen (*Felis s. sylvestris* Schreber 1777). *Säugetierk. Mitt.* **1**, 73–4.

Lockie, J. D. (1964). The distribution and fluctuations of the pine marten, *Martes martes* L., in Scotland. *J. Anim. Ecol.* **33**, 349–356.

Lockie, J. D. and Day, M. G. (1964). The use of anaesthesia in the handling of stoats and weasels. *In* "Symposium on Small Mammal Anaesthesia" (O. Graham Jones, ed.), pp. 187–189. Pergamon Press, Oxford.

Marshall, W. H. (1951). Pine marten as a forest product. *J. For.* **49**, 899–905.

Nasimovich, A. A. (1949). The biology of the weasel in the Kola peninsula in connection with its competitive relations with the ermine (trans.). *Zool. Zh.* **28**, 177–82.

Neal, E. G. (1948). "The Badger." Pelican Books, London.

Nyholm, E. S. (1959). On stoat and weasel and their winter habitat. *Suom. Riista* **13**, 106–116.

Polderboer, E. B. (1942). Habits of the least weasel (*Mustela rixosa*) in north-eastern Iowa. *J. Mammal.* **23**, 145–7.

Quick, H. F. (1951). Notes on the ecology of weasels in Gunnison County, Colorado. *J. Mammal.* **32** (3), 281–90.

Quick, H. F. (1956). Analysis of marten exploitation as criteria of management. *Trans. 21st N. Am. Wildl. Conf.*, 355–363.

Raievsky, V. V. (1946). Quantitative checking of sables (*Mustela zibellina* L.) in their winter nests (trans.). *Zool. Zh.* **259**, 171–174.

Schmidt, F. (1943). Naturgeschichte des Baum-und des Stein-marders, mit vergleichenden Betrachtungen ihrer nächsten Versandten, besonderes des Sibirischen Zobels und des Amerikanisches Fichtenmarders. *Monogrn. Wildsäugetiere* **10**, 1–528.

Southern, H. N. (Ed.) (1964). "Handbook of British Mammals." Blackwells, Oxford.

Storm, G. L. (1965). Movements and activities of foxes as determined by radio-tracking. *J. Wildl. Mgmt* **29** (1), 1–13.

Tinbergen, N. (1953). "The Herring Gull's World." Collins, London.

Weckworth, R. P. and Hawley, V. D. (1962). Marten food habits and population fluctuations in Montana. *J. Wildl. Mgmt* **26** (1), 55–74.

Wynne-Edwards, V. C. (1962). "Animal Dispersion in Relation to Social Behaviour." Oliver and Boyd, Edinburgh.

APPENDIXES

1. *Study areas*

Three study areas have been used, a young forest plantation in the Carron Valley, Stirlingshire, as the main live-trapping study area, a small plantation in Midlothian as a subsidiary live-trapping area and part of an estate in Midlothian where intensive spring-trapping was carried out. The first two areas gave information on resident animals, and a little about transients, while the third, which was initially cleared of weasels and stoats, gave information about transient animals.

The study area in the forest plantation in the Carron Valley was about 80 acres with 2 000 acres of similar plantation all around it. The trees, mostly Scots Pine and Sitka Spruce, varied in height from 1 to 6 ft; grasses, mostly *Deschampsia caespitosa*, *D. flexuosa*, *Holcus mollis*, *Molina caerulea* and *Agrostis* spp., grew luxuriantly.

Weasels had been numerous before the study began but had become scarcer by November 1961. A feature was the unbalanced sex ratio. Indeed, from February 1961 for more than one year no females could be found and almost certainly none or few were present in the forest, since no young appeared in the traps in July 1961 when young animals should become independent. In this respect, the study area was atypical but from subsequent work in Midlothian it seems that males behaved, nevertheless, normally.

The Midlothian live-trapping study area was a shelter belt of 30 acres in its initial stages. The trees were small, the grass luxuriant. The spring-trapping area was on the same estate. Trapping was intensive over about 500 acres using sixty to seventy Fenn spring traps. The area was cleared of weasels and stoats at the beginning. Thereafter, the traps were visited every 3 or 4 days for three years. Since there were periods when no animals were caught, it is presumed that all or most animals entering the study area were caught soon after entry.

2. *Trapping*

When traps are used for, say, small mammals each animal must be enticed to the trap. Some come readily, some less so and some not at all. Thus the captures are not only a sample but possibly a biased one. However, weasels and stoats cannot resist heaps of stones (as every gamekeeper knows) and my traps were set in these. They were left *in situ* and open between trappings so that the weasels used them regularly and incorporated them in their daily movements. Thus, at every trapping session most and sometimes all the residents were caught. The owners of only two territories were missed on occasions and I presumed that these animals only had part of their territory outside the study area (Table III). The ease of capture and recapture compensates in some degree for the fact that the animals are of necessity thin on the ground.

TABLE III

The proportion of trapping sessions at which each resident weasel was caught one or more times

Animal*	No. of trapping sessions	Percentage of trapping sessions at which each animal was caught one or more times
A†	18	67
B	18	100
C	18	100
D	9	100
E	20	100
F	19	100
G	18	100
H	18	100
I	15	100
J†	18	77

* Lettering of animals as in Fig. 1.

† A and J are presumed on this evidence to have part of their territory outside the study area, the remainder not.

The traps were home made wooden boxes (10 in. long × 6 in. high × 5 in.) with a galvanized iron guillotine door operated with a nylon line from a treadle at the back of the trap. Inside, I provided a hay loft and fresh meat. The food was not needed to attract the weasels and stoats to the trap but to keep them alive overnight once captured. I found that both weasels and stoats were very susceptible to lack of food and chilling. The back of each trap was made of plate glass to allow the operator to see what he had caught. The traps were set as "dead end" traps, that is, the animal could not look through but instead explored a dark cavity.

In areas where wood mice *Apodemus sylvaticus* entered the traps they invariably when caught chewed through the nylon line. We therefore made treadle traps in which the treadle acts also as the door. By nailing weights to the treadle, the traps could be made to capture only animals heavier than wood mice. The Cotswold Game Farm, Stroud, Gloucestershire, make weasel traps of this sort. They are most efficient but are too narrow if the wish is to keep weasels alive overnight in cold weather.

3. *Handling*

Weasels and stoats are fierce and active. Heavy gloves and a wire cone are difficult, if not impossible to use. I therefore, anaesthetized all weasels before handling with anaesthetic ether. Because of the variety of field conditions and the variability of individuals, I could not determine a standard dose. Instead I had to judge by experience when the animal was sufficiently anaesthetized. (See Lockie and Day (1964) for a fuller explanation.)

4. *Marking*

At first, I tried plastic collars hoping to be able to observe marked and unmarked weasels and also hoping to get returns of animals which had left the district. In general, the collars were difficult to adjust and while some lasted for up to 9 months in the field with no inconvenience to the owner, others chafed.

I therefore, ceased using collars and marked all weasels and stoats by punching the ears, there being three positions on each and sixty-three combinations which was adequate for my purpose. (See also Lockie and Day, 1964.)

5. *Age determination*

The age of weasels and stoats was determined by the degree of wear on the upper canine teeth. I now have records of the wear of canine teeth in twenty animals of known age in the wild. The length of time that individuals could be followed after independence varied from a few months to three years. This information shows that age determination by the wear of canines is accurate for the first 12 months but is less accurate in the older age classes. The errors involved are being estimated and the technique will be published elsewhere. It has the obvious advantage that it can be used on unmarked live animals.

Symp. zool. Soc. Lond. (1966) No. 18, 167–177.

SCENT MARKING IN THE CANIDAE

DEVRA KLEIMAN

The Zoological Society of London, London, England

SYNOPSIS

Scent marking has been defined as urination, defaecation, or rubbing of certain areas of the body which is (1) oriented to specific objects, (2) elicited by familiar conspicuous landmarks and novel objects or odours, and (3) repeated frequently on the same object. Comparisons have been made of the marking postures of the members of fourteen species in the family Canidae. Scent marking postures in conjunction with other behavioural and anatomical characters were shown to be effective in establishing taxonomic relationships. The bush dog and bat-eared fox, two anatomically aberrant members of the family, differed considerably from the other species in the methods which they used for marking and the postures which they adopted.

Several theories concerning the functions of marking are discussed, and it is suggested that scent marking probably originated as a device for familiarizing and reassuring the animal when he entered a strange environment. The methods used for dispersing scent arose from the association of the unknown with autonomic responses, such as urination and defaecation, which occur in strange and frightening situations. Secondary functions have arisen such as the bringing together of the sexes and the maintenance of territory, and these have assumed an important function in the survival of the species.

INTRODUCTION

The significance of olfaction in communication amongst mammals has been largely ignored by biologists, mainly because they have been so ill-equipped to deal with the problem. Our own feeble olfactory sense has inhibited both research and interest in this field. We know next to nothing about the quantity and quality of information conveyed by the odours which many mammals deposit with such conspicuous behaviour throughout their environment, and we have scanty knowledge of the behaviour patterns which have evolved in association with the dispersal of scent. Our ignorance in this area is rather disturbing when we consider the sophisticated methods which have been devised to analyse the visual, tactile, and acoustic senses.

This paper will deal with scent marking in the family Canidae. The behaviour patterns which are utilized for depositing scent will be described. Several comments will be made on species-specific differences in the motor patterns and their possible use as taxonomic characters. Lastly, I will discuss the functions of scent marking and its possible evolution as well as the types of information which can be conveyed by the odours.

ANIMALS AND METHODS

Fifty-three members of the family Canidae were observed in the gardens of the Zoological Society of London. The following is a list of the distribution of sexes and numbers:

	Species	No. of males	No. of females
1.	Wolf (*Canis lupus*)	4	6
2.	Coyote (*Canis latrans*)	1	2
3.	Black-backed jackal (*Canis mesomelas*)		1
4.	Side-striped jackal (*Canis adustus*)		3
5.	Domestic dogs including dingoes and New Guinea singing dogs (*Canis familiaris*)	5	5
6.	Red fox (*Vulpes vulpes*)	2	1
7.	Fennec fox (*Fennecus zerda*)		1
8.	Arctic fox (*Alopex lagopus*)	3	3
9.	Raccoon dog (*Nyctereutes procyonoides*)	2	1
10.	Paraguayan fox (*Dusicyon gymnocercus*)		1
11.	Maned wolf (*Chrysocyon brachyurus*)	2	1
12.	Bush dog (*Speothos venaticus*)	3	1
13.	Cape hunting dog (*Lycaon pictus*)		1
14.	Bat-eared fox (*Otocyon megalotis*)	3	1
		25	28

All of the animals observed were on exhibition in the gardens throughout most of the year. They were fed a diet of horse-meat and freshly killed chicks and mice. Fruits and vegetables were fed to those species which are thought to be more omnivorous in the wild.

Generally, the animals were interfered with as little as possible by the observer, and a hide was set up in front of the cages of those individuals who appeared disturbed by the observer's presence. Occasionally, novel odour-bearing and visual objects were placed in the cages of all of the animals, and the responses to these stimuli were recorded. Balloons, herbs, perfumed cloths, and the faeces of different species were among the objects presented. Where possible, the faeces and urine of conspecifics with whom the subject was unfamiliar and familiar were presented.

RESULTS

Before describing the means by which members of the Canidae deposit their scent, it is necessary to define what is meant by the term "scent marking". In mammals, odour can be dispersed by urination, defaecation, and the secretion of glandular material. The latter method is frequently associated with some form of body rubbing. In order to distinguish between mere elimination in the case of urination and defaecation and a comfort movement such as a scratch in the case of body rubbing, certain quantitative and qualitative differences that are not visible in the original postures must be found in scent marking. The behaviour patterns used, therefore, should be changed.

There are three characters which serve to distinguish scent marking in the family Canidae. First, there is a directional quality in the posture, i.e. the animal orients itself towards a specific object or to the source of an odour. Secondly, the stimuli which elicit the patterns are either entirely new objects or objects with which the animal is well acquainted and on which he has previously deposited scent. In both cases, the object marked is conspicuous. Lastly, the motor patterns are repeated frequently in response to the same stimulus.

It should be emphasized that the use of the term "territorial marking" has been deliberately omitted since this would immediately ascribe a function to the behaviour.

Urination patterns

Elimination of urine in members of the family Canidae differs between the sexes. Females generally squat deeply into nearly a sitting position. The tail is held parallel with the ground. Males also squat; however, they lower their hindquarters less than females.

Males exhibit three marking postures depending upon the intended orientation of the urine. If sprinkling urine on a vertical surface, the well-known leg-lifting pattern occurs. The animal stands parallel with the object, twists his hindquarters, raises his leg from the hip and crooks it (Fig. 1). When directing urine onto the ground, males either stand with all four legs slightly spread or stand and elevate one hindleg under the body. In the latter posture, there is generally a slight depression of the hindquarters. Tembrock (1957) has described male red foxes marking with urine using a squatting posture, but this was not observed in the present study.

Most males and some females of the genus *Canis* (the domestic dog, wolf, coyote and jackals) scratch at the ground with their fore and hind feet after marking with urine.

In the males of two species (maned wolf and bush dog) little seasonal change was seen in the frequency of urine sprinkling. The members of most species observed did, however, show an increase during the rutting season.

Studies of the male domestic dog (Berg, 1944) have shown that the leg-lifting posture of males does not appear until the animal has become mature. Berg showed that animals prevented from leg-lifting until after reaching maturity showed the correct pattern as soon as they were released from a confined state. Although leg-lifting normally appears at 19 weeks in the domestic dog, it can be induced at 8 weeks by daily injections of testosterone. Thus, Berg's experiments demonstrate that the leg-lifting marking posture in the domestic dog is inborn and hormonally controlled.

FIG. 1. A male maned wolf urinating on a post using the leg-lift posture.

Females who are directing their urine towards an object on the ground either squat in the normal urination posture or squat and elevate one hindleg under the body (Fig. 2). When they orient towards a vertical surface they initially stand parallel with the surface and then turn so that they are facing away from the surface. One hindleg is lifted under the body and the root of the tail is twisted to the side as they urinate. A female may lightly touch the vertical surface with her ano-genital region. There is no depression of the hindquarters.

While the squat or the squat-with-leg-lift was used by the females of most of the species observed. the completely upright posture with the leg lift was seen only in the raccoon dog, the Arctic fox, the maned wolf, and the side-striped jackal.

Fig. 2. A female Paraguayan fox using the squat-with-leg-lift posture. She is just rising after having urinated.

The bush dog female uses an entirely distinct marking posture (Fig. 3). She directs her urine onto a vertical surface by climbing up backwards onto the surface with her hindlegs, urinating while standing on her forelegs, and then sliding her ano-genital region down the vertical surface.

Among the females, the Paraguayan fox and side-striped jackal use urine as a marking device throughout the year. The raccoon dog, domestic dog, coyote, and bat-eared fox females only mark during the period preceding oestrus and during oestrus itself. During this study, female Cape hunting dogs, wolves, red foxes, and black-backed jackals were never observed marking with urine. The female bush dog marked throughout the year, but more intensively during heat. Neither the fennec fox nor the maned wolf were observed for the entire year, and there is therefore no data on seasonal changes in marking behaviour for them. Neither of these females showed signs of an oestrous period.

Fig. 3. A female bush dog urinating in the raised-hindquarters posture. (Taken from a colour film.)

Defaecation patterns

Although dogs and foxes could use faeces as material for marking, defaecation is not used by the members of most species as a means of depositing odour on a specific object or landmark. The fennec fox and Arctic fox were occasionally observed defaecating in response to novel stimuli; however, the act was never repeated more than once. The motor pattern used was the same as the eliminative pattern. The back is slightly hunched, the tail root raised, and the hindlegs bent. In the cases of the Arctic foxes and fennec fox, faeces were considered to be a marking substance because they were directed onto novel objects.

Rubbing and rolling patterns

Rolling on the ground and body rubbing are well-known phenomena in the family Canidae, but have not generally been considered to be a means of dispersing scent. Since rubbing and rolling possess an orientation component, are repeated frequently upon the same object, and are elicited by both novel objects and well-known landmarks, I feel that they should be considered as marking. Members of the Canidae do not have scent glands located on the trunk of the body (they do have anal scent glands and a gland on the dorsal side of the tail near the root; Hildebrand, 1952). There is now, however, some evidence from observations on the domestic dog (T. J. Pickvance, personal communication) that the odours of some areas of the body have a greater attraction for conspecifics than others.

When rubbing its body on an object on the ground, the animal will generally begin by bending its forelegs and thus dropping its forequarters. It will then rub the side of its neck and temple on the object or odour-bearing object several times in succession, sometimes alternating sides. This may be followed by the animal turning over completely on its back. When on its back the animal exhibits the wriggling and writhing pattern with which dog owners are so familiar.

When rubbing its body against a vertical surface the animal successively presses the side of its temple, neck, and trunk against the surface. The tail is usually raised at the root.

The body rubbing postures which have just been described occur throughout the family with the exception of the bat-eared fox who shows a slightly modified pattern. When on its back, the bat-eared fox will generally roll from side to side using quick jerky movements. The writhing behaviour has never been observed in these animals.

Stimuli releasing marking behaviour

Urination, defaecation, and body rubbing, the three methods of dispersing scent employed by members of the family Canidae, are released by two types of stimuli. The first type of stimulus is provided by familiar, conspicuous objects, and all members of the family concentrate some of their marking activities on objects such as wooden posts which are a permanent part of their environment. The second type of stimulus is provided by novel odour-bearing and visual objects.

DISCUSSION

Species-specific differences in marking methods

Lorenz (1941) has shown how a comparison of fixed motor patterns in closely related species of the Anatinae could be used in clarifying phylogenetic relationships. A preliminary study of the family Canidae (Kleiman, in preparation) using much the same approach has just been completed. The relationships of the various species are best revealed by differences in social behaviour, but a comparison of scent-marking postures reveals that they too can be used for taxonomic purposes.

Heimburger (1959) and Seitz (1955) in their studies of certain species in the family have implied that there are species-specific patterns of response to visual and odour-bearing objects, i.e. the members of one species will respond to certain objects by rubbing and to others by urinating. These differences were not observed during the present study. For example, most strong odours can and do elicit both patterns separately and together. The response is probably not completely random, but until we obtain more information about both the qualities of the stimuli being used and the responses to them, it is not possible to make any generalizations.

There are, however, two statements which can be made on the preference of marking method. (1) Some species use one marking method to the exclusion of others. (2) Species differ in the posture which they adopt for marking.

1. *Use of one marking method to the exclusion of others*

Bush dogs, a morphologically aberrant member of the family, have never been observed rubbing their bodies on either old landmarks or new objects. Only urine is used for depositing scent. The fennec fox and Arctic foxes were observed occasionally using their faeces as a marking substance and were the only members of the family to do so.

2. *Different postures employed for marking*

The males of ten species were observed. Although most of the animals urinated on both horizontal and vertical surfaces using the marking patterns which have been described, the males of two species showed a preference for one method of marking. Bat-eared fox males were never observed marking on vertical objects. All urine sprinkling was directed towards the ground, and the animals either stood with their legs slightly spread or stood and raised a hindleg. Bush dog males, on the other hand, were seen using only the posture in which the leg is lifted out from the body at a ninety degree angle, and they used this method even when they were urinating on objects which were on the ground.

In females, the most common postures used for marking with urine are the ones in which the female simply squats, or squats and elevates a hindleg. This pattern has been observed in the domestic dog, the coyote, the side-striped jackal, the bat-eared fox, the Paraguayan fox, the fennec fox, the wolf, and the Arctic fox. It has been reported in the red fox (Tembrock, 1957). The more unusual pattern of urinating on vertical objects by directing the anogenital region towards a surface has been observed only in the maned wolf, the raccoon dog, the Arctic fox, and the side-striped jackal. The bush dog female's posture which has been described has been neither observed nor described for females of any other species in the family: the bush dog female used this method almost exclusively and only once displayed the squat-with-leg-lift posture.

With one exception there are no species-specific differences in rubbing and rolling patterns. The exception is the bat-eared fox whose side-to-side rolling behaviour has been mentioned. This behaviour pattern may be related to the fact that there is a hair split in the centre of its back which may contain a scent gland. It would be most interesting if the evolution of a new scent gland had been associated with a modification of the normal canine rolling pattern.

The bush dog and bat-eared fox stand out as having the most specialized means of dispersing their scent. This behavioural analysis is in accord with the palaeontological and morphological evidence through which these two species have been placed in separate subfamilies, the Simocyoninae and Otocyoninae, respectively. Of course, the analysis of one type of behaviour is inadequate for reaching conclusions regarding phylogenetic relationships. All aspects of the animal's behaviour must be considered together with its ecological status before any definite statements can be made regarding its taxonomic position.

Functions of marking behaviour

Several theories have been proposed to account for the occurrence of scent-marking. Wynne-Edwards (1962) has presented the view that scent marks serve to inform animals of the population density of conspecifics, hence information can be gained on the number of rivals, the number of oestrous females, and their health and age. He considers urination to be a social phenomenon with a display function solely confined to males. Schenkel (1947) in his study of wolf behaviour concluded that scent marking has several functions which include the demarcation of territory, the making of acquaintances, the formation of the pair, and the legitimization of the leader. Lorenz (1954) has likened scent marking in dogs to a nightingale's song. The scent is deposited in a dog's territory in order to ward off intruders.

The above views consider the behaviour to be mainly a social phenomenon. Lyall-Watson (1964) (among others) in his study of the acouchi has made several interesting comments on the function of scent marking that might have a more general application. His statements are useful in explaining the occurrence of the behaviour and easily lend themselves to an hypothesis concerning its evolution. He favours the interpretation that scent marking serves to maintain the animal's familiarity with its environment and that odour is added to specific visual landmarks both to familiarize the animal with new territory and to refamiliarize it with old terrain.

From this hypothesis arises a possible understanding of the evolution of the behaviour. Most mammals show autonomic responses such as defaecating, urinating, and sympathetic reactions in the skin in response to unfamiliar terrain or situations. Primitive mammalian forms could have responded in this way to the unknown, and the smell of their own scent would have reinforced the assurance that was gained from a known home range. These autonomic responses might have evolved into more voluntary actions. The specialized postures which are used today for depositing scent might have developed for directing the scent onto more conspicuous landmarks in the environment.

In analysing the possible evolution of social displays, Morris (1955) uses the same argument:

> "Considering all that is known about the type of behaviour involved in territorial defence, it is highly probable that these methods of marking (urination and defaecation) have evolved from the alimentary effects of parasympathetic stimulation that occurs with thwarting." (p. 104).

The thesis that scent marking in mammals arose from autonomic responses and evolved into a means of familiarizing the animal with its environment and reassuring it in unknown situations is very useful. It certainly does not exclude the numerous social functions which scent-marking has gained during the evolution of the behaviour, but it does imply that they developed secondarily. This thesis also suggests that scent marking is not used as an agonistic display for territorial defence even though the behaviour is effective in maintaining a territory. Its efficiency simply lies in the avoidance responses which are shown by the intruding individuals.

Acknowledgements

This research was supported by the National Institutes of Mental Health grant number 03361. The author is deeply indebted to Dr. B. Ginsburg for making the research possible. The author is also grateful to Drs. P. Jewell and D. Morris for their helpful criticisms of this manuscript and to Dr. G. Manley for his many valuable discussions.

References

Berg, I. A. (1944). Development of behavior: The micturition pattern in the dog. *J. exp. Psychol.* **34**, 343–368.

Heimburger, N. (1959). Das Markierungsverhalten einigen Caniden. *Z. Tierpsychol.* **16**, 104–113.

Hildebrand, M. (1952). The integument in Canidae. *J. Mammal.* **33**, 419–428.

Lorenz, K. (1941). Vergleichende Bewegungsstudien an Anatiden. *J. Orn., Lpz.* **89**, 194–294.

Lorenz, K. (1954). "Man Meets Dog", p. 94. Methuen, London.

Lyall-Watson, M. (1964). The ethology of food-hoarding in mammals—with special reference to the green acouchi *Myoprocta pratti* Pocock. pp. 384–386. Ph.D. thesis, University of London.

Morris, D. (1955). The feather postures of birds and the problem of the origin of social signals. *Behaviour* **9**, 75–113.

Schenkel, R. (1947). Ausdruck-studien an Wölfen. *Behaviour* **1**, 81–129.

Seitz, A. (1955). Untersuchungen über angeborene Verhaltensweisen bei Caniden. *Z. Tierpsychol.* **12**, 463–489.

Tembrock, G. (1957). Zur Ethologie des Rotfuchses (*Vulpes vulpes* L.). *Zool. Gart., Lpz.* **23**, 289–532.

Wynne-Edwards, V. C. (1962). "Animal Dispersion in Relation to Social Behaviour", pp. 102–103. Oliver and Boyd, London.

Symp. zool. Soc. Lond. (1966) No. 18, 179–210.

SOCIAL GROUPING AND HOME RANGE IN FERAL SOAY SHEEP

P. GRUBB and P. A. JEWELL*

Wellcome Institute of Camparative Physiology, The Zoological Society of London, London, England

SYNOPSIS

The Soay sheep of Hirta, St. Kilda, are feral and under no human restraint or control. This study is concerned with the manner in which their movements and social grouping are employed in making use of the resources of the island. Details are given of the study area. Methods of marking and identifying individual sheep are discussed and the system of mapping their movements is described.

The sheep are formed into social groups, each restricted in its range. A ewe home range group includes ewes, lambs and young rams, totalling about thirty head. Ram home range groups are much smaller, with between two and twelve members. Coherence of the group is promoted by physical barriers, and maintained by isolation of grazing areas and specific social ties. The age class distribution and social grouping of the sheep are listed.

The ranges of ewe groups overlap but regions exclusive to the occupants are maintained within the range although there is no overt aggressive interaction between groups. Ewes have retained the same home range for at least five years. Daily movements are extremely regular in summer but less repetitive and more extensive in winter. There are also seasonal changes in daily activity. Adverse weather conditions disrupt movement. Sheep shelter in cleits (drystone cells) and certain cleits are used by specific groups of sheep. The adequacy of the pasture is important in determining the home range. The locations of lambing and death are described.

The nature of ram home range groups is discussed. During the mating season, these groups split up and each ram wanders widely. This wandering is halted only when a ewe on heat is encountered. Groups of rams reform after the mating season with the same composition and on the same ground.

Ram lambs in most respects behave like adult rams during the mating season though this may lead to new associations for the young animals.

INTRODUCTION

The Soay sheep of Hirta are not indigenous wild animals but are a population of feral domestic sheep. This circumstance must always be borne in mind when comparing their behaviour with that of wild ungulates. These sheep have not recently escaped, however, but are of a very primitive, unimproved type, and have been feral for a long time (see description of their history in Boyd *et al.*, 1964). They were first recorded in the seventeenth century when they already existed as a feral flock on the small island of Soay (244 acres in extent). In 1930, the larger island of Hirta (1 575 acres) was evacuated and a part of the Soay flock

* Present address: Department of Zoology and Comparative Anatomy, University College, London, England.

was subsequently transferred there. These introduced sheep have not been interfered with since that time; a large flock has descended from them, and the population now stands at about 1 000 head but fluctuates in numbers from year to year.

The sheep occupy all parts of the island of Hirta and there is virtually no part of it that is not accessible to them. Several sub-flocks can be identified that appear to remain within small sectors of the island, and there are further subdivisions into small parties of sheep that are resident on areas of about 100 acres. Thus, although the movements of the sheep are not restricted in any way, each individual prefers to inhabit a relatively small area that can be identified as its home range. Feral goats in New Zealand have been observed to behave in a similar way (Riney and Caughley, 1959).

A discussion of the concept of home range is presented elsewhere (Jewell, pp. 85–109). The exhibition of home range behaviour by mammals implies a self-imposed restriction to movement, and it was shown by Hunter (1964) that the concept can be applied appropriately to commercial hill sheep. He found that a flock in a large hill enclosure was composed of several home range groups and each group grazed only a part of the enclosure. These observations were made on flocks of ewes and their lambs, and rams were not present. Moreover, it might be suspected that some of the behavioural attributes of husbanded sheep are maintained by constant contact with man. In view of these considerations the study of feral sheep gains particular interest. A full complement of rams is present on Hirta, their numbers being determined solely by factors of natural mortality. The flocks on Hirta have never been shepherded or rounded-up by man.

The observations that we shall describe have been made as part of a broad co-operative research programme to study fully the ecology of the Soay sheep (see Boyd *et al.*, 1964). This study has been in progress since 1959 and has yielded a great deal of background information on which we have been able to draw. During this past year one of us (P.G.) has been resident on the island.

METHODS

The period of intensive observation extended from September 1964 to June 1965 inclusive and covered the rutting season, winter and the birth of a fresh crop of lambs.

Area of study

The study area was restricted to the Village Glen. This glen is a semicircular area of ground rising from the sea with a gradient of 1 in 6 and backed by the much steeper slopes of two hills, Oiseval (948 ft) to the east and Conachair (1 397 ft) to the north. In addition, the south-east slope of a ridge extending from Conachair and culminating in a plateau, Mullach Sgar (715 ft), bounds this area on the west side. These features are shown on the map (Fig. 1). The gradient of these high

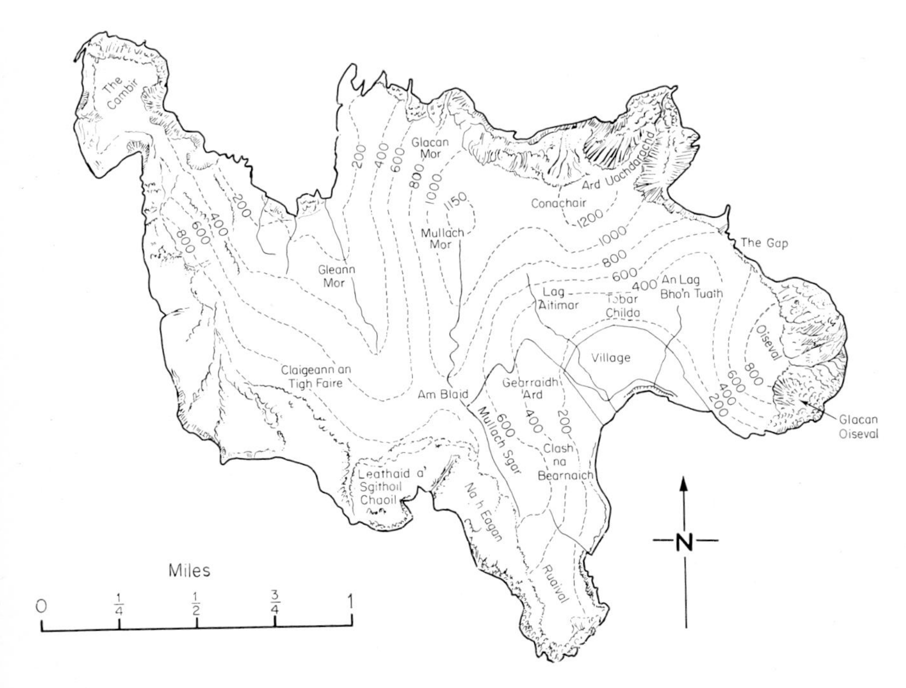

Fig. 1. Map of Hirta, St. Kilda, showing the localities mentioned in the text.

slopes varies from 1 in 1·5 to 1 in 3·5. The last mentioned ridge is broken by a col at Am Blaid, below which the slope is less uniform and interrupted by small corries. Set between Oiseval and Conachair is a subsidiary hanging valley, An Lag Bho'n Tuath (see Fig. 2). The central part of the Glen is bounded by a drystone wall that follows the contours and encloses those areas formerly cultivated. Centred within this are the deserted cottages of the St. Kildans arranged along a single street. The whole area within the wall is here referred to as the Village and this ground is divided into sectors by streams, dykes and cultivation ridges. Drystone storage houses or cleits are numerous throughout the Glen but are especially concentrated at the back of the Village and in

Tobar Childa. An Army garrison is installed in the south-east corner of the Village and a new road leads from the Army camp parallel to the shore and then sweeps up into the hills.

Above the Village, the slopes are covered by a grass-heath, within which heather is predominant on Oiseval and Conachair. Mixed grassland, on the other hand, is almost confined within the perimeter wall, although patches of such grassland occur in An Lag Bho'n Tuath (Fig. 2) and in depressions lying in the western slopes. Here, also, are isolated

FIG. 2. Conachair and An Lag Bho'n Tuath from the east, photographed from a vantage point on Oiseval. The fanks in An Lag Bho'n Tuath are shown, together with the Village perimeter wall and cleits in Tobar Childa to the left of the picture. The rather sharp demarcation between the heather on Conachair and the grassland in An Lag Bho'n Tuath is evident.

areas of *Molinia-Sphagnum* grassland. Other plant communities are sparsely represented within the Village Glen.

Boyd (1959) presents an aerial photograph of the Village Glen and there is a photograph of the Village in Boyd *et al.* (1964). A general account of the climate of the Outer Hebrides will be found in Manley (1948). A recent account of the history of St. Kilda is given by Steel

(1965) and many excellent photographs that illustrate the habitat of the sheep are published in this book.

Identification of individual sheep

The sheep had been marked with plastic tags and nylon swatches to indicate age, and year and locality of capture. Combined with natural variation in colour, and the presence or absence of horns, these produced a set of characters by which each tagged sheep could be positively identified. Identification of a number of untagged individuals, including all rams, was also possible and marking of untagged sheep continued during the period of study. Sheep with tags alone could not be safely identified at a distance even with binoculars and the more conspicuous coloured swatches used to indicate area of capture had in many cases faded. Sheep which had been given coloured nylon collars could be seen from any part of the village, as long as they were not hidden in dead ground. These conspicuous animals were chosen as representatives of home range groups and their ranges were mapped.

Recording ranges of sheep

Sightings of individual sheep were represented as dots on a map of scale 17 in. to 1 mile. This map was prepared from aerial photographs. There is an element of distortion in the result as these photographs were not true verticals.

In the latter half of October and November 1964, as many sightings as possible were recorded. In December to April 1965, in an attempt at standardization, sightings were systematically plotted for 09.00 h, 12.00 h and 15.00 h only, but this did not appreciably alter the results. In May, additional sightings for 06.00 h and 18.00 h were taken. Sometimes certain sheep could not be found and as a thorough search would cause too much disturbance, their positions were not recorded for that hour.

It was inevitable that whilst an attempt to map home ranges of sheep could be accurate within the Village itself, where landmarks were numerous, it could be misleading outside, since sightings would be too few to distinguish regular from exceptional occurrences.

The sub-population of sheep in the Village Glen is quite distinct from others, although the marking schemes discussed by Boyd *et al.* (1964) have also involved sheep from the peninsula of Ruaival and the cliff terraces of Oiseval. A group of sheep whose home range is centred on Oiseval spends the late summer in the east Village, but they are not considered in the present paper.

Recording of daily activity

For one day each week, half-hourly counts were made during the daylight hours of the numbers of sheep engaged in different activities. Observations were made from a vantage point on the lip of An Lag Bho'n Tuath. Three categories of sheep were recognized: ram lambs (born in 1964), other males, and all other sheep (ewes, ewe lambs and misidentified males). Activities recorded were grazing, lying, standing, walking, fighting, suckling and mating.

OBSERVATIONS

Ewe home range groups

Recognition of ewe home range groups

Soay sheep on Hirta commonly graze in small numbers (grazing parties), although it is a subjective matter to decide how closely animals must be grazing before they are regarded as forming a single party. In any case, in whatever way such groups are defined, they vary in composition during the day. Sheep may form into larger groups when moving away on being disturbed or when moving from one area to another during grazing. That individual sheep keep to particular parts of the Village has already been shown (Boyd *et al.*, 1964) by marking them with plastic collars and coloured ear swatches and by observing naturally marked animals. It is, therefore, likely that the same sheep will tend to graze together from day to day. On certain occasions numbers of the order of thirty sheep became isolated from all others in the Village Glen, for instance in An Lag Bho'n Tuath, on the south-west slopes of Oiseval or on the slopes below Clash na Bearnaish (see Fig. 1). In these fortuitous circumstances all those animals tending to graze together and forming an apparent association separate from other sheep, could be distinguished. Such groups can be called home range groups (Fig. 3). Having noted all the constituent individuals that could be recognized, it was then possible to verify subsequently the reality of the group. In this way, it was found that all the ewe parties in the village could be ascribed to one of seven home range groups (see Table I). The positions and extent of these ranges is indicated in Fig. 4. Within a home range group it was possible to discern smaller parties that frequently grazed and moved as sub-units. Such parties were particularly noticeable in the West Village area (Table I). Again, individual sheep could show preferences in the area that they would use within the group home range during a particular period. The home ranges during May 1965 of four members of the Signal's Meadow group illustrate this phenomenon (Fig. 5 A–D).

Fig. 3. Part of a ewe home range group, showing ewes and young lambs. The animal at top centre of the picture is an old ewe with long horns, accompanied by twin lambs. Immediately below her is a yearling ram.

The structure of ewe home range groups

It seems probable that several diverse factors contribute to the formation and maintenance of home range groups. Firstly, natural features of topography and the man-made structures in the Village Glen reduce freedom of movement of the sheep. Dykes, streams and walls divide the area into regions showing some correspondence with the ranges of home range groups. A dry burn, for instance, serves to demarcate the Factor's Meadow group from the Signal's Meadow group (see Figs. 4 and 5).

Secondly, the grassland communities which the sheep favour most are restricted in area but are distributed throughout the lower part of the village. These areas form focal points of attraction for the sheep and each area tends to be monopolized by a particular group of animals.

Thirdly, sheep are observed to associate closely. The most important of these associations is the family of matrilinearly related animals. Ewe lambs accompany their dams closely through summer and autumn, though by mid-November some are to be seen occasionally grazing apart or with others of the same age. Again, some yearling ewes accompany particular older ewes. There is no evidence to show whether those that do not do so have lost their dams or have lost the tendency to follow them. Older sheep of different age classes are also seen to keep with each other, suggesting that the attachment of the ewe lamb to her dam lasts for a long time, probably until the death of the dam. The

TABLE I

Age class distribution and social grouping of St. Kilda Village sheep for autumn 1964

(The figures in parentheses refer to the number of sheep whose minimal age is known, as they were first caught in a "full mouth" condition.)

	Age classes of ewes by year of birth												Age classes of rams by year of birth											Total in home range group
	1964	1963	1962	1961	1960	1959	1958	1957	1956	1955	1954	Not known	1964	1963	1962	1961	1960	1959	1958	1957	1956	1955	1954	
Ewe home range groups																								
Factor's Meadow	4	1	4	5	2			4	1(1)				4	1										26
Signal's Meadow		1	3	3	2	1(1)	3	5(1)		3(2)	1(1)	2	6	4										34
Mid Village fields	3	1	1	4	1(1)	1			2(2)				4											17
Village seafront		1					2	1					3											7
Tobar Childa	8	4	8	4	5(5)	3(2)	2(1)		1(1)			9	5											49
West Village: 1	2	3	2		2(1)		2(2)	2(1)					4											17
2	6	4	4	2	1	5(3)	3(1)		3(3)			3	10											41
3	1	2			1				1(1)				1											6
4	5		4	2	2(1)			1	1(1)			3	3	4										25
5	2	1		5			1					2	2	1										14
Gearraidh Ard	9	1	4	5	2(2)	1		1	1			4	2	3	1									34
Ram home range groups																								
Group 1																2	2							4
2																8								8
3															5	2	4	1		1				13
4															3	2								5
5															4									4
6															1	5								6
Solitary rams																	1					1		2
Total in each age class:	40	19	30	30	18(10)	11(6)	13(4)	14(2)	10(9)	3(2)	1(1)	23	44	13	14	19	7	1		1		1		312

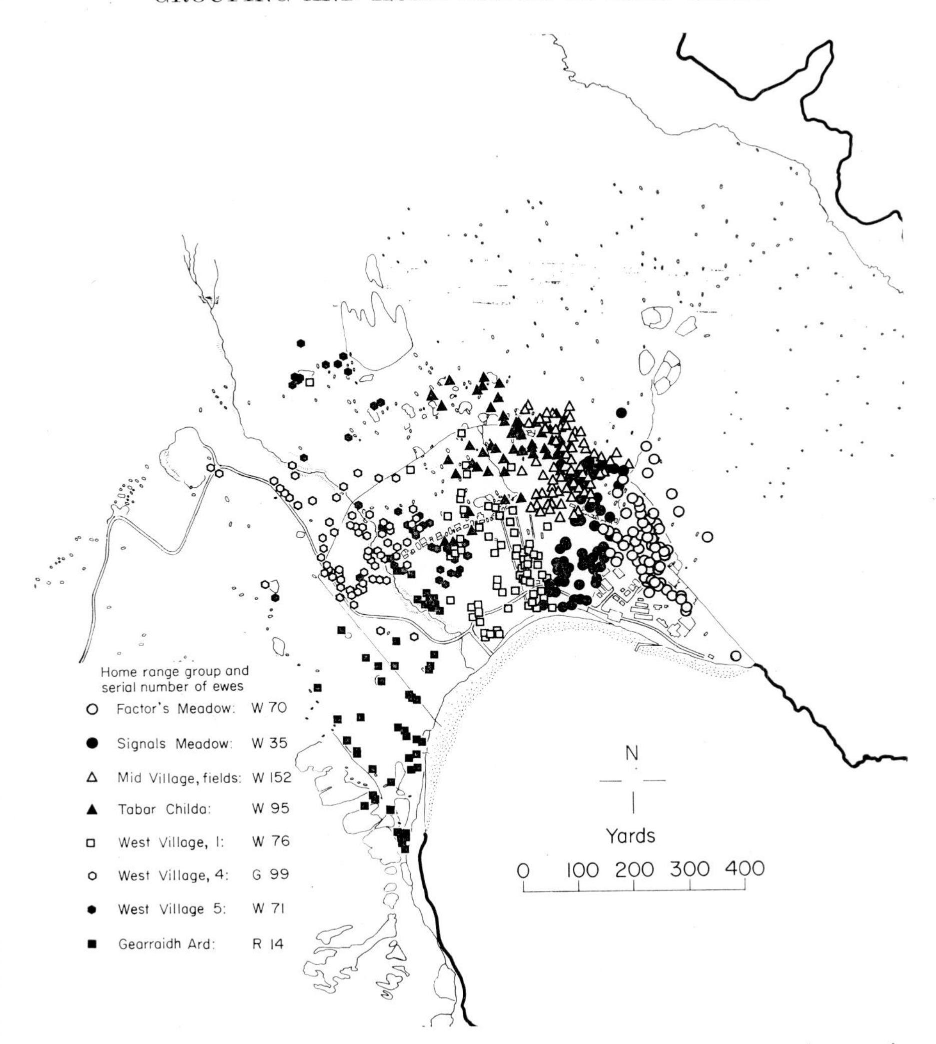

FIG. 4. Ranges of eight ewes, each representing a home range group or subgroup, in May 1965. The groups are listed in Table I. Each symbol represents one sighting. The range of the small Village Seafront group is omitted; it is completely overlapped by the ranges of the Signals Meadow and West Village groups. Of the West Village subgroups, 2 and 3 are intermediate in range between 1 and 4 and 5, and their ranges are also omitted.

tendency to follow the dam remains even after the time the lamb might be expected to have become fully acquainted with its range. In a few instances known marked sheep have offered proof of the family relationship within a party, whilst in other instances it could be reasonably

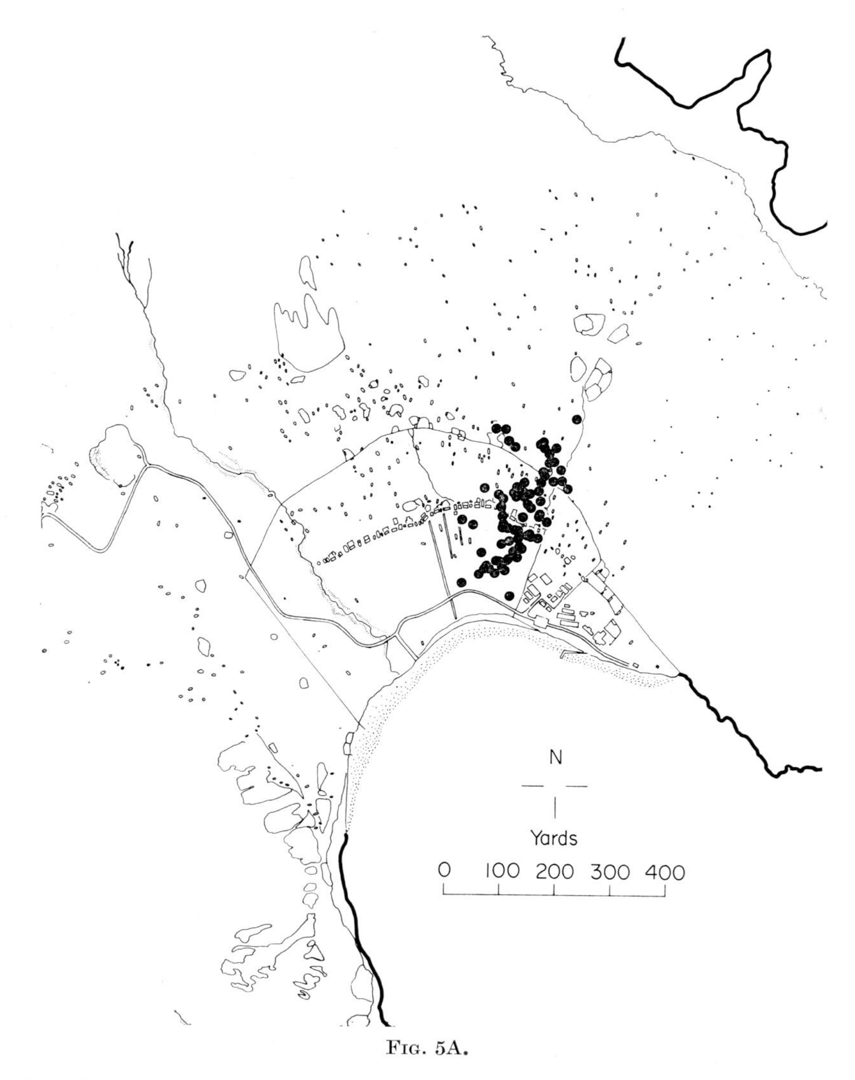

Fig. 5A.

inferred from their possession in common of some distinctive coat-colour marking.

Young lambs spend much of their time in each other's company and these associations may persist in later life. Parties of ewes of the same age were quite often seen, and in a year of exceptionally good lamb survival (as in 1961; see Jewell, 1966), when the chances of ewe lambs grazing together are greater, such associations could be of long-lasting significance.

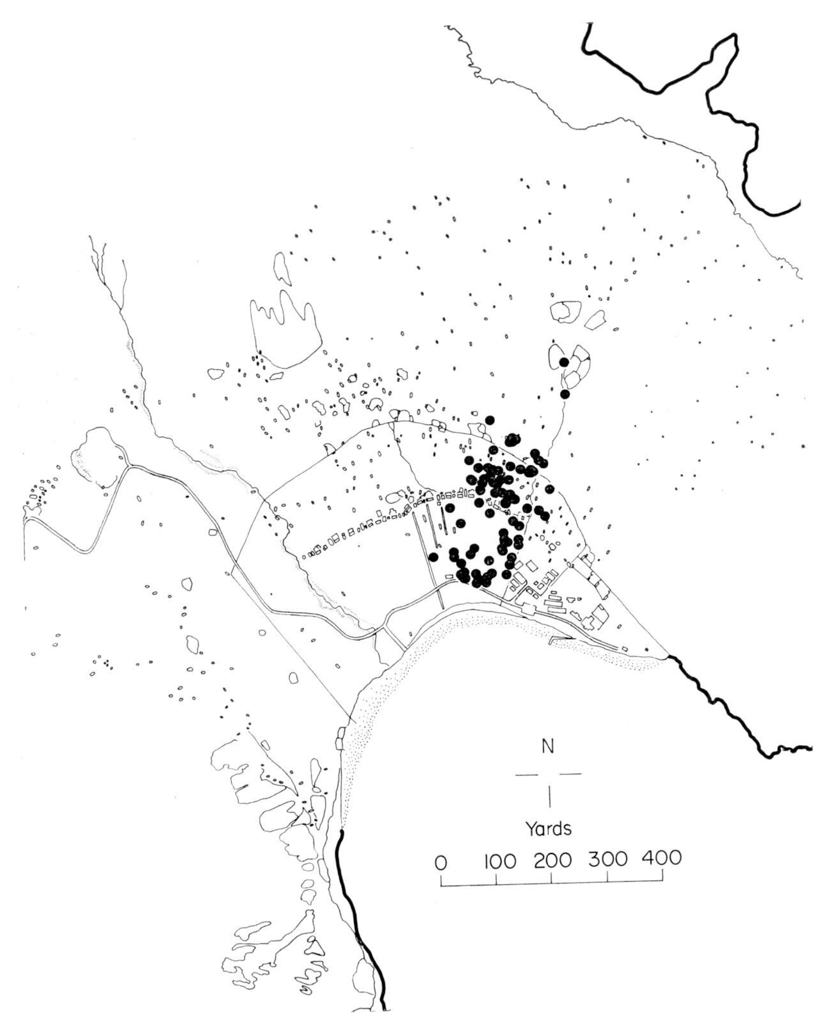

FIG. 5B.

In any one home range group there are, of course, many families (see Table I) but their ultimate relationships are not known. It can be inferred that many parties have members without a close filial relationship, but the nature of the bond between them is not known. In a number of cases, a ewe (and in one case a mature ram) has been seen to call for its companions when they have wandered far away or have moved out of sight.

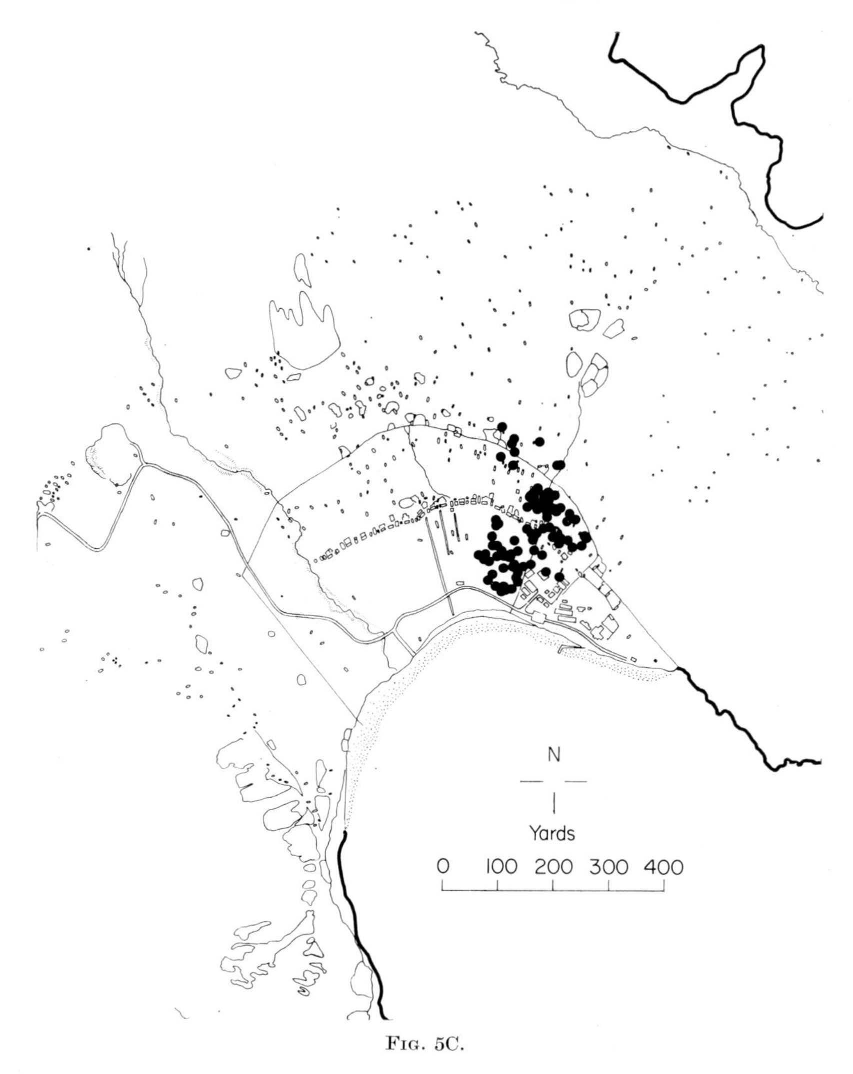

FIG. 5C.

The presence of male sheep in ewe home range groups

Through summer and autumn ram lambs accompany their dams, although by September they already show greater independence than ewe lambs. Their ranges, however, are still those of their maternal groups. Yearling rams in the village area also demonstrated a persistent adherence to ewe home ranges (see Figs. 3 and 5D). Older rams were never members of ewe home range groups and their movements will be described in a later section.

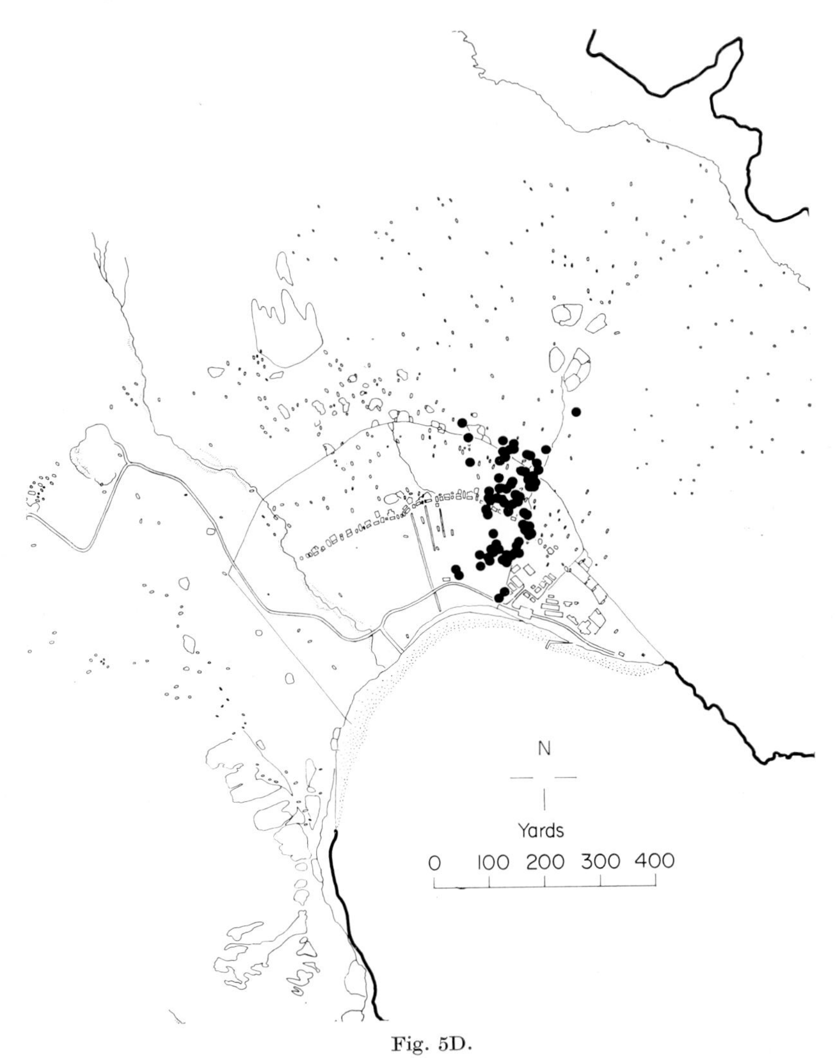

Fig. 5D.

FIG. 5. Ranges of four sheep of the Signals Meadow home range group in May 1965. The animals are (A) ewe W52, (B) ewe W54, (C) ewe BL87 and (D) a young ram, G84. BL87 was exceptional in that she ranged widely into the area used by the Factor's Meadow home range group, although her range was otherwise similar to those of the other sheep in her group.

Home range behaviour

Relations between home range groups

Sightings have been recorded for several individuals within each home range group and the maps prepared have afforded a series of comparisons. From these and from general observations, it is clear that the ranges of individual sheep within a group are generally very similar (Fig. 5) although there is some variation. The ranges of groups overlap, but compared with the area used exclusively by one group, the zone of overlap is small (Fig. 4). The extent to which sheep of one group will move into the range of another group, varies from individual to individual. In Fig. 5 it will be seen that one individual of the four animals illustrated persistently grazed east of the dry burn (ewe BL 87, Fig. 5B) in an area dominantly occupied by the neighbouring home range group.

The West Village sheep are interesting in that they present a situation that might represent incipient splitting into several home range groups. The West Village sheep are, as a whole, quite separate from other home range groups, but are, nevertheless, subdivided into smaller groups with different ranges. These ranges overlap considerably and members of distinct subgroups will often mix in grazing parties. Moreover, some interchange between members of the subgroups was seen in spring, thus testifying to the reality of a larger cohesive group.

The fact that certain areas are occupied exclusively by one home range group does not imply that territories, in the sense of defended areas, are being maintained, but the sheep do provide a good example of the establishment of "monopolized zones". Within a group of ewes it is unusual to see any overt interaction between individuals although recognition of regular companions is implicit. Strange ewes which wander among other groups are subjected to an investigation, consisting of sniffing of the flanks and anal region. The degree of interest shown in a stranger can be very slight. Occasionally a butting bout has developed, but similar butting encounters are not uncommon between sheep within a group. It is significant that sheep only transgress the bounds of the range of another group when the latter are elsewhere in their range.

Adherence to range

Ewes first marked in 1961 have stayed in the same range through to 1964–65 (see the example in Jewell, p. 91). Amongst the several hundred sheep that have been marked since the Soay sheep study started, there have been remarkably few observed shifts of range. The only record of far-ranging movement was in February 1965. Following a snow storm, some ewes moved from the Village Glen to the Cambir and did not return until the lambing season. Another shift occurred when a ewe changed home range groups. It grazed with the Mid Village group in September and October, 1964, and moved to the Village Seafront group in November. Other departures from ranges have been temporary and have always been provoked by disturbance of the sheep. Attempts to catch them in nets may lead to their being chased far from their home range, yet within a matter of hours they will return to it.

Daily movements

Daily movement of sheep includes comparatively rapid excursions between the Village itself and the slopes above, alternating with periods of grazing and resting involving less movement. Arrival and departure do not coincide with sunrise and sunset. Sheep may be present in the Village at dawn but if not they arrive soon after. On doing so they move quickly down to areas near the periphery of their range before starting to graze and then move slowly back across the Village fields. By late afternoon, sheep are travelling more rapidly to their evening grazing areas.

When approaching or departing from a grazing area, sheep would keep in strict file and travel along well-defined tracks. If the leader of the file halted, so would the others, although often another animal would move round onto the track ahead, continuing movement. The file would periodically break up as pockets of good grazing were encountered. This was most clearly seen as sheep moved across the slopes of An Lag, stopping at the grassy surrounds of each cleit they passed. Files were never led by very young sheep if older ones were present; activity was generally initiated by the older animals. Though no individuals stood out as "flock leaders", some older sheep were clearly more alert and wary than others.

The most well-marked sheep tracks are those followed by the sheep in their early morning movement into the grazing areas. The tracks (Fig. 6) are oriented in relation to the pattern of home ranges and their presence implies a regular traffic of sheep.

The movement of different groups and even different individuals within groups was not entirely similar. Sheep of one group might descend into the Village while those of another were moving out. Members of a group may ascend and descend at different times. In spite of these variations, the position of a sheep at a particular hour of the day could vary by less than 100 m over a period of days, during spring and summer. The great regularity of the movements of a sheep through the hours of the day is illustrated in Fig. 7. Such regularity of movement can allow the same area to be grazed by different groups of sheep at different times of day without the groups encountering each other.

With the passage of autumn and winter, there was a progressive change in the timing of movements. Ascent to higher ground came earlier relative to sunset even as the days shortened, and often the Village was not visited at all by sheep which earlier in the season would only have begun to leave it at dusk.

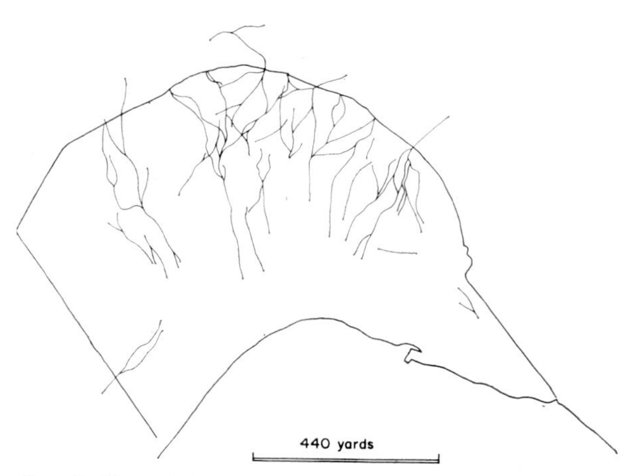

FIG. 6. Map of sheep tracks in the Village in spring 1965.

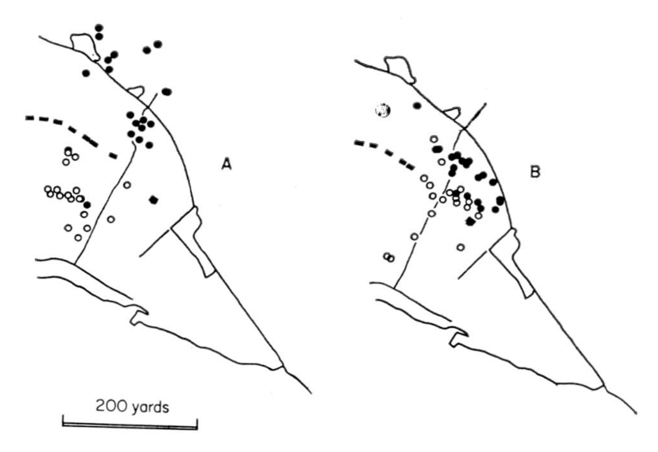

FIG. 7. Sightings of a ewe BL87 at different hours of the day in May 1965. A at 06.00 h (○) and 18.00 h (●); B at 12.00 h (○) and 15.00 h (●).

In parts of the Village Glen grazings of the type present within the perimeter wall are isolated among grass heath and sheep would stay in such places during the day. When they came into the village fields, the time of arrival and departure of the sheep varied and the paths taken were not necessarily the same each day. For instance, the same animals might ascend Gearraidh Ard or Lag Aitimir on different afternoons.

Changes in the daily cycle were associated also with a deterioration of the grazings during winter and a consequent search for food. As a result, ranges were recorded as being more extensive during, for instance, January, than in May (Fig. 9) even though fewer sightings per day were being recorded. For a given hour of the day, the area being grazed was different, say, in March, before the spring growth of grass, from what it was in May, when grass was actively growing (Fig. 8). The effect was for the home range groups to be concentrated together on the best grazings in May, whereas in earlier months they had been more widely dispersed.

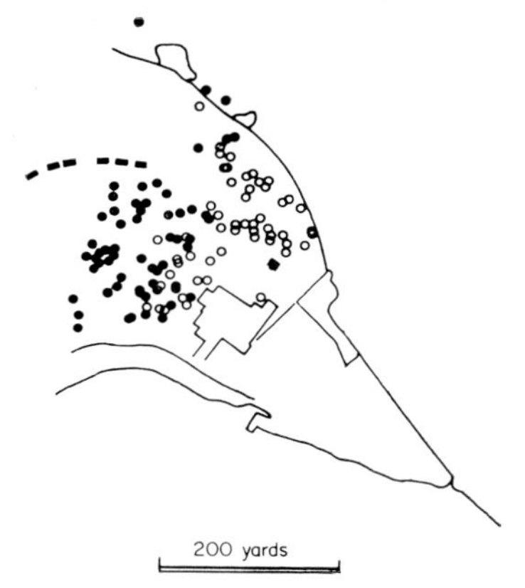

FIG. 8. Sightings of the ewe BL87 at 09.00, 12.00 and 15.00 h for March (●) and May (○) 1965.

Daily activity

A full analysis of daily activity will form the subject of another paper. Here it may simply be noted that during the late summer after intensive grazing in the morning, the animals would usually lie down and chew the cud. The proportion doing so at any one time was never large but there was a noticeable midday peak in this activity in both rams and ewes. As winter advanced, the proportion spending any part of the daytime lying down became very small and this was especially so amongst rams. With the spring flush of grass and the lengthening day, grazing became less continuous and at this time there was an additional peak of resting and cud chewing after the morning descent. The proportion of sheep lying down and cudding was always higher on sunny days.

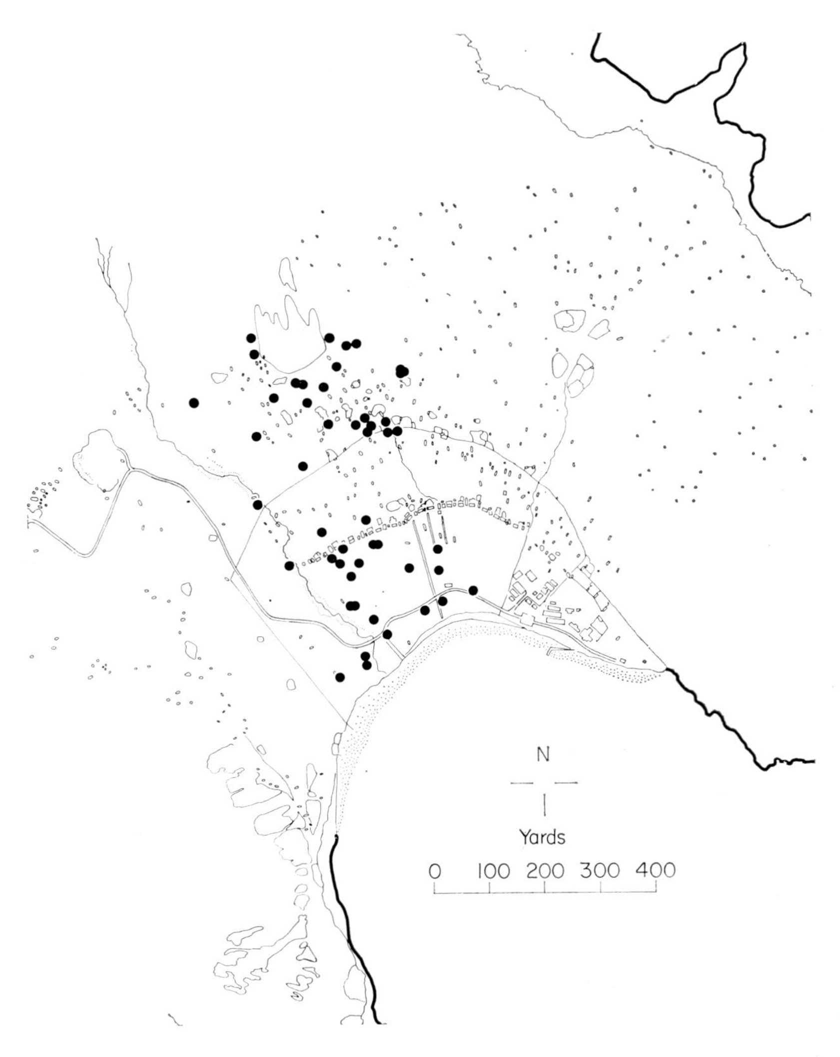

Fig. 9A.

Before the mating season, in September and October, rams would often lie down during the day and spend time cudding. After cudding they would frequently rest with the head stretched out on the ground before rising to graze again. This habit was rarely seen in ewes. The proportion of males engaged in activities other than grazing or cudding became much higher during the mating season.

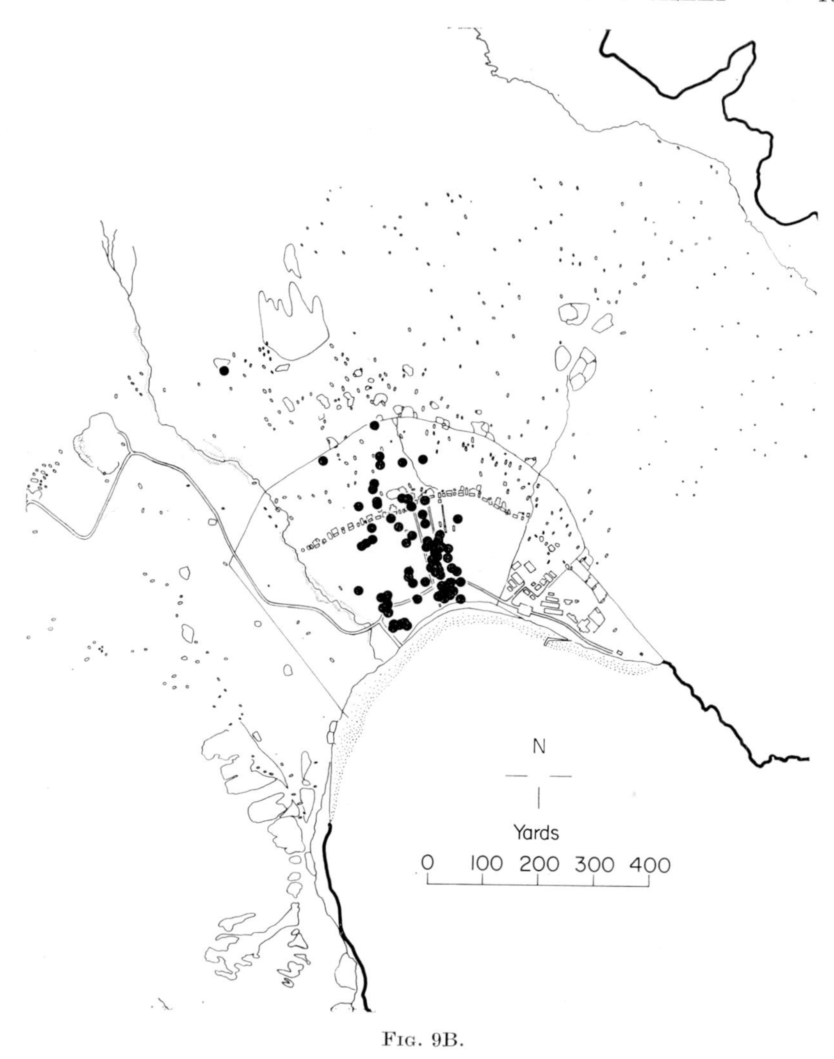

Fig. 9B.

Fig. 9. Sightings of a ewe W76 taken at 3-hourly intervals over the day in (A) January and (B) May 1965.

Influence of weather

On fine days there were fewer sheep in the Village and more on the slopes above and some sheep would spend the day there without descending to the Village grazings. On exceptionally sunny days, sheep would range farthest from their normal haunts. Conversely, during severe weather, Village sheep would keep within the perimeter wall and retire to cleits towards evening. A sudden shower would make sheep return rapidly to the Village from An Lag Bho'n Tuath or the lower slopes of Oiseval and clouding over on a sunny day also sometimes had this effect. But sheep also made additional cycles of movement during the day without any clear relation to weather conditions.

There were varied reactions to hail and heavy rain. Sometimes sheep would continue grazing. At other times, especially with a driving wind, they would shelter behind walls or cleits or even small banks. Males often entered cleits under weather conditions which did not prevent ewes grazing, and sheep appeared more ready to shelter in summer and autumn when they were physically most fit.

Following a snow fall, sheep wandered in troops until thawing commenced. Few attempted to dig through the snow for food (Fig. 10).

FIG. 10. An old ewe pawing away snow to reach the grass.

The use of shelter

The village cleits are the most important places of shelter. The sheep have preferences for certain cleits some of which have regular and frequent use. Such cleits are used only by the members of a given home range group, even when they are situated in a region of overlap between two home range groups. (There are exceptions, to be mentioned later, in that the use of certain cleits is the prerogative of ram groups.) Cleits with partly broken walls, allowing a through draught, are not entered, but sheep can get into cleits the doorways of which have become so blocked with debris that the remaining gap is no higher than the lying height of a sheep. Within each home range group, no evidence was found to suggest that any particular family of sheep had the exclusive possession, or use, of any given cleit.

Several places outside cleits were frequently used for resting, judging by accumulations of sheep dung. In the village, such sites were under the wall bordering the Manse in Gun Meadow and on the Village Street near the graveyard. Elsewhere, rock outcrops and concrete buildings formed shelter for conspicuous resting sites and many of the ruins in Glen Mor were similarly used. The pattern of deposition of dung indicates how sheep will take advantage of shelter. Lying-up positions often occur to the leeward of very small banks or rocks and even tussocks of grass less than a foot high.

Grazing on cleits

Sheep sometimes graze the turf roofing of cleits. This habit reveals some interesting individual variation. Only six ewes in the Village area fed on cleits, and of these some did so far more frequently than others. A few ram lambs were also seen several times on cleits but only one adult ram was ever seen in such a position, and then only after the mating season. At this time it grazed alone and after completing grazing on one cleit would climb down and search for another, spending most of the day on them.

Lambing and the home range

Observations on the behaviour of ewes at lambing were limited, but it can be noted that they did not depart from their usual routine in any significant way. Sometimes, before they gave birth, it was noted that ewes would retire to secluded areas, and this took them to parts of the home range that were not usually used at that time of the year. They were very wary for a short time after parturition and would graze apart from their usual companions but after a few days they returned. Older lambs would play together; although such groups of lambs would not necessarily all belong to one home range group, it was the usual tendency for this to happen.

Death and the home range

Relatively few sheep died during the period of study, and these mostly in March. Characteristically, a dying sheep would graze apart from its fellows and retreat more readily into the shelter of cleits. Most sheep die in the cleits which they have been regularly frequenting. Certain cleits frequented by rams were found to contain a number of rams' skulls but not the remains of any ewes. Here was evidence that rams had died in the seclusion of their "traditional" cleits (see later).

There was a heavy mortality among yearling rams. Many of these were seen to wander aimlessly and eventually collapse well away from the home range of their first few months of life. This wandering could not be explained simply as a disorientation following sickness as ewe yearlings did not wander in the same way. It should be noted that these yearlings cannot be regarded as having established permanent ranges at this stage of their life.

Grazing and the home range

As grazing is the chief activity of sheep, the area grazed and the home range are virtually the same, although there may be zones of passage within this area where animals rarely stop to feed. The areas where grazing is most intensive are also those where the home range can be most sharply defined. In the Village Glen, swards including species of *Holcus*, *Agrostis*, *Festuca*, *Poa* and *Anthoxanthum* are confined to the Village itself and some outlying patches. It is on such pastures that the sheep feed for most of the time and for most of the year. There are local variations in the species composition of such grassland, but the most favoured swards are scattered about the Village and occur for instance in damp places or where there is trampling. Sheep do not feed exclusively on such patches but they clearly prefer them and the distribution of these swards bears a relation to the organization of sheep into home range groups. The presence of an isolated patch of especially good grazing may influence the separation and isolation of a group of sheep whose movements centre around it. Within the range of a home range group, there may be several pockets of good grazing. Some of these may be visited more often by certain individuals and not at all by others, resulting in minor variations in home range within the group (Fig. 5).

Seasonal changes in day-length and the condition of food plants were associated with changes in the route and timing of the daily cycle of movement of the sheep. Although showing such strict adherence to range the sheep were obliged to roam more widely when grazings deteriorated, but there was no wholesale shift of range. The animals moved over what were the best grazings but, in addition, they incorporated into their daily cycle visits to other plant communities, by going up the slopes earlier in the day and ranging further over the higher grazing. In the Village Glen, grass heaths and communities dominated by purple moor grass occur on the hills above the Village. These food sources had been ignored when more attractive herbage was available.

Activities of rams and ram lambs

Home range groups and ranges

Adult rams grazed in small groups during September and October and were completely independent of ewe parties (Fig. 11). These groups

FIG. 11. A group of rams grazing within a drystone fank in An Lag Bho'n Tuath. The tussocky appearance of the grass results from the grazing methods of the sheep.

comprised two to twelve individuals (Fig. 12) although at times some rams led a solitary existence. Ram lambs, however, and yearling rams (that is young adults born in 1963) grazed with particular ewe groups and shared their general movements and home range (see Fig. 5). Close observation showed that these young rams were nevertheless expressing some measure of independence from the ewes. They often grazed a little apart, frequently in pairs, and as will be described later, the advent of the mating season disrupted their association with ewes.

There were six groupings of adult rams in the village (Table I) although one split into three units in the early part of 1965, and their home ranges were quite different from those of any ewe group. The home ranges of the rams cut across those of the ewes and also included some areas not inhabited by ewes (Fig. 13). Even so, they were somewhat restricted in distribution, and this feature was more evident in other parts of the island, outside the study area. The ram ranges were oriented on good grazings and some of them overlapped considerably.

Fig. 12. A home range group of rams in spring.

Sometimes several neighbouring groups of rams would graze or lie together and as many as twenty-one rams have been seen congregated in this way, but the formation was a temporary one and the several groups always dispersed again.

Certain cleits were used exclusively by the adult rams, and at some periods of the year one or two cleits would be used regularly every night by a group. During the period of study some ram lambs began to use these "ram cleits" and this could evidently lead to their use by rams over a long period. Confirmation of the existence of traditional ram cleits came from finding the skulls of rams only in some of them (see p. 200).

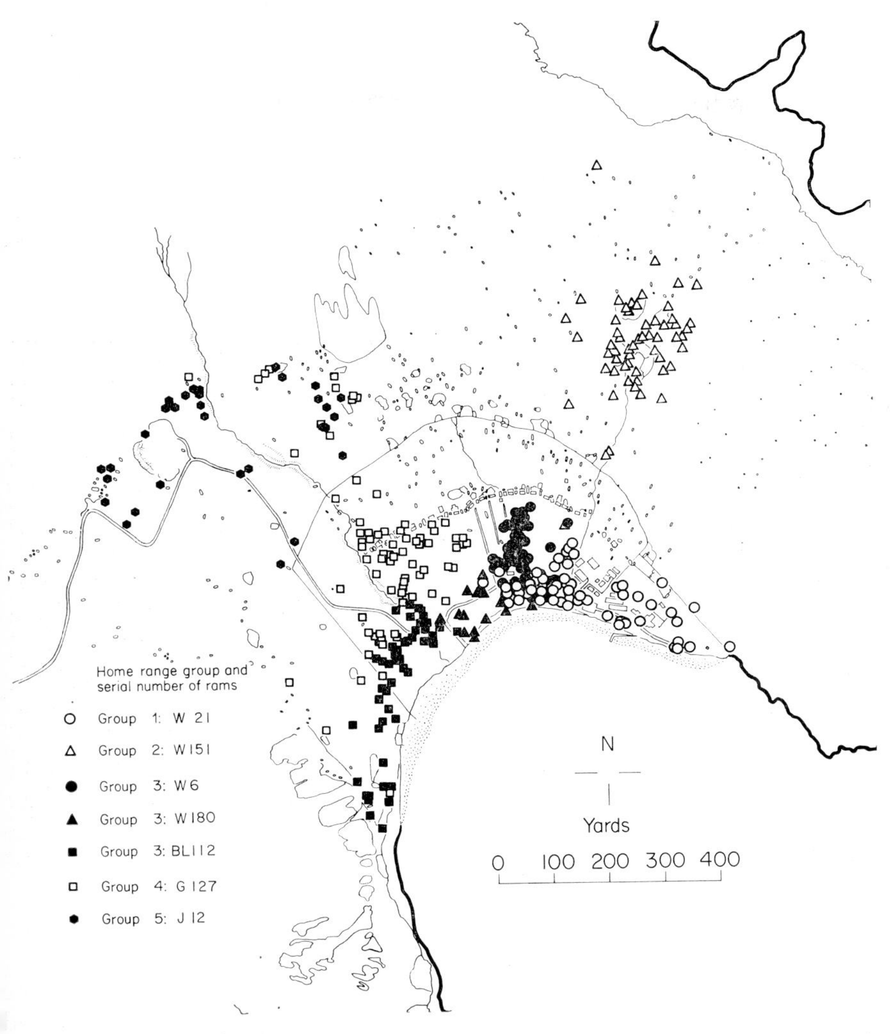

Fig. 13. Ranges of eight rams, each representing a home range group (or subgroup) in May 1965. The groups are listed in Table I. Each symbol represents a sighting. At the time records were made, group 3 was split into three subgroups with different ranges.

Ranges and the mating season

At the beginning of October some of the ram groups altered their ranges. Rams which had formerly grazed in An Lag Bho'n Tuath in the evening, retired instead to Lag Aitimir together with those that had formerly moved onto Gearraidh Ard. At about the same time some individuals departed from the Village Glen and others began arriving from other parts of the island. The first strange ram appeared in the Village on 29 September. It may have come from Glacan Mor as it returned to this area in December. As early as 23 September, Village rams had been seen making excursions outside their normal ranges. In the first week of October two rams had gone to other parts of the island, but general daily activity had not changed.

As October progressed, more strange rams arrived, in some cases in groups which kept together even as the mating season advanced, and Village rams started wandering outside their earlier ranges more frequently. Although often grazing with former companions the organization of groups gradually disappeared. During the middle of November, at the height of the mating season, many strange rams appeared within the Village but a proportion of Village rams remained the whole time in the vicinity of the Village Glen. Visiting rams remained for various periods of time, from a few hours to a week or two, and Village rams, equally, were absent for various periods.

During late October and November rams from the Village Glen were seen on the eastern terraces of Oiseval, on the slopes of Mullach Sgar, on Ruaival, Leathaid a'Sgithoil Chaoil, east Glen Mor, the Cambir neck and the slopes of Ard Uachdarachd (see Fig. 1). Visiting rams which were identified had come from the Oiseval terraces, Ruaival, east Gleann Mor, Ard Uachdarachd and the Gap and others were seen, in December, to have returned to Glacan Mor, Claigeann an Tigh Faire and Claigeann Mor. Visitors of known provenance returned to their old haunts.

Daily activity and the mating season

In September daily activity consisted of emergence from cleits at or after first light when ewes had already begun to graze, movement to a grazing site, grazing within a circumscribed area of this site and a steady movement away from this area towards evening. Rams usually entered cleits after dark. By November, daily activity had radically changed. Rams never grazed together or remained in one area for any length of time. At any one time a high proportion were neither grazing nor lying cudding but were either wandering through the Village, investigating ewes, or engaging in sexual or agonistic behaviour. Rams were often seen in quite different parts of the Village within a few hours and crossed and recrossed it in no set pattern. A conspicuous feature of the mating season was the formation of a consort pair between a ram and a ewe that was approaching oestrus. Such rams became temporarily sedentary and spent much of the time grazing. Other males often grazed in the vicinity of such pairs. It was concluded that less time was being spent grazing than before but that rams that were forming consort pairs with ewes were less affected.

Although there was this change amongst rams to greater activity during the day, there was also a tendency to remain within a certain part of the Village for several days and movements of the ewes in that area were in general followed.

The end of the mating season

The roaming activity of rams subsided as the peak of the incidence of oestrus in the ewe population was passed, although there were many ewes to come on heat. This contrasts with the situation before the peak, when few ewes had been recorded on heat but the rams had started wandering. In several cases the re-establishment of range took the form of a shift within a day from a range that had been occupied for only a few days to a permanent one corresponding to old haunts. Rams were seen making these movements. Some rams, however, did not return until the summer of 1965.

With the mating season ended, daily activity was almost entirely confined to grazing. Rams no longer lay together cudding or idling. Movement was now very clearly centred round cleits, into which they would retire while it was still light and from which they would not emerge until some time after dawn.

Activities of ram lambs

In September ram lambs were still sucking their dams occasionally, although they were large enough to raise the hindquarters of their dams off the ground with one thrust of the muzzle. It was, nevertheless, clear that the larger ram lambs were losing attachment to their dams and grazed independently or with other ram lambs. The associations between ram lambs appeared to be temporary, however, and the smaller individuals kept with their mothers well into January, except for a brief period of independence during the mating season in mid-November. During this season, some ram lambs moved far afield, one visiting Ruaival from Glacan Oiseval and another Gearraidh Ard from Na h'Eagan (distances of about $1\frac{1}{2}$ miles). These movements were probably not as extensive as those of adult rams, as relatively few strange ram lambs were identified in the Village. Smaller and presumably less mature ram lambs changed their ranges hardly at all or for a short period only.

At the end of the mating season, most ram lambs returned to their old ranges. It was common to see several ram lambs grazing together, but in only one case was a permanent partnership formed (Fig. 14).

Many individuals grazed for the whole or a large part of the time as individuals among ewe groups. In the north-west of the Village area, ram lambs were using cleits also used by rams but not frequented by ewes. In other parts of the Village ram lambs have been caught in cleits with rams although they had not been associating with them while grazing. One or two ram lambs which had not been seen before the mating season established ranges in the Village Glen. A few Village lambs made changes of range well after mating activity had ceased.

FIG. 14. Two ram yearlings which have formed a permanent partnership.

Residency and dispersion amongst rams

The mating season acts disruptively on established ram associations, but it is also a time that leads to the formation of new associations by young rams. Nevertheless, the old rams in general show great loyalty to their home ranges and each other, and their groups are reformed. It also appears that the majority of rams establish a home range near the area of their birth. The fifty-six rams grazing within the range of ewe groups included thirty-nine tagged rams of which twenty-eight had first been captured as lambs or yearlings. These rams had remained in the general vicinity of their birth place, though there is no doubt that rams do not show the same life-long fidelity to an area of residence as do ewes. Examples of dispersion and new home range formation far from the area of birth were seen in the five rams tagged in the village; they had subsequently settled in outlying parts of the island—on the Cambir Neck, Ard Uachdarachd, the Gap, Ruaival, and in east Glen Mhor.

DISCUSSION

The selection imposed under domestication profoundly affects the physique and behaviour of domesticated species (Spurway, 1955; Hale, 1962; Jewell, 1962). In particular, in relation to behaviour, there is selection for docility and presumably for tolerance to crowding. Soay sheep are much more timid than commercial flocks and do not bunch when chased, but they no doubt possess the qualities imposed by domestication and their fertility appears to be unimpaired by crowding. On the other hand, many of the behavioural attributes of domestic animals may be maintained by constant contact with man, and escape into the feral state could reveal previously disguised behavioural potentialities, whilst the feral state will itself impose new conditions of selection. The Soay sheep flocks may possess attributes, therefore, that are unique to their situation, but their home range behaviour can probably be taken as a useful model for many ungulate associations.

The present studies have established the pertinence of Hunter's (1964) work to unmanaged sheep, and feral Soay sheep are seen to have ranges that differ little in extent from those of partially confined hill sheep. The presence of a full complement of rams on Hirta does not disrupt the home range organization of ewe groups, although the rams themselves are seen to have their own type of behaviour in relation to home range. Moreover, the present studies have shown the fidelity with which ewe groups will adhere to a given small home range throughout their lifetime.

Hunter's method of recording home range, by simply mapping the positions of marked sheep at certain times of day, has given considerable insight into sheep movements. It has obvious limitations, but it avoids the artificiality of attempting to define a range boundary and in the present paper we have not been concerned to translate observations into actual home range areas. Some indication of the size of these areas, and their variation, can be judged from Figs. 4, 5, 9 and 13.

The range of the whole home range group is more extensive than that of any one of the individuals that comprise the group. As there is some variation in the home ranges of sheep within a group, a useful representation of the group home range would be a map of the distribution of density of occurrences of all group members. The nature of the joint home range in relation to that of the individual demands further examination. Nevertheless, in the case of a close-knit home range group, the difference between the group and individual ranges is not very great in terms of area. Certain conditions may promote the evolution of several home range groups from one original group (the status of the sheep in the west part of the Village could be interpreted in this way).

This could arise from the idiosyncracies of movement of an individual, if taken up by many sheep (as could happen if there was exceptionally favourable survival of lambs and the consequent build up of a very large family).

The relations between groups of rams is not clear at present but the following picture of the social grouping and ranging of ewes is suggested. The movements of the individual are dictated by an innate daily rhythm and an active search for food, but they are strongly influenced by the tendency to follow the movements of other individuals and inhibited by the "resistance" provided by the presence of sheep that belong to neighbouring groups. Some sheep will be less affected by these last two factors than others. The area of overlap between adjacent home range groups will not be precisely definable. It is suggested that this overlap of range is greatest when the group is small but, other things being equal, intrusion is least in areas where most time is spent by the group. The use of one area by several groups does not obtain when ranges are small (in early summer) but this condition will operate when wide ranging movements are made, increasing the extent of overlap. The home ranges of groups of sheep will be in equilibrium, the position of vague psychological boundaries moving as grazing conditions change. Bearing in mind the variation in the overlap part of the range, the group home range can be divided into an overlap area and a monopolized zone (Jewell, p. 105).

Ewe groups are large, include ewes of all age classes and young rams, and consist of matrilinearly related sheep. Family associations begin with the behaviour of the lamb and dam which ensures that they keep together (Hafez and Scott, 1962). In late life some of this behaviour is lost and a ewe and its dam may or may not be seen together frequently, but, as Hunter and Milner (1963) have shown, a family relationship typifies most home range groups. The play groups of young lambs show a tendency to reform after the completion of weaning, with the difference that the sexes are in separate groups, and in the ewe home range group this sub-association forms an alternative attraction to that of the family. What it is that makes one rather than the other predominate in a particular case is not clear.

The ewe associations may evolve from family groups under some particularly favourable circumstances. In an established home range group (and particularly at high population densities) the relatively poor chances of survival of lambs, and the birth of males which soon depart from the dam, reduce the chances of large families developing within the group. Thus, although members of a home range group may be ultimately more closely related amongst themselves than they are to ewes in other groups, the relation between most of them may be so indirect that it is hardly likely to contribute in any significant way to the cohesion of the group. The general synchrony of activity within the home range group, the calling of sheep isolated from others, suggesting that the presence of companions is sought, and the recognition of ewes from other groups as strangers, all imply an acquaintance and familiarity with grazing companions and form the basis for the perpetuation of the company. Perhaps the associations within the family group, the single age-class group and the home range group, can be explained in terms of the initiation of activities by the older, dominant, experienced animals and the following of such activity by the younger, subordinate, inexperienced ones. This remains to be examined. However, the specificity of the association between mother and daughter does appear to have a special importance as a primary bond amongst ewes and it ensures that the groups are naturally self-perpetuating.

Hunter and Davies (1963) carried out some experiments on ewe-lambs associations. They removed groups of ewes with their lambs from the hill and kept them elsewhere in pens. On being returned to the hill, those sheep amongst which ewes and lambs had been penned together, returned to their appropriate home range areas. But groups of lambs that had been weaned and then kept apart from their dams for 6 months stayed in small companies together and adopted new home ranges that cut across the boundaries of the existing ones.

Young rams, once they have given up trying to suck their dams, make no further attempt to keep with them and group together with the male playmates of their first few weeks of life. The presence of young rams in a ewe group is temporary. Later they will keep apart or join up with the older rams. Such a change is in contrast to the sedentary life history of ewes, and involves the adoption of a new range. Certainly, the members of a ram group keep very close together outside the rut in a way not usually seen among members of a ewe group. The end of the rut is the significant occasion in the forming of new associations among males, and in general these associations appear very firm.

Ram groups are small and comprise animals that are mostly 3–5 years old. The death rate of males is higher than that of females, so that few old rams survive, and the youngest rams remain with the ewes. Members of a ram group need not be related at all closely. Whether recruitment of new members is adequate to maintain ram home range groups indefinitely is not known.

The home range groups of ewes and rams differ in size, age-class composition, relationships between members and the way in which they are perpetuated. In addition, the rams tend to frequent different ground from ewes. These differences in social grouping and spatial distribution and the distinctions in physical characteristics and in behaviour, are ultimately a result of the different selection pressures imposed on the two sexes. These in turn result from the different contribution that each male or female is potentially capable of making to future generations.

Acknowledgements

We gratefully acknowledge the support given to this work through research grants from the Agricultural Research Council and the Nature Conservancy. The Commandant of the Royal Artillery Guided Weapons Range (Hebrides) has greatly assisted the work by making transport facilities available to us.

References

Boyd, J. M. (1959). Observations on the St. Kilda field-mouse (*Apodemus sylvaticus hirtensis* Barrett-Hamilton). *Proc. zool. Soc. Lond.* **133**, 47–65.

Boyd, J. M., Doney, J. M., Gunn, R. G. and Jewell, P. A. (1964). The Soay sheep of the island of Hirta, St. Kilda. A study of a feral population. *Proc. zool. Soc. Lond.* **142**, 129–163.

Hafez, E. S. E. and Scott, J. P. (1962). The behaviour of sheep and goats. *In* "The Behaviour of Domestic Animals" (E. S. E. Hafez, ed.). Baillière, Tindall and Cox, London.

Hale, E. B. (1962). Domestication and the evolution of behaviour. *In* "The Behaviour of Domestic Animals" (E. S. E. Hafez, ed.). Baillière, Tindall and Cox, London.

Hunter, R. F. (1964). Home range behaviour in hill sheep. *In* "Grazing in Terrestrial and Marine Environments" (D. J. Crisp, ed.). *Symp. Br. ecol. Soc.* No. 4, 155–171.

Hunter, R. F. and Davies, G. E. (1963). The effect of method of rearing on the social behaviour of Scottish Blackface hoggets. *Anim. Prod.* **5**, 183–194.

Hunter, R. F. and Milner, C. (1963). The behaviour of individual, related and groups of south country Cheviot hill sheep. *Anim. Behav.* **11**, 507–513.

Jewell, P. A. (1962). Changes in size and type of cattle from prehistoric to medieval times in Britain. *Z. Tierzücht. ZuchtBiol.* **77**, 159–161.

Jewell, P. A. (1966). Breeding season and recruitment in some British mammals confined on small islands. *In* "Comparative Biology of Reproduction in Mammals" (I. W. Rowlands, ed.). *Symp. zool. Soc. Lond.* No. 15, pp. 89–116. Academic Press, London and New York.

Manley, G. (1948). The climate of the Hebrides. *New Nat.* 1948, 77–82.

Riney, T. and Caughley, G. (1959). A study of home range in a feral goat herd. *N.Z. Jl Sci.* **2**, 157–170.

Spurway, M. (1955). The causes of domestication: an attempt to integrate some ideas of Konrad Lorentz with evolution theory. *J. Genet.* **53**, 325–362.

Steel, T. (1965). "The Life and Death of St. Kilda." The National Trust for Scotland, Edinburgh.

Symp. zool. Soc. Lond. (1966) No. 18, 211–228.

OBSERVATIONS ON THE DISPERSAL OF RED DEER ON RHUM

V. P. W. LOWE

The Nature Conservancy, Speyside Research Station, Aviemore, Inverness-shire, Scotland

SYNOPSIS

Owing to the nature and overall importance of the work on population dynamics of the red deer (*Cervus elaphus* L.) on Rhum, observations of their social organization and behaviour have until this year been largely adventitious.

The data, although limited, do however suggest that both the dispersal and dispersion of the deer are ordered by well-established patterns of behaviour.

Larger or smaller groups of each sex consistently occur together within each of the natural catchment areas, usually on south-facing slopes. The stags invariably occupy a particular area; generally below the hinds and followers in the winter and spring, and above them in the late summer. In spite of the large-scale changes consequent upon the removal of the sheep from the island in 1957, this spatial arrangement of the herds has not been affected. When the hinds' wintering ground in Kinloch Glen was fenced for afforestation, however, no compensatory regrouping took place and only a few stag groups remained on their much reduced, but traditional, grazings.

Segregation of the sexes, even in winter, is largely incomplete on Rhum; less than half the sexually mature individuals of either sex being wholly dissociated from the other at any one time. As yet, no individual of either sex has been observed to be territorial in the strict sense of defending an area of ground. On the contrary, all the grazings are shared and a natural ranking order appears to dictate the grazing behaviour. The larger or older hinds appear to be dominant to all other classes of either sex within their own home ranges; the yearling stags occupying the lowest rank.

These home ranges, within which individuals live throughout the year, appear to be surprisingly constant in size regardless of topographic variation; extending to approximately 400 ha for a hind and 500 ha for a stag. The limits are not, however, fixed but vary with the year; each home range being based on an area of maximum utilization, which will include the more important winter grazings.

The mechanism of dispersal appears to be an almost continuous process beginning at birth and reaching completion by the age of 3 years. The data suggest that the pattern of dispersion is determined largely by the combination of the individual's exploratory behaviour with its reactions to encounters with other deer of varying social dominance.

With a uniform annual cull of one-sixth of the adult stock from all parts of the island, there should theoretically be no need for any individual of either sex to move far to establish its own home range. Yet, of the fifteen marked deer recovered in the cull, aged 3 years or older, only two out of nine stags had moved less than 1·5 km from their places of birth, and all six hinds had moved more than 800 m. The stags had, on average, moved 2·5 km, almost twice as far as the hinds with their average of 1·4 km.

These behavioural differences, associated with sex, are apparent even during the first year of life.

Amongst the natural deaths during the late winter and early spring, the marked stag calves have been found to have moved more than three times as far as the hind calves. Their descent in altitude was also more than four times that of the hinds. Whether these calves were solely responsible for their movements or were induced to move in this way by their parent hinds or other deer is not known.

There are indications that the diurnal and seasonal movements may also be largely determined by age; in general the older the individual, of either sex, the lower its position on the hill in respect of its place of birth. The five marked stags, over the age of 3 years shot accidentally during the August–September period, were all occupying ground, level with their respective places of birth, whilst the four 3-year-old stags were all considerably higher. Similarly the four marked hinds, over the age of 3 years, were all lower than their places of birth in order of age, whilst the five 2- and 3-year-old hinds, were all as high, or higher, during the same winter period, November–January.

Because of its bearing on the problem of marauding and colonization, the behaviour work, which started this year, has as its main aim the elucidation of the principal factors determining these differences in dispersal and home range utilization.

INTRODUCTION

Most of the data discussed in this paper have arisen adventitiously in the course of a study of red deer (*Cervus elaphus* L.) population dynamics. This work was started on Rhum immediately following its declaration as a National Nature Reserve in 1957; the immediate aim being to establish and then maintain a stable deer population at a sub-maximal density as part of an experiment in land management (Eggeling, 1964).

The total number of deer has varied between 1 691 and 1 842 since an annual cull of one-sixth of the adults, counted each spring, was introduced in 1958. The population counted in the spring of 1965 was 1 760. Advantage is being taken of the present stability to study the deer's grazing regime and behaviour.

With the development in 1963 of calf ear-tagging materials suitable for field recognition, the present population contains most of the 228 marked individuals from three age classes, covering all the most important stages in population dispersion and reproduction.

Because of their importance in the allied problems of colonization and marauding, the mechanics of dispersal and home range utilization are now receiving special attention.

HABITAT

The island of Rhum lies some 24 km due west of Mallaig, off the west coast of Scotland.

It is approximately 10 684 ha in extent, most of it bleak and mountainous except where the larger glens level off near the coast.

The hills, largely consisting of igneous rocks, were formed during the Tertiary period by intrusion through the Pre-Cambrian Torridonian sandstone. The subsequent action of the glaciers carved out many steep-sided corries and glens from these hills of ultra-basic and acid rocks.

Most of the ground above 305 m is sparsely covered with vegetation and affords little grazing outside the summer months; three of the hills exceed 762 m in height. For more than half the year this high ground is enshrouded in mists and exposed to frequent gales and rain. During the winter months it is commonly subject to frost conditions and is often snow-covered. Snow lay on average 107 days each year between 1960 and 1963.

The ground below 305 m is mostly poorly drained or boggy and largely dominated by *Molinia*, *Scirpus*, *Schoenus* and *Eriophorum*, with relatively smaller areas of *Calluna* heaths and *Agrostis-Festuca* grasslands on the better drained soils. These latter constitute the most important source of food for the deer for the greater part of the year.

The island is almost entirely treeless, so that the deer have to seek shelter in hard weather behind natural topographic features.

SEASONAL DISTRIBUTION AND MOVEMENT

With the prevailing south-west wind, the eastern half of the island, though not so exposed to gales, receives less sunshine and considerably more rain than the western half. Partly perhaps because of the contrast in climate, the better pastures appear to be more numerous and extensive in the west, and inspection of the maps (Figs. 1 and 2) shows the movement of deer into this region after the removal of the sheep stock from it in September 1957.

The maps show the late winter/early spring distribution of those deer groups where one sex predominates, so as to clarify the social arrangement. It will be noted that the hind groups are invariably flanked by stags, and both are usually located on the lower ground on south-facing slopes in each of the larger natural catchment areas, the higher ground being almost uninhabited. This spatial arrangement was not affected by the changes in distribution following the removal of the sheep. But the fencing-off of the traditional hind ground in Kinloch Glen for afforestation appears to have produced a permanent change, only a few of the stags remaining on their much reduced, but traditional, grazings.

Delap (1957) has described a similar dispersion of the red deer on the Wicklow Hills during the period 1932–33, and has observed a similar arrangement in north Westmorland, where the larger stags tend to gravitate downwards and outwards each year after the rutting period.

Ahlén (1965, p. 325) has noted the same tendency amongst the

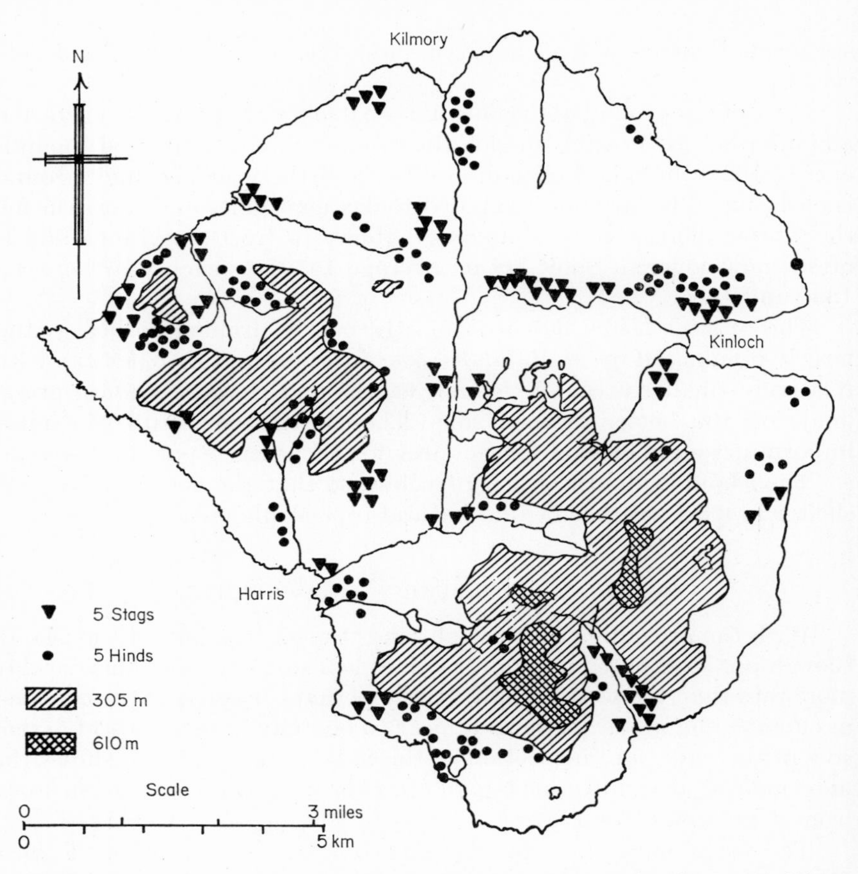

FIG. 1. Distribution of deer groups, composed predominantly of one sex. Rhum, April 1957.

vestigial herds of Swedish red deer in Scania. In this case the stags live in the smaller woods on the periphery of the hinds' range except during the rut.

On Rhum, the mapped groups indicate the normal resting positions of both the segregated and mixed parties of deer. If undisturbed many of the older animals stay on, or near, their main feeding areas during the day. Each evening, however, almost all the deer will come down to collect on these low level *Agrostis-Festuca* grasslands and feed there during the night.

It will also be observed from Table I that in most years 60% of the deer, irrespective of sex, age or the prevailing weather, were distributed on ground insolated from the south. Areas facing east and west, and

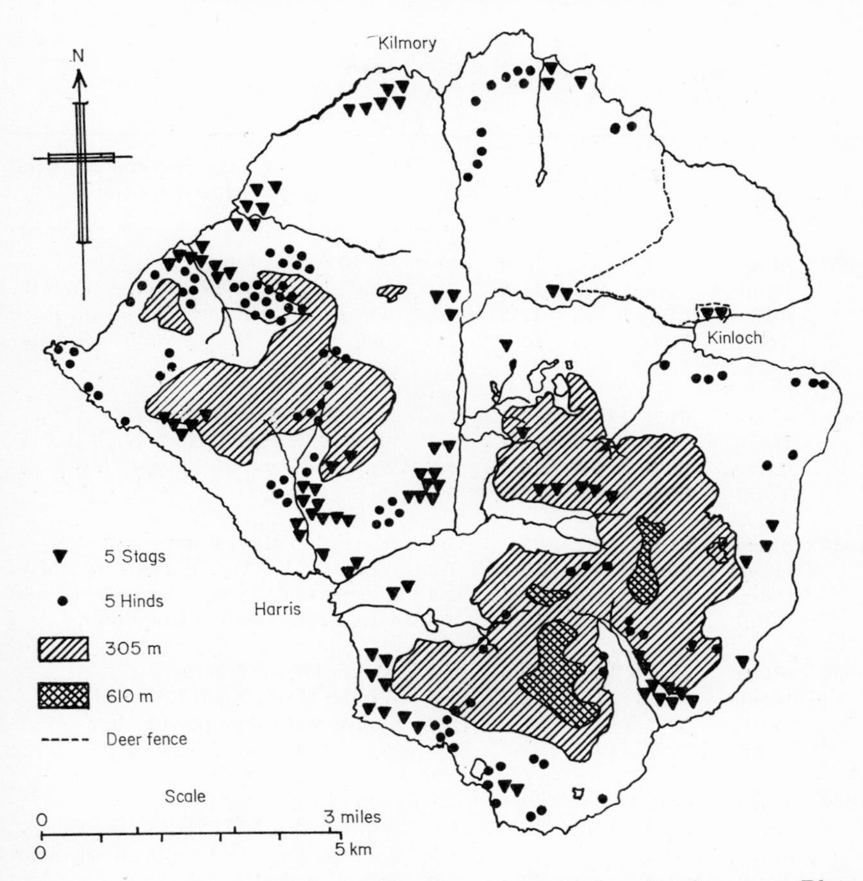

FIG. 2. Distribution of deer groups, composed predominantly of one sex. Rhum, March 1965.

receiving only a few hours sunshine each day, appear to be the least favoured, whilst the north-facing slopes, insolated obliquely but throughout the day, attracted slightly more than 20% of the deer. It will be noted, however, that in the spring of 1957, whilst the island still carried a sheep stock of 1 000 breeding ewes, 70% of all the deer appeared to prefer ground insolated from the south, suggesting that when the better quality grazings were less available, aspect assumed relatively greater importance.

Although there could be slight differences between classes in their selection of ground according to aspect, these are not at present significant. On the other hand, in relation to altitude the various classes, which can be distinguished in the field, show quite definite preferences

TABLE I

Percentage distribution of the deer in relation to incidence of insolation

Year	Class	S.	W.	N.	E.	Dates, no. of days of counting, wind and weather conditions
1957	Stags	67·2	10·8	14·0	8·0	24–30 April. 6 days
	Hinds	71·5	9·2	11·9	7·4	Winds: N., N., NW., SW., NW., NW.
	Calves	71·7	9·3	12·2	6·8	(The island still carried a sheep stock
	Total	70·0	9·8	12·7	7·5	this year.) Warm and pleasant throughout
1958	Stags	61·2	13·9	17·4	7·5	5–13 May. 6 days
	Hinds	59·6	8·6	25·1	6·7	Winds: SE., NW., NW., N., NW., W.
	Calves	60·3	8·5	26·4	4·8	Warm or very warm each day
	Total	60·3	10·4	22·6	6·7	
1959	Stags	61·5	10·2	23·2	5·1	28 April–6 May. 6 days
	Hinds	66·3	10·3	15·8	7·6	Winds: NE., W., W., N., W., NW.
	Calves	61·0	11·4	20·4	7·2	Except for the last day it was cold
	Total	63·8	10·5	19·1	6·6	with strong winds throughout
1960	Stags	57·1	13·0	20·6	9·3	20 April–2 May. 5 days
	Hinds	49·8	14·0	21·7	14·5	Winds: NW., N., N., SE., SE.
	Calves	52·2	14·0	21·0	12·8	Sunny and warm or very hot
	Total	52·7	13·7	21·2	12·4	
1961	Stags	64·1	8·3	20·4	7·1	5–14 April. 5 days
	Hinds	61·0	10·2	20·3	8·4	Winds: SE., NE., NE., NE., E.
	Calves	60·3	9·8	21·2	8·6	Cool or very cold with all the high
	Total	62·0	9·5	20·5	8·0	ground frozen
1962	Stags	61·5	12·6	19·7	6·2	26–30 March. 5 days
	Hinds	58·7	10·6	24·3	6·4	Winds: N., NW., E., SE., N.
	Calves	54·6	9·8	29·2	6·4	Very cold with strong winds, accom-
	Total	59·2	11·3	23·2	6·3	panied by hail and snow showers
1963	Stags	62·1	9·1	17·7	11·1	3–7 April. 5 days
	Hinds	62·3	6·7	21·9	9·1	Winds: NW., N., NE., SE., E.
	Calves	62·7	6·4	22·5	8·4	Very cold with hard frosts and strong
	Total	62·3	7·7	20·2	9·8	winds throughout
Average 1958–63						n
	Stags	61·3	11·1	19·8	7·8	660 ± 21
	Hinds	59·6	10·2	21·4	8·8	807 ± 25
	Calves	58·3	10·1	23·5	8·1	286 ± 15
	Total	60·0	10·5	21·2	8·3	1 753 ± 22

TABLE II—*Percentage distribution of the deer in relation to altitude*
(Measured in 76 m intervals.)

Class	0–76	152	228	305	381	457	533	610	*n*
1957									
Stags	28·2	27·3	20·7	14·2	7·5	1·6	0·5	—	564
Yearling ♂♂	Included with stags								
Hinds	25·1	30·4	11·3	20·1	8·9	2·7	1·5	—	741
Calves	26·9	31·2	12·5	17·9	7·9	2·5	1·1	—	279
Total	26·5	29·4	14·9	17·6	8·2	2·3	1·1	—	1 584
1958									
Stags	56·7	7·4	17·6	11·5	3·0	3·5	0·3	—	598
Yearling ♂♂	Included with stags								
Hinds	37·5	16·6	12·5	23·6	3·5	4·8	1·5	—	818
Calves	37·6	19·7	11·1	25·4	3·1	2·4	0·7	—	295
Total	44·3	13·9	14·0	19·7	3·3	3·9	0·9	—	1 711
1959									
Stags	37·4	31·4	16·4	11·8	2·0	1·0	—	—	500
Yearling ♂♂	38·9	19·0	15·1	16·7	7·1	3·2	—	—	126
Hinds	41·2	20·2	11·7	15·2	9·9	1·8	—	—	871
Calves	42·4	20·8	13·1	16·1	5·5	2·1	—	—	236
Total	40·1	23·4	13·5	14·5	6·8	1·7	—	—	1 733
1960									
Stags	49·1	19·3	15·2	5·7	7·9	2·8	—	—	506
Yearling ♂♂	41·0	18·0	16·3	11·1	8·5	3·4	1·7	—	118
Hinds	45·3	15·3	12·5	11·5	8·7	5·8	0·9	—	862
Calves	46·2	17·2	11·5	10·8	8·3	5·1	0·9	—	314
Total	46·2	17·0	13·3	9·7	8·4	4·7	0·7	—	1 800
1961									
Stags	45·1	23·9	15·7	10·5	3·0	1·8	—	—	544
Yearling ♂♂	46·6	22·9	9·9	7·6	6·1	6·1	0·8	—	130
Hinds	55·7	17·8	9·6	6·4	4·1	4·8	1·2	0·4	831
Calves	58·8	16·0	10·2	5·2	4·3	4·0	1·2	0·3	325
Total	52·5	19·7	11·5	7·5	3·9	3·9	0·8	0·2	1 830
1962									
Stags	40·8	28·1	15·2	13·1	2·5	0·4	—	—	564
Yearling ♂♂	40·0	16·1	16·1	17·4	6·5	3·2	0·7	—	157
Hinds	36·0	18·5	14·0	20·1	6·2	4·9	0·4	—	737
Calves	33·9	18·0	16·6	19·7	6·1	4·4	—	—	295
Total	37·5	21·5	15·0	17·5	5·0	3·2	0·2	—	1 753
1963									
Stags	39·5	25·3	16·6	12·5	4·2	1·9	—	—	593
Yearling ♂♂	35·7	18·3	8·7	19·0	4·8	13·5	—	—	125
Hinds	31·9	19·7	9·5	24·6	6·2	8·1	—	—	725
Calves	30·2	21·0	9·7	23·4	4·8	10·9	—	—	248
Total	34·6	21·8	11·9	19·8	5·2	6·7	—	—	1 691
Average 1959–63									
Stags	42·3	25·6	25·8	10·8	3·9	1·6	—	—	541 ± 18
Yearling ♂♂	40·4	18·8	13·3	14·5	6·6	5·8	0·6	—	131 ± 7
Hinds	42·4	18·3	11·5	15·1	7·1	5·0	0·5	0·07	805 ± 31
Calves	43·1	18·6	12·2	14·5	5·8	5·2	0·5	0·07	284 ± 18
Total	42·4	20·6	13·0	13·6	5·9	4·0	0·4	0·05	1 761 ± 25

(Table II). Constructing a contingency Table for the four classes of deer, arranged according to seven intervals in height, a X^2 value of 202·1 with 18 degrees of freedom is obtained. The greatest contribution is from the stags with 135·3, due to their being more numerous than expected between 76 m and 228 m and much less numerous than expected between 228 m and 533 m.

In the five spring counts, 1959–63, the average height of these stags was 86 m above sea-level. The hinds and followers were significantly higher, with slight differences between each class. The yearling stags had the highest average mean of 113 m, whilst the hinds averaged 109 m and the calves were lowest at 106 m. In 1957 the deer were kept off many of the lowest grazings by the shepherds, which explains the rather different distribution.

In the only complete summer count, undertaken in the first week of August 1965, all the deer were on the highest parts of their range and, as expected, the stags had reversed positions with the hinds and followers (Table III). The latter classes were, however, distributed in the same order of average height as in the spring.

	Stags	Yearling stags	Hinds	Calves
Metres	280	265	263	251

TABLE III

Percentage distribution of the deer in relation to altitude

(Measured in 76 m intervals in August 1965.)

Class	0–76	152	228	305	381	457	533	610	686	*n*
Stags	6·9	14·8	11·5	19·8	28·5	10·7	3·8	1·5	2·5	696
Yearling ♂ ♂	11·1	11·1	17·9	28·2	13·7	6·0	6·0	2·6	3·4	109
Hinds	13·7	10·0	10·3	32·1	14·7	11·3	2·5	4·8	0·6	904
Calves	15·3	12·0	10·8	33·3	13·8	9·3	2·4	2·4	0·6	333
Total	11·5	12·0	11·2	28·0	19·1	10·5	3·1	3·2	1·4	2 042

The explanation of this distribution would appear to be that the non-breeding classes, because of their superior physical condition (unpublished material), are able to move higher up the hills than the breeding hinds. This is supported by percentage figures of hinds with calves taken at 152 m intervals.

Metres	0–152	305	457	over 457
Percentage of hinds with calves	42·3	38·3	32·6	25·0

DISPERSAL

Group size and segregation of the sexes

The size of the groups and the degree of segregation of the sexes in red deer appear to depend largely on the scale of the country, the number and dispersion of feeding areas and the availability of shelter. Where woodland is accessible, and food and shelter are abundant, deer appear to live in small family parties. Eygenraam (1963) gives figures for Holland, which show that two-thirds of all the groups observed in the 1960 and 1961 counts were composed of five or less individuals; and only 4% of all the groups exceeded twelve in number. By inspection of the various groups tabulated, it appears that 70% of the stags, excluding yearlings, and 98% of the hinds were clearly segregated into groups of their own sex.

Ahlén (1965) includes the yearling with the older stags in the totals, but states that most of his observations were of single stags. Since only 9·2% of all observations were of stags over the age of 2 years, most of them living outside his study area, almost all the stags associating with the hinds must have been yearlings. The Scanian deer appear therefore to be equally well segregated. Again the average group is composed of about four individuals. By contrast, in Scotland where the deer are living in a largely tree-less habitat, the groups tend to be considerably larger, the actual size varying with the scale of the topography.

On Rhum the glens are small, and sheltered hollows and corries are numerous. Grazings likewise are not generally extensive but are widely distributed. During the 1964 and 1965 spring censuses, particular attention was paid to noting the size and composition of each group before it coalesced with others after being disturbed. The average group size was 9·2 and the two years hardly differed in this respect. In the August 1965 census the average group increased in size to eleven, largely due to the addition of the current year's calves.

On two forests in the eastern uplands of Scotland, Glen Fiddich and Invermark, which are being used as complementary study areas, the country is altogether on a larger scale, and the average group consists of about forty deer.

Even the roe deer (*Capreolus capreolus* L.) in the Speyside area in the Central Highlands show a similar trend in winter. In woodland conditions the wintering groups remain as family parties but in the open these parties tend to form larger groups of two or three families in each. On one exposed and almost tree-less hill near the research station, the only shelter is limited to one small area in a large summer range. Throughout the late winter of 1965, there were twenty-six roe in this area, living and behaving as a herd until the spring.

Perhaps, because of this tendency for deer to herd on open hills, the red deer in Scotland are probably never as well segregated as those on the continent. On Glen Fiddich 41% of all the groups counted during the last four years' spring censuses, have been mixed. This figure does not include yearling stags. On Rhum the figures are lower, being 34% in the spring and 38% in the summer. The slight summer decline in segregation might appear to be due to both sexes moving up to the same high ground, where the grazings are more restricted, thus producing apparent aggregations of groups, with no obvious limits; and certainly not sufficiently obvious in the limited time available during a census (Lowe, 1961).

However, in terms of deer numbers, rather than groups, the difference is greater and appears to be real. In the spring of 1964, 50% of the hinds were mixed with 58% of the stags, excluding yearlings. In the two spring counts of 1965, the figures were 58% and 56% of the hinds associating with 60% and 54% of the stags respectively. This suggests that the degree of mixing at any one time is probably roughly constant when measured in this way. In the August count, 66% of the stags were found in association with 74% of the hinds; the smaller family parties and some of the stags being almost the only strictly segregated groups.

Under this system, therefore, it appears that an individual of either sex is under no compulsion to move far from its place of birth through social pressures.

Territory and home range

Territory in the original sense used by Howard (1920) and re-defined by Burt (1943) as that part of the home range, protected "... by fighting or aggressive gestures from others of their kind, during some phase of their lives ..." has not been observed on Rhum; unless the occasional aggressive gesture made by one individual towards another, usually of junior rank, when it approaches too closely and gets in the way, indicates a system of micro-territoriality rather than one of social dominance.

In the same way during the rut, the stags cannot be said to hold territories as defined above, because they are not usually within their own home ranges, and the hinds, rather than the area on which they happen to be at any one time, briefly constitute the protected property.

Through marking calves in the neighbourhood of Kinloch, the only human settlement on the island, it has been possible to follow closely the dispersal of some individuals and their success in establishing home ranges. From these observations, it would appear that only the physically mature and breeding members of the local groups of both sexes have established home ranges and the limits to these are not strictly defined except along the lower margins of their more important winter grazings.

Because the total population is small in this area, normally consisting of about thirty hinds and followers, it has been possible to identify the few well-established and dominant hinds individually. For three of these it has been possible, by experiment, to determine the limits of the areas over which each is dominant in respect of the others, since their home ranges overlap to some extent on the low ground. If these three are labelled A, B, and C; hind A feeds and is fed scraps at the north end of the settlement only. Hind B, probably the oldest of them, feeds on all the grazings round the bay but is not given food anywhere. Hind C also feeds on all the grazings, but is used to being fed scraps on one area only at the south end. When all three are grazing at the north end and food is thrown to them, all the deer within about 5 m of hind A, make way for her. Elsewhere, except for the one area at the south end, hind B is dominant to C throughout.

Normally, such responses are difficult to observe, except between the old and the immature classes, because the relationships between mature individuals are too well established.

Because of the configuration of A's home range in relation to the others, these three hinds can only graze communally again when on the highest parts of their summer range. B and C, on the other hand, have overlapping home ranges throughout all the seasons of the year but are rarely members of the same group by day. Because home ranges overlap or separate to varying extents at different levels on the hill, the possible combinations of groups or individuals are to some extent dependent on season and prevailing weather conditions.

The possible compositions are further complicated by the exploratory movements of the immature individuals. This was well illustrated during the 1964 census. Hinds B and C were in one party of eleven, consisting of three stags, five other hinds and one unmarked calf. Both their marked calves were in another party of seven, consisting of a yearling stag, a marked hind with her first but unmarked calf and two young non-breeding hinds; the two groups being separated by about 400 m. The implications are discussed later.

The inconstancy of group size and composition due to movements of this type has become increasingly obvious as the marked proportion of the groups has been raised through calf marking. In the spring of 1965, two counts were made of the deer just south of Kinloch, the results of which demonstrate just how easily an impression of constancy might have been formed if all the deer had been unmarked; especially since

10-month-old calves closely resemble young hinds superficially. On 23 March 1965, the largest group was one of fifteen deer, consisting of one yearling stag, ten hinds, one of which had a blue tag and two were the marked yearlings of hinds B and C; and four calves, three of which were marked, one with an orange flash and two with white flashes. On 1 April 1965, the largest group was in the same place and was again one of fifteen deer, consisting of one yearling stag, eight hinds and six calves. But none of the hinds and five of the calves were marked, two with orange and three with white flashes. The two marked yearling hinds were this time with another group of seven, some 300 m further west.

Schloeth (1961) found a similar inconstancy amongst the deer in the Swiss National Park, once he had a marked sample as a basis for his observations. Within a year, he found that only 25% of the deer, originally observed in the company of the marked deer, were still present.

It is difficult to reconcile these observations with group territorial behaviour, postulated by Darling (1937, pp. 68–70), when the only relatively stable elements in each group appear to be the physically mature individuals with their well established individual home ranges; and none of these has ever been observed to assume overall leadership.

The present data do not suggest that there is any social organization extending beyond the family and the mother's home range.

The distinctive and recurring pattern of distribution of stags and hinds appears most probably to emanate from their social preferences, which are quite different but complementary; the stags disliking and the hinds preferring to be surrounded by other groups of deer.

Stages in dispersal

First year

Within a few hours of birth, most calves begin to explore their hinds' home range, their first steps being in search of a comfortable bed. Within about a fortnight these explorations include making brief contact with other calves and groups of deer. These encounters may elicit a variety of reactions. Very occasionally it may be temporarily or permanently adopted by another milk hind. In one such case on Rhum the hind reared both calves successfully. More often, but still infrequently, a hind may allow a strange calf a drink, but normally calves are suckled by their own hinds only and are repulsed by others. Later in the winter, calves are more often observed, by themselves, with stags, with other calves or associating with other hinds. With the cessation of lactation, towards the end of March amongst the pregnant hinds, calves of both sexes are regularly found in the company of other groups as already described, suggesting a temporary disruption of family ties. This situation tends to continue until after the calves are born in June.

If the marked calves, dying from natural causes each late winter, are tabulated in accordance with the distances they have covered from their original point of capture, it appears that the two sexes have quite different behaviour patterns (Tables IV and V). The stag calves have been found on average three times as far from their place of marking as the hind calves and more than four times lower in altitude. On Invermark a similar pattern of behaviour was observed in the severe winter of 1962–63, when fourteen of the marked calves (seven stags and seven hinds) died. The stag calves had moved on average 5·6 km from their original positions of marking compared with 4 km moved by the hind calves. Whether these movements signify that stag calves explore more

TABLE IV

Distance between original point of capture as a calf and recovery when shot or found dead

	Metres				Kilometres				Sample size (n)	Mean distance (km)
	100	200	400	800	1·6	3·2	4·8	6·4		
Age of stags										
6 months	(1)	(1)		(3)	(3)	(2)			(10)	1·1
1 year									—	—
2					(1)	(1)			(2)	1·7
3						2	1	1	4	3·6
4			1		1				2	0·7
5	1						1		2	1·7
6									—	—
7									—	—
8						1			1	3·1
Age of hinds										
6 months		(1)	(2)	(1)					(4)	0·3
1 year				(1)					(1)	0·6
2			1		2				3	0·9
3				1		1			2	1·7
4				1		1			2	1·5
5									—	—
6				1					1	0·6
7					1				1	1·2

Figures in parentheses refer to deer found dead outwith the shooting season.

TABLE V

Change in altitude from original point of capture as a calf, when subsequently shot or found dead

	Metres −305	−152	−76	±30	+76	+152	+305	+457	Sample size (n)	Mean change (m)
Age of stags										
6 months	(3)	(2)	(2)	(3)					(10)	−104
1 year									—	—
2	(1)		(1)						(2)	−122
3						2	1	1	4	+213
4				2					2	−8
5				2					2	−15
6									—	—
7									—	—
8				1					1	0
Age of hinds										
6 months				(4)					(4)	−23
1 year					(1)				(1)	+61
2				3					3	0
3						2			2	+99
4			1	1					2	−38
5									—	—
6			1						1	−76
7	1								1	−183

Figures in parentheses refer to deer found dead outwith the shooting season.

extensively than hind calves, react differently to approaching death, or demonstrate a difference in parental behaviour is not known.

In general, calves, during their first year, explore most parts of their hinds' home ranges but seldom stray far from them.

Second year

In their second year most yearlings suffer at least one period of temporary expulsion at the time of parturition or mating (the rut). But the variety of responses observed together with the dearth of marked breeding hinds, make any quantitative evaluation impossible at the present time. Much depends on the breeding condition of the mother and the sex of the yearling, but three main categories of behaviour can be distinguished.

1. *Non-breeding mothers and their yearlings.* Hinds not pregnant for a second year are termed yeld; these usually continue to suckle their

yearlings throughout the summer and in some cases until the following November regardless of their sex.

2. *Breeding mothers and their yearling hinds.* Some yearling hinds have been seen to remain near their mothers throughout parturition and to have rejoined them shortly afterwards. Others have become completely independent and have joined other non-breeding hind groups, usually in the neighbourhood; but normally the reunion is probably delayed only for a few days or weeks.

3. *Yearling stags.* The yearling stags appear to be less acceptable socially than the yearling hinds and are often seen singly or in loose groups after leaving their pregnant mother. Almost invariably any solitary antlerless deer encountered on the hill between June and October will be found to be a yearling stag. Some of these yearlings leave their mothers' home ranges at the age of 9 months as described and only return for brief visits in the late summer. But most of them probably rejoin their families sometime before September. During the rut many of these yearlings are again forced to leave the family group temporarily, although some are allowed to remain, being ignored by the stag holding the group.

At present the percentage of yearling stags becoming independent as a result of either of these two events is unknown. But, by the end of their second year, it appears from the census figures that at least one-sixth of them are no longer with their families. In the 1964 census, 21·4% of all the yearling stags were on their own, with other stags or with other hinds, in roughly equal numbers. In 1965, the figure was 16·8%.

However, with some groups containing as many as eight yearling stags with only seven hinds, it appears likely that more than one of them was a stranger. In another instance, two marked yearling stags were counted with hind groups, to which they appeared to, but did not in fact, belong. Since some single yearling stags may, moreover, have joined hind groups on being disturbed before being counted and classified, it appears probable that at least 25% of this class of stags have become independent by the end of their second year.

In Holland, Eygenraam (1963) was unable to locate most of the yearling stags expected during the 1960 and 1961 censuses, and since the yearling hinds outnumbered the yearling stags by seven to one, it suggests that most of them must have become independent towards the end of their second year.

Third and fourth year

Until the introduction of a new type of ear tag in 1963, observations of movements made by marked 2- and 3-year-old deer were not possible, because by that age the numbers on the tags had either fallen out or were obscured by grease and dirt, only being legible in the hand.

Few marked deer have been shot, and those by accident, because they are required alive for a full documentation of their development, growth and breeding histories, etc. Data are therefore limited. But if those available (Tables IV and V) are examined, they appear to indicate that final dispersion is probably not complete before the end of the fourth year.

During the third year, the disruptive forces, bearing on the family groups at the time of calving and mating, appear to be more effective, but not total. The two 2-year-old stags found amongst the winter deaths, although not strictly comparable with the other shot stags, were both still in the neighbourhood of their mothers' home ranges. Similarly, the three 2-year-old hinds, shot in the early winter, did not appear to be far from their previous home ranges. But being still on their summer ranges when shot, these hinds were in fact probably independent.

By the end of their fourth year, both the stags and the hinds appear to have moved as great a distance from their original point of capture as that recorded by any other older age class. It also appears that both sexes in this age class were higher up the hills than any other older deer. The older stags appear to go no higher than the calving and rutting grounds during the months of August and September, the period during which all the marked stags were shot.

The marked hinds, all of which were yeld, were all shot in the period November–January. Although only very small samples are involved, it does appear that there is a marked change in the relative height on the hills after the age of 3 years, only one of the older hinds being as high as the area on which it was marked as a calf. This is in agreement with Darling's observations (1937, p. 74).

Whether this pattern of behaviour is maintained by hinds breeding in their third year and calving in their fourth, is not known. One marked hind did calve as a 3-year-old on Rhum in 1964, but perhaps because there are no grazings between the highest parts of their summer range and the grasslands near sea-level, no hinds have ever been seen wintering much above the 100–150 m contour in that area.

CONCLUSIONS

The dispersal of deer on Rhum therefore appears to follow a definite pattern and is perhaps never quite complete.

During the first three years, the family ties are gradually dissolved and the sub-adult 2- or 3-year-old moves up to the water-shed, which it then explores during the summer months.

A home range is next selected from above and gradually established below as it matures and begins to breed.

Ultimately, in old age, only the lower parts of the home range are utilized and the summer range is abandoned.

SUMMARY

1. Information about the distribution, dispersal and social organization of red deer on Rhum was gathered incidentally during a study of their population dynamics between 1957 and 1965.

2. General daytime distribution of red deer in the catchment basins of this mountainous island favours slopes and ground isolated from the south with little or no distinction between sex and age.

3. In spring, daytime distribution of the distinguishable classes, stags, yearling males, hinds and calves, shows most of the deer ($>60\%$) below a height of 152 m with the stags the lowest class (av. 86 m). In one summer count (August 1965) these positions were reversed, the stags being the highest class (av. 280 m.)

4. Group size and composition by sex. On Rhum, where feeding grounds and shelter are of assorted sizes and dispersion, average group size is about nine, and about one-third of the groups contain deer of both sexes. Where the country is on a larger scale, as in the eastern highlands of Scotland, group size is larger (*ca* 40) and more groups (40%) include both sexes. By contrast, in mixed open and wooded country, e.g. Holland and Sweden, groups are small—seldom more than family parties—and the sexes are generally segregated.

5. Dispersal of young. From observations of individuals marked as calves, there appears to be a gradual dispersal (perhaps stimulated by enforced separation during the periods of calving and mating) over the first three years of life, the males tending to establish home ranges further from their place of birth (av. 2·5 km) than the hinds (av. 1·4 km). Following the evacuation of the sheep stock in 1957, and with the deer population being held at about 1 700–1 800 by means of an annual cull (17% excluding yearlings), dispersal over distances of this order appears to be independent of competition for food. Further, aggressive behaviour of adults does not appear to contribute to dispersal. In fact marked animals may be found sometimes with one group, sometimes with another. There appears to be no group territorial behaviour, as has been sometimes reported. Since, however, such movements probably

underlie the problems of marauding and colonization and appear to be greater in other parts of Scotland, this investigation is now receiving special attention in preparation for similar work on the mainland.

References

Ahlén, I. (1965). Studies on the red deer, *Cervus elaphus* L., in Scandinavia. III. Ecological investigations. *Viltrevy* **3**, 178–376.

Burt, W. H. (1943). Territoriality and home range concepts as applied to mammals. *J. Mammal.* **24**, 346–352.

Darling, F. Fraser. (1937). "A Herd of Red Deer." Oxford University Press, London.

Delap, P. (1957). Some notes on the social habits of the British deer. *Proc. zool. Soc. Lond.* **128**, 608–612.

Eggeling, W. J. (1964). A nature reserve management plan for the island of Rhum, Inner Hebrides. *J. appl. Ecol.* **1**, 405–419.

Eygenraam, J. A. (1963). Het sociale level van edelherten (*Cervus elaphus*, L.). *Lutra* **5**, 1–8.

Howard, H. E. (1920). "Territory in Bird Life." John Murray, London.

Lowe, V. P. W. (1961). A discussion on the history, present status and future conservation of red deer (*Cervus elaphus* L.) in Scotland. *Terre Vie* **1**, 9–40.

Schloeth, R. (1961). Markierung und erste Beobachtungen von markiertem Rotwild im schwiezerischen Nationalpark und dessen Umgebung. *Ergebn. wiss. Unters. schweiz. NatnParks* **7**, 197–227.

Symp. zool. Soc. Lond. (1966) No. 18, 229–235.

HOME RANGE AND AGONISTIC BEHAVIOUR IN THE GREY SQUIRREL

JAN C. TAYLOR

Ministry of Agriculture, Fisheries and Food, Infestation Control Laboratory, Tangley Place, Worplesdon, Guildford, Surrey, England

SYNOPSIS

Observations have been made on clearly marked grey squirrels (*Sciurus carolinensis* Gmelin) in a small woodlot. The range of movement of individual squirrels varied according to sex and age, and some of these differences have been correlated with agonistic and sexual behaviour.

INTRODUCTION

During the 12-month period from November 1964 a study has been made on the social behaviour of grey squirrels in an attempt to understand their destructive habit of stripping living bark from trees, and some interesting aspects are emerging. Most of the work has been done in a $4\frac{1}{2}$ ha woodlot at Imperial College Field Station, Silwood Park, Berkshire, where squirrels have been trapped periodically to maintain a population individually identifiable by dye-marked pelage and toe-clipping. Two hundred hours have been spent on observations, chiefly from vantage points scattered through the wood, but also from a hide overlooking a feeding point, where more intensive behaviour studies have been made.

RANGE OF MOVEMENT

There have been several studies on range of movement of grey squirrels; principally by Robinson and Cowan (1954) who observed a range of about 20 ha for males and 2–6 ha for females, and Flyger (1960) who by trapping and visual observation detected much smaller ranges of 0·77 ha for males and 0·49 ha for females. Although estimates of range vary, there is agreement that the grey squirrel is a "home range" species, and that the majority live in areas familiar to them for most of their lives. There is also agreement that male range is greater than that of female, and that juvenile range, which is more erratic, is probably associated with dispersal.

Most of the data from Silwood refer to sight records of marked animals, which are preferable to the use of baiting points (as in trapping), but suffer from some bias due to the non-uniformity of the habitat resulting in differences in ease of observation, as well as the observer being unable to give equal attention to all parts of the wood. Also the squirrels' habitat was not continuous because the woodland was small. The linear movements observed (Table I), however, were similar to those found by Robinson and Cowan (1954), and K. D. Taylor (unpublished), but were larger than those observed by Flyger (1960), probably because most of his records were obtained by a method involving a high density of traps, a method shown by Taylor (1963) to reveal only relatively small movements.

TABLE I

Captures and sightings of all squirrels, and range of movement of animals with over nine records during the period November 1964 to October 1965

Section of population	No. of animals	Mean no. of captures	Mean no. of sightings	No. of animals with more than 9 records	Greatest distance between observations		Area defined by observations	
					Mean (m)	Maximum (m)	Mean (ha)	Maximum (ha)
Adult ♂	18	3	9	6	314	488	1·46	3·04
Adult ♀	14	5·4	16·4	12	132	174	0·53	0·93
1964 born juvenile ♂	13	6	20	10	214	348	0·89	1·66
1964 born juvenile ♀	10	5·2	13·6	6	167	283	0·97	2·15
1965 born juvenile ♂	17	4·6	5·7	7	221	381	0·77	1·82
1965 born juvenile ♀	9	2·8	2·8	1	(95)	(140)	—	—

BEHAVIOUR

Little meaning can be attached to range of movement without considering behaviour; this has been well demonstrated by Eisenberg (1962) in a study of two species of *Peromyscus*, when he showed how their differing social behaviour was accompanied by differing breeding performance and accounted for the constant, locally distributed population of the one species and the fluctuating, quickly spreading population of the other. In grey squirrels agonistic and sexual behaviour appear to have great influence on their movements.

Agonistic behaviour

The most conspicuous form of agonistic behaviour is when one animal chases another at speed round a tree-trunk and across the woodland floor; under some circumstances this can be heard at a distance of at least 100 m. Less conspicuous behaviour, such as avoidance, is more difficult to observe and needs more careful interpretation, requiring a knowledge of the system of visual, auditory and possibly olfactory signals. The signals mainly associated with dominance appear to be: narrowing of the eye, which is ringed by pale fur, bringing the ears forward to expose the puff of white hair behind, raising of hair along the mid-dorsal line of the back, erection of tail hair and flapping the tail, paddling the hind feet, teeth chattering, and finally (that which is important to this project), taking chips out of whatever is to hand, which includes strips of green bark during March to August. Signs of submission include: wide open eyes, covering white hair behind the ears, relaxing tail hairs, avoidance by altering course or by rushing past at speed, squealing when hard-pressed in a chase, and a high-pitched growl, often accompanied by striking with the forepaws when at close range (also found in the red squirrel by Eibl-Eibesfeldt, 1951). The latter may perhaps be more a sign of defiance than submission as it is frequently directed towards an unquestionably dominant animal, and it is not a sign of dominance as Flyger (1955) describes for American squirrels.

Observations made at feeding points indicate that there is a well-defined scale of precedence which has been noted before by Flyger (1955) and others. This seemed to be strongest between adults towards juveniles, but in addition both sexes appeared to have separate social scales which are loosely linked in such a way that the dominant male takes precedence over all females, and the dominant female takes precedence only over males low in the social order. Since the study is still at an early stage it has not yet been possible to determine over what area a dominant animal exercises its rank, nor whether males hold it over their full annual range of movement, or only part of it, and whether or not subordinate females assume dominance over higher ranking animals when defending their broods. However, the relatively few observations on dominance made other than at the baiting points did not reveal reversal in the social scale. How the rank order is arrived at is uncertain; open combat is unlikely since only one case of this was seen, yet torn ears and broken tails often occur. The only fight witnessed occurred between two spring-born juveniles disputing the use of the feeding hopper, the movement was too quick to analyse, but appeared to involve biting and scratching and was accompanied by much growling. The number of chases heard per unit time each month perhaps give a clue as to when the social order is determined, for these rise to a peak in the late autumn and fall off to only one-eighth of this value in June and the amount of chasing suggests that rank is decided before actual combat; one animal conceding to another by avoidance or escape. Since many of these chases consist of a juvenile being pursued by an adult it is probable that older animals are likely to be more dominant; this is borne out by examination of dominant squirrels. Chasing of juveniles may also be one of the reasons for the erratic juvenile ranges, as they may be attempting to find areas where adult aggression is minimal.

It is interesting to compare the frequency of chases with readiness to call at predators or intruders (such as myself); autumn calling has been noted by Hazard (1960) and Shorten (1962) and during the year at Silwood the frequency and origin of calls has been noted. As with chasing, this reaches a peak in the autumn, falling to one-eighth of this level in March, and Gordon (1936) suggests that the autumn calling of the pine squirrel is connected with a territorial system. Grey squirrel calling, often heard at distances up to 300 m, is usually accompanied by vigorous tail flagging. On one occasion six animals, only a few metres apart, were seen to call at the same time, apparently showing no antagonism towards each other. Flyger (1955) concludes that these calls are purely alarm notes, but this does not explain their differential frequency each month throughout the year. As with the pine squirrel, the main activity at the time of most frequent calling is burial of the food crop; this suggests that it could be the period of annual stocktaking suggested by Wynne-Edwards (1962), calling acting as a means of population census and storage as a measurement of food availability.

Breeding behaviour

Range of movement and agonistic behaviour become more meaningful when considered with breeding behaviour; when a female is coming on heat she gives a call similar to that heard in the autumn; this can bring males from a distance of at least 100 m and in a short time there may be as many as twelve animals, including some immature ones of both sexes, following and chasing her through the trees. In chases where I have been able to identify most of the animals present, the animal nearest to the female is the most dominant male. The female is chased to the extremity of a branch or into a nest where she turns and holds off the leading male, and he in his turn tries to keep the other males away; while the male is thus engaged, the female may rush past and be chased to another point. It is during the confusion of the chase from one perch to another that copulation often takes place, intromission being accomplished without courtship by a male—not invariably the leader—which succeeds in catching and holding the female for perhaps a minute, during which time the other males stay still and quiet and the female emits the defiant growls described under agonistic behaviour. In the confusion other chases often develop after the wrong female, and excited juvenile males have been observed to attempt reciprocal copulation. These chases often lead the oestrous female away from her usual range.

The larger male range appears to be connected with their behaviour during the period of oestrus in the females, which at Silwood occurred from late December to February and June to early July. During these times males systematically search through the woodland sniffing along "highway" branches in the trees and along fallen branches and stumps on the ground, sometimes cutting chips from them (also described by Eibl-Eibesfeldt (1951) in red squirrel courtship), and approaching females with a stilt-like walk which enables them to come close enough to smell at the base of their tails, and later the ground below as the female moves on. Males will often "test" the same female in this way a number of times before moving off, approaching her each time she stops to dig in the leaflitter. Male searching activity, female calling, a short grunting call given by males after they have sensed a female on heat and, apparently, a scent marker, all help to ensure the presence of a number of males attending an oestrous female. That male behaviour during the oestrous months accounts for their greater movements is supported by the observed maximum linear range (including the seven males with large movements), being reduced to less than the average for the year, if the months of January, February and June are excluded (see Table I). During chases after an oestrous female there is considerable antagonism between males, with a great show of the signals, including chipping bark (also noted by Shorten, 1954) and, in June, stripping off shreds of living bark; up to 200 cm^2 of green bark were seen to be removed in this way.

Much of the bark stripping at Silwood occurred a little while after oestrus in the breeding period, and only occurred at points where two or more ranges of the seven observed summer breeding females overlapped. This suggests that this damage is also associated with breeding females, and the only animal seen stripping bark at this time was a pregnant female which had on several occasions been seen chasing another summer breeding female. Defence of nest trees by breeding females is well known, and Robinson and Cowan (1954) report considerable aggression, particularly towards other females. It is interesting to note that summer-breeding females are the last to moult the tail and ear hairs which are so important in displays of aggression.

The movements of the different sections of the population appear to be closely connected to their behaviour, sexually quiescent animals having medium overlapping range, breeding females having reduced range connected with defence of nest trees and possibly a marked territorial system, while fecund males have extended range connected with the search for females on heat. Much of the bark stripped at Silwood, amounting in all to about 1 m^2, was apparently connected with breeding, but observations made at Wytham Wood suggest that other factors are involved, since adult females and spring-born young were seen returning daily to the same trees to feed on the inner layers of bark. A habit which may also be connected is that of gnawing superficial bark from under the first branch of major trees, but as yet it has not been possible to identify the squirrels concerned.

Acknowledgements

I wish to express my thanks to Professor O. W. Richards for use of the facilities at Silwood Park, and Mr. H. N. Southern and the Oxford University Chest for permission to make observations at Wytham Wood. I am also indebted to Imperial Chemical Industries Ltd. for the use of Durafur Black R. Flake Dye. My thanks are also due to Mr. H. G. Lloyd and Mr. H. V. Thompson of the M.A.F.F., Infestation Control Laboratory, for encouragement in this work and help in preparing this paper.

References

Eibl-Eibesfeldt, I. (1951). Beobachtungen zur Fortpflanzungsbiologie und Jugendentwicklung des Eichhörnchens (*Sciurus vulgaris* L.). *Z. Tierpsychol.* **8**, 370–400.

Eisenberg, J. F. (1962). Studies on the behaviour of *Peromyscus maniculatus gambelii* and *P. californicus parasiticus*. *Behaviour* **19**, 177–207.

Flyger, V. F. (1955). Implications of social behaviour in grey squirrel management. *Trans. 20th N. Am. Wildl. Conf.*, 381–389.

Flyger, V. F. (1960). Movements and home range of the gray squirrel, *Sciurus carolinensis*, in two Maryland woodlots. *Ecology* **41** (2), 365–369.

Gordon, K. (1936). Territorial behaviour and social dominance among Sciuridae. *J. Mammal.* **17**, 171–172.

Hazard, E. B. (1960). A field study of activity among squirrels (*Sciurus*) in southern Michigan. Ph.D. Thesis, University of Michigan.

Robinson, D. T. and Cowan, I. McT. (1954). An introduced population of the grey squirrel (*Sciurus carolinensis* Gmelin) in British Colombia. *Can. J. Zool.* **32**, 261–282.

Shorten, M. (1954). "Squirrels." New Naturalist Monograph. Collins, London.

Shorten, M. (1962). Grey squirrels. "Animals of Britain" No. 5 (L. Harrison Matthews, ed.). Sunday Times Publication, London.

Taylor, K. D. (1963). Some aspects of grey squirrel control. *Ann. appl. Biol.* **51**, 334–338.

Wynne-Edwards, V. C. (1962). "Animal Dispersion in Relation to Social Behaviour." Oliver and Boyd, London.

Symp. zool. Soc. Lond. (1966) No. 18, 237–258.

GELADA BABOON HERD STRUCTURE AND MOVEMENT
A COMPARATIVE REPORT

JOHN HURRELL CROOK
Department of Psychology, University of Bristol, England

SYNOPSIS

Theropithecus gelada, a cercopithecoid primate, is found only in the mountains of Ethiopia. This vegetarian inhabits the slopes of steep precipices and gorges forming herds of up to 400 strong composed of "one-male groups", "all male groups" and parties of infants, juveniles etc. Under poor feeding conditions herds tend to fragment into smaller parties and many "one-male groups" then forage separately. Herds may range up to 4 miles a day but do not return to the same cliff sleeping sites—rather they move along a line of precipices for several days before returning. Although local populations are concentrated in particularly favourable localities, the one-male groups wander freely and there is probably considerable interchange between herds. Herds show no defensive behaviour of any kind in relation to other geladas and a male's aggressive behaviour occurs in relation to his "harem" only. Geladas never move far from cliffs and retreat to them on the least alarm and for sleeping. Their ranges are thus linear—along the crag-lines of gorges and escarpments. A herd is dispersed in such a way that females and young remain nearest the cliffs, and males, particularly non-breeding and juvenile individuals, form the periphery.

The social system resembles that of *Papio hamadryas* closely and that of *Erythrocebus patas* to a lesser extent. It differs markedly from the better known multimale troop of *Papio cynocephalus* and *Macaca* species. It is argued that these contrasting types of social systems in terrestrial open country primates are essentially functions of habitats differing with respect to food availability, predation pressure and the availability and nature of secure places for protection and sleeping.

INTRODUCTION

The gelada baboon (*Theropithecus gelada*) is a ground dwelling vegetarian primate of open precipitous country found only between 2 000 and 5 000 m in the high mountains of central and northern Ethiopia. Strictly speaking it would be better named gelada "monkey", since it is not a close relation of the typical "baboons" of the genus *Papio* and certain similarities to them in terms of ecological adaptation in morphology and behaviour may be regarded as examples of convergent evolution. The animals are large (adult males may weigh about 45 lb, twice that of females; Matthews, 1956) and sexually dimorphic, the adult males sporting lengthy dark brown capes from their shoulders and enormous canines. The smaller females are not unlike macaques in superficial appearance.

The gelada was first "discovered" by the German explorer and naturalist Rüppell (1835) during a collecting safari in the Begemdir province of Ethiopia in the last century. Apart from a few brief accounts from skin collectors and taxonomic reports the animal has remained unstudied in the field until the present writer's expedition to Ethiopia in 1965. Two races have been described, one from northern Ethiopia and one from the eastern escarpment and the central highlands, but local variations observed by the writer suggest that the distinctions are not very meaningful. The name "Tschelada" is given to the animal only by the Amhara inhabitants of Begemdir where Rüppell first collected it.

In 1965 a preliminary survey of the animal's ecology and behaviour was completed and the results are being prepared for publication. The present paper reports briefly on certain aspects of herd composition, population dispersion and movement of interest in the context of this symposium. A more detailed account will follow. Comprehensive studies in Ethiopia are planned for the near future.

Washburn and De Vore (1961) have pointed out the great interest of comparative studies of ground dwelling African primates in view of possible parallels between cercopithecid, pongid and protohominid evolution in similar terrain. Apart from the forest dwelling gorilla and mandrill, and the montane gelada, the terrestrial primates are savannah or forest fringe animals. Of these *Papio cynocephalus* has been extensively studied (Hall and De Vore, 1965) and preliminary accounts of *Papio hamadryas* and *Erythrocebus patas* have appeared (Kummer and Kurt, 1963; Hall, 1966). Gartlan is completing a study of the semi-terrestrial *Cercopithecus aethiops* (Hall and Gartlan, 1965) and will begin work on *Mandrillus* in October 1966. This study of the gelada provides new information for the analysis of the markedly contrasting social systems now known to occur among terrestrial primates.

ECOLOGY

The Ethiopian highlands comprise an elevated tableland, rising to near 5 000 m at Ras Dashan in Semyen, dramatically dissected into enormous gorges belonging mostly either to the Blue Nile or Takazze river systems. In the north and east the highlands fall away along escarpments of tremendous height and grandeur into arid lowlands which, to the east, rapidly disappear into the Danakil Desert. The highlands have a temperate climate with a dry season approximately from September till June broken only for the small rains in April (for details see Kebede Tato, 1964). Occasional showers may, however, be experienced throughout the dry part of the year. In the main study area, in the Semyen mountains of Begemdir (between 3 500 and 4 400 m), ground frost was experienced before dawn on several days in February and after storms frozen hail may lie for several hours in April. The higher peaks may be white for several days during this month. More severe climatic conditions occur during the main rains between June and September.

Apart from taking small quantities of insects the geladas appear entirely vegetarian, feeding mainly on grasses and bulbs. They occur only in the vicinity of precipices to which they run on the least alarm and on the ledges of which they sleep. To study them it is thus essential to camp on the edges of escarpments and gorges and to observe the animals as they move up and down them and along the cliff edges. On the eastern side of the highlands geladas were found mainly near the cliff-girt summits of high crags (Ambas) occurring at intervals along the escarpment and also on cliffs often very close to agricultural land. Some of these localities were accessible by Landrover but in Semyen the finest herds in most natural conditions were only reached during extensive safaris by mule caravan.

The main study areas were (1) the districts of Geech, Ambaras and Addis Gey in the Semyen mountains (February to April 1965), (2) the gorge at Debra Libanos some 70 km north of Addis Ababa in Shoa (May and July 1965), and (3) a chain of localities down the eastern escarpment from Lalibela to Sendafa in the provinces of Wollo and Shoa (Mount Abuna Joseph, Limba Amba, Dessye, Tarmaber, Ankober and Aliltu) visited in June 1965. (See Scott, 1955, for a map of High Semyen; more correct map now in preparation.)

HERD SIZES AND POPULATION DISPERSION

Geladas are gregarious and were observed in herds of up to 400 strong. These herds are, however, not social units of relatively stable composition such as baboon troops. They comprise several types of social unit, "one-male groups" (see below), "all-male groups", juvenile groups and infant play groups which tend to separate easily, forming a constellation of smaller herds which may later reunite to form the original large congregation. The larger herds result primarily from animals coming together on particularly favourable feeding grounds. This is, however, by no means a passive aggregation (Allee, 1931) but an active congregation dependent upon the animals' responsiveness to their fellows. Social responses tend to bring individual groups into the vicinity of food.

In Semyen during February the harvests are being gathered and threshing floors are in active use. Particularly large herds were observed near the village of Ambaras and the animals gathered around threshing floors where the food supply was particularly ample. The hillsides are excessively cultivated in this area and erosion is heavy. Following the harvests the soil bakes hard and there is little food. The animals congregate on the few patches of dried sward left by villagers for their domestic animals or wander up and down craggy slopes too steep for farming. Observations of population size in April, in the latter half of the rainy season, showed numerical differences in population from February. Near the villages of Ambaras and Addis Gey the population as a whole was smaller but this effect was not apparent on the high plateau of Geech mountain where there is no agriculture; the animals feed in a more or less untouched habitat of grassland dotted with tall mountain lobelias.

In February twenty-four herd counts were made in Semyen, providing a maximum count of about 400 individuals and a minimum of thirty ($\bar{x} = 156$). In April, however, when thirty-five herds were counted, the largest was only 300 and the smallest twenty-five ($\bar{x} = 90$). A comparison between these two figures shows that in February herd size was significantly larger than in April ($\chi^2 = 17{\cdot}69$, significant at $0{\cdot}1\%$). Leslie Brown (personal communication), who was in Semyen in November 1963, saw large herds 300–400 strong at that time. It appears therefore that following the rains large herds pillage the crops in agricultural areas and remain around the villages during harvest. Later, however, as the food supply visibly decreases, the animals are forced increasingly off the agricultural land and decreases in herd size occur. It seems probable that the local movements involve shifts onto gorge sides or into areas where grassland is more extensive. Since the gelada never moves far from cliff edges any gap in the line of precipices appears to impose a natural barrier to population movements. Nevertheless fairly large local displacements along gorges in Semyen are probable.

In other areas herds were counted late in the dry season. Food was visibly scarce and herd sizes were small. Counts of eleven herds from the eastern escarpment and Debra Libanos averaged eighty-five individuals with a maximum of 200 and a minimum of forty. While these figures are significantly smaller than counts from Semyen in February they do not differ significantly from counts made there in April. Local populations were, however, much smaller—an effect of range and habitat restriction by intensive agriculture and human settlement. In most of these localities shooting and/or trapping of geladas occurs on a scale much greater than in Semyen. In these areas also the frequency with which one-male groups (see below) were recorded moving separately from other groupings was especially high. Thus, whereas in Semyen there were fifty-nine herd counts and thirty-three of one-male groups, elsewhere there were only eleven herd counts and thirty one-male group determinations.

All the available evidence thus suggests that the population dispersion of geladas at different places and seasons is largely a function of food availability. With abundant local food sources large herds congregate together—with food sparse and irregularly distributed the herds scatter and a high incidence of one-male groups travelling separately is recorded. While local human predation may also affect dispersion to some extent this is considered a minor factor. Along the escarpments and gorges cliff sleeping sites are commonly available and their relative abundance does not affect the herd sizes under discussion. An observation especially pertinent to this conclusion was made near Debra Libanos during the early part of the rainy season in July. The first storms caused little visible change in the food situation and small dispersed parties of geladas were observed. As soon as a carpet of green grass appeared changes in dispersion were apparent. A rich gently sloping meadow-land developed near a stream bed and the animals took to assembling there in large herds of up to 150–200 individuals. All fed eagerly and for many hours on the freshly growing vegetation. Elsewhere, on the more barren gorge sides and on ploughed land, at this time only relatively small parties were seen.

HERD COMPOSITION

Large herds consist of several types of social unit. The "one-male group" (Kummer and Kurt, 1963) is the reproductive unit of a gelada population. It consists of a large adult male, a group of females including both mothers and non-maternal animals in all stages of the oestrous cycle, variable numbers of juvenile animals, infants and babies and an occasional sub-adult male often almost fully grown but not sexually mature. In areas where the population is widely dispersed such social units are the commonest, observed associating inconstantly with small groups consisting wholly of large sub-adult males and mature males (possibly old animals) not possessing "harems". These "all-male groups" likewise move independently from other units and show considerable cohesion over several weeks.

In large herds the one-male groups become totally intermingled so that to the casual observer their presence is completely disguised. In fact that it took the writer five weeks of hard observation before he was certain of their presence. Evidence of the following types finally demonstrated their occurrence without any doubt. (1) Groups were identified by observing identifiable females (chest patches in contrasting stages of oestrus; Matthews, 1956; Crook, in preparation) and their movements. (2) While scattering widely throughout the herd the females of a group periodically gathered close to their male and appeared to interact sexually only with him. (3) The group of females together with their babies move synchronously with a male and independently from other members of the herd both in space and time. (4) The male normally determines the direction of movement of the group. (5) Observation of a few well-known groups over periods of up to 3 weeks reveals a considerable membership consistency. In two groups studied an additional female joined the group during the period but no females were lost. Juveniles and infants frequently move from one group to another when the groups unite to join temporary herds. In large herds juveniles tend to congregate together and infants form play groups quite distinct from the overdispersed adults. Likewise in large herds the all-male groups coalesce to form a well marked section in which few females or young ever occur. One-male groups varied in size from five to thirty monkeys with a noticeable, but not statistically significant, trend to increased group size outside Semyen in areas where shooting occurred.

After several weeks' observation it became possible to make counts of the herd composition in terms of sex and age categories. These comprised adult males, large sub-adult males, non-maternal adult females, females with babies, juveniles and infants. While every attempt was made to make these determinations as accurate as possible, a degree of error was inevitable and probably varied with the number of animals and the distance of the herd from the observer. Repeat counts were made until the best possible estimate had been obtained. Particular difficulty was experienced in distinguishing large juvenile males from females, especially when animals had their backs to the observer for long periods. Since the distinction between small juveniles and infants depended on a size estimate, difficulty was experienced with herds at differing distances from the observer. Results nevertheless showed sufficient consistency to allow a reasonable confidence in the estimates. Details are provided in Table I permitting the following conclusions.

(1) The adult sex-ratio in herds differed when herds in Semyen were compared with those from elsewhere, more males being observed in the Semyen. This is almost certainly the consequence of shooting. Adult males are not only the largest animals in herds but also the boldest and the last to retreat onto the cliffs. Near Debra Libanos in particular, army

Table I

Ratios of population categories in herds and one-male groups of gelada baboons. Ethiopia 1965

	Herds in Semyen ($n = 17$)				Herds outside Semyen ($n = 6$)				One male groups in Semyen ($n = 30$)				One male groups outside Semyen ($n = 21$)				One male groups at Mount Abuna Joseph and Debra Libanos ($n = 11$)			
	No. of individuals	max.	min.	$\bar{x}$	No. of individuals	max.	min.	$\bar{x}$	No. of individuals	max.	min.	$\bar{x}$	No. of individuals	max.	min.	$\bar{x}$	No. of individuals	max.	min.	$\bar{x}$
Adult males	168	26	2	9·9	24	5	3	4	30	1	1	1	19	1	0(×2)	0·9	10	1	0(×1)	0·9
Sub-adult males	88	15	0	5·2	13	4	0	2·2	7	2	0	0·02	12	5	0	0·6	2	1	0	0·2
Females	321	47	3	18·9	106	43	7	17·7	58	6	0	1·9	92	10	1	4·4	26	4	0	2·4
Females with babies	170	23	3	10	61	17	6	10·2	60	4	0	2·0	77	8	0	3·2	18	4	0	1·7
Juveniles	197	22	0	11·6	84	22	9	14·8	20	5	0	1	68	6	1	3·2	26	5	1	2·4
Infants	149	26	0	8·8	85	26	6	14·2	20	7	0	0·7	61	10	0	2·9	32	5	0	2·9
Babies	170	23	3	10	61	17	7	10·2	60	4	0	2·0	77	8	0	3·2	18	4	0	1·6

parties from a nearby camp used to shoot up geladas at irregular intervals, doubtless selecting males as the main targets. (Semyen sex ratios 1 : 2·4, elsewhere 1 : 6·9.)

(2) The socionomic sex-ratio for the "one-male groups" also reveals a higher proportion of females outside Semyen. Some of these groups were extraordinarily large (one of thirty being recorded at Debra Libanos) and only in those areas where shooting was reported were groups ever seen being led by large sub-adult males. (One-male group ratios in Semyen 1 : 3·9, elsewhere in areas where shooting was reported 1 : 8). The fact that in two areas outside Semyen where shooting does not occur (slopes of Mount Abuna Joseph and the monastery forest area at Debra Libanos) the ratio was 1 :4·6, resembling the figures from Semyen, suggests that human predation is indeed the main factor producing the differences.

(3) When herd sex ratios are compared to one-male group ratios relatively more adult males were counted in the herds. This is attributed to the herd counts including large adult males otherwise occurring only in all-male groups.

(4) The ratio of adult females to maternal females in herds differed little in the contrasting areas counted, although a slight increase in mothers is apparent outside Semyen. Since the mean numbers for infants and babies in Semyen herds in February–April summate to 18·8 individuals compared with a figure of 24·4 from herds outside Semyen in March–July, the contrast is probably due to a higher incidence of births in the early dry season yielding higher numbers of females with babies late in the dry season.

(5) The ratio of non-maternal to maternal females is larger in one-male groups than in herds. In Semyen this may be due to counts of one-male groups being made mostly late in the visit there. The ratios for one-male groups from shooting and non-shooting localities outside Semyen are identical. A further analysis of these data is in preparation.

HERD STRUCTURE AND MOVEMENT

A gelada herd shows a distinct organization that is not simply a summation of scattered "one-male groups" and "all-male groups" into a mixed population. A browsing herd is dispersed over a wide area but is never seen more than a mile from the nearest cliff edges. Its organization is intimately related to the position of the cliff. Nearest the edges one observes parties of infants and small juveniles either feeding or playing together interspersed among numbers of females and mothers.

Scattered irregularly among them are several adult males, the leaders of "one-male groups". As one traverses the herd away from the cliff edge the numbers of infants and babies rapidly decrease while that of adult and large sub-adult males increases until, on the outside flank, only males are observed. The herd may be divided conveniently into two sections—the mothers, infants and females nearest the cliff and adult and sub-adult males "inland" from them (Table II).

TABLE II

Proportion of individual categories in two herds from sections near the cliff, furthest from the cliff, and intermediate, expressed as percentages of animals sampled in each section.

Geech, Semyen Mountains, January 1965

	Near cliff	Intermediate	Furthest from cliff
Herd A			
Adult males	8·6	16·7	45·8
Sub-adult males	3·5	—	29·2
Females	34·5	33·3	—
Juveniles	19·0	25·0	25
Babies	34·5	25·0	—
Herd B			
Large males	28·3	54·6	89·2
Mothers with babies	71·7	45·5	10·8

During the greater part of the day a herd moves slowly forwards, its speed determined by the numbers of individuals respectively sitting, grooming, feeding or walking. A fairly regular sequence of speed changes may be observed. Table III provides data showing the numbers of animals in sample counts performing these four activities at half-hour intervals. From such records we may categorize the manner of movement of a herd into several main types: Groom-sitting (usually in early morning and late evening), Groom-feeding, Feeding, Travel-feeding (which may be fast or slow depending on the percentage of individuals feeding or walking), and Travelling, the latter being a rapid cross country march. During the typical record shown, extensive forward movements occurred just before recording was started and again at roughly hourly intervals. Each displacement continued for 10–15 min when the pace slowed as individuals sat down to feed. The following

TABLE III

Activity counts of a herd in Semyen

Time	Grooming	Feeding	Walking	Sitting	Total	Herd activity designation
14.00	13	9	6	3	31	Groom-feeding
14.30	2	37	8	0	47	Slow travel-feeding
15.00	0	34	34	0	68	Travel-feeding
15.30	2	21	60	0	83	Fast travel-feeding
16.00	0	38	12	0	50	Slow travel-feeding
16.30	Moved too far to count and settled again					—
17.00	2	38	36	0	76	Travel-feeding
17.45	Start of descent onto cliff face					—
Next day						
10.30	12	32	2	10	56	Groom-feeding
11.00	47	26	1	6	80	Groom-feeding
11.15	0	27	36	0	63	Travel-feeding
11.30	0	41	15	0	56	Travel-feeding
12.00	0	48	0	0	48	Feeding
12.30	2	47	4	0	53	Feeding
13.00	2	45	0	0	47	Feeding
13.30	14	28	22	0	64	Travel-feeding

morning two main displacements occurred between 11.15 and 11.30 and again 2 h later. Throughout the day the main activities are feeding and walking. Grooming occurs mainly in the early morning and during short rest periods throughout the day.

Forward movement is commonly initiated by the male section of the herd—an increasing number of individuals rising and striding forward plucking up a food object here and there. After pacing approximately 300 m they settle down one by one and resume feeding. Sometimes, however, individual monkeys get up here and there all over the herd and move forward. Their going gradually activates the feeding animals who likewise rise and move until eventually the whole herd moves slowly forward. During Slow Travel-feeding movement occurs through the sporadic walking forward of individual males in the van. An animal moves a few metres and sits down again to feed. Another monkey strolls up behind it and, on reaching it, also sits down. Following animals very rarely pass a monkey that has sat down so that forward speed depends particularly on the distance the initiators walk rather than on the number of them moving. There are no "leaders"—first one then another of the monkeys in front initiates a movement. It is apparent, however, that males move more frequently, further and range outwards from the cliff more than females and this greater activity accounts for their relative positions on the ground and their role in activating movement. Travelling resembles a forced march. It was seen once when a herd had moved far from a cliff sleeping place and appeared anxious to retrace its steps, and frequently during March and April at Ambaras when the food supply was scarce—the smaller herds then travelled rapidly from one patch of dried sward to another or up and down over the gorge-side crags in an evident search for feeding places.

In Fig. 1, the relative positions of the male and predominantly female sections of a herd during a day's ranging are shown. As commonly happens the herd reversed directions in the middle of the day, this being initiated within the rear part of the herd. The males followed and their greater pace soon brought them back into the forward and "inland" position characterizing the outward march. On the march one-male groups often become sufficiently separated to reveal their identity (Fig. 2A). A more confusing distribution of individuals during a herd feeding period is shown in Fig. 2B.

DIURNAL ACTIVITY AND RANGING

The monkeys sleep on small ledges on vertical rock faces. In Semyen they show a preference for clefts and chimneys in the cliffs where the

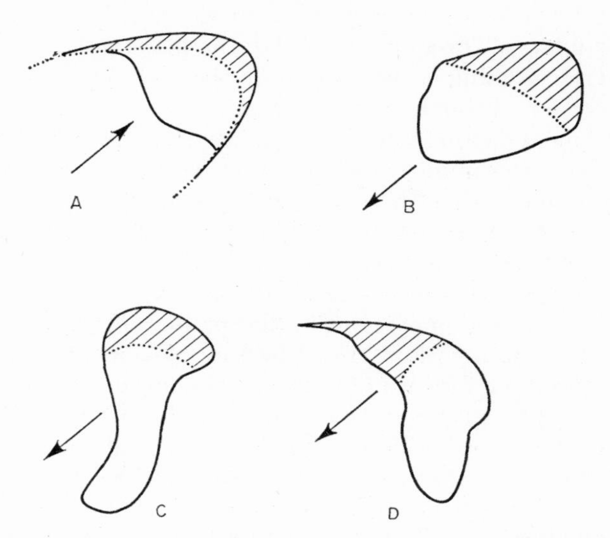

Fig. 1. Gelada herd movement. Male section lined. A. Herd moving forward with males in front. B. Reversal. C and D. Males recovering frontal position on side of herd away from cliff. (From field sketches.)

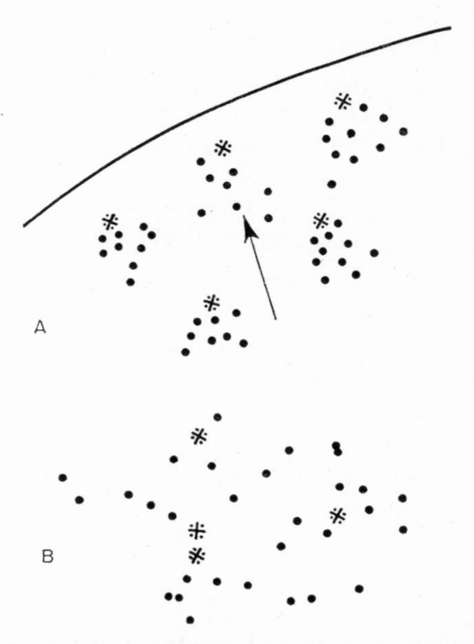

Fig. 2. A. Herd progression up hillside with one-male groups separated. Males leading. B. Intermingled groups of feeding herd. (From field sketches.)

rock is broken by an abundance of ledges and often overshadowed by an overhang. At dusk they climb down into these places and scatter in small groups or singletons about the available ledges. Geladas are seldom about before full daylight and only gradually disentangle themselves from the huddles in which they spend the night to sit or groom nearby. On deeply shaded cliffs they soon move out of the cold air and climb out of the mountain shadow into the sunlight where at once they sit down and groom. Later the groups coalesce into the herd for the daily ranging. In one area (Addis Gey) in Semyen a herd spent the night on the slopes of a vast gorge where crags and cliffs were well separated. This appeared to impose a considerable scatter on the groups and on the following morning many single one-male groups and a few small herds formed by the fusion of two or three groups were seen moving in parallel up the gorge sides to the flat land above. Here they coalesced to form a large herd of some 264 individuals.

In the Semyen gorges in February the herds gradually climbed the scarped slopes until they reached relatively flat land near the villages in the middle of the day. They then reversed their movement and returned slowly downwards for some part of the morning journey. In late March and April, however, they remained below the villages on the steeper slopes less denuded of food than higher areas. At Aliltu near Addis Ababa small groups were kept low in a gorge by village boys at harvest time (December) but in June, when the boys were less active, they came up over the top of the gorge rim reputedly to work the recently sown fields.

In Semyen and again at Debra Libanos a reversal of movement in the middle of the day was frequently observed. Also in the late afternoon in Semyen the animals often descended the cliffs into rich vegetation with trees where they drank. They did not ascend again except on one day after a storm which had driven them to shelter in the vegetation earlier. Herds on these gorges commonly moved west in the morning and east in the afternoon. It appeared that they were avoiding moving towards the bright sun. The pattern did not occur, however, on differently oriented gorges elsewhere.

The distance travelled in the course of a day varies with the locality and time of year. Montane grassland herds appeared to have a fairly stable long distance range every day while herds near villages at harvest time moved only short distances and kept near the threshing floors. One herd watched on the Geech mountain grasslands travelled for 3 miles outward in the morning and returned $1\frac{1}{2}$ miles in the afternoon —a total of $4\frac{1}{2}$ miles in the day. Most herds probably do not move as far as this unless feeding conditions are poor or the animals disturbed. In the same area and at the same time a herd in heather forest spent most of the morning in one locality and travelled only about $1\frac{1}{2}$ miles in the rest of the day. Herds do not normally return to sleep in the same cliffs on succeeding nights and this is linked with the longer outward journey compared with the afternoon return. On succeeding nights on sleeping cliffs immediately below our camp at Ambaras we counted 14, 40, 14 (different animals), 60, 20, about 100, 20, 51, 0, 25, 21 and 0 monkeys, thus demonstrating the inconsistency with which the ledges were occupied.

Attempts were made to follow herds on successive days but this revealed major difficulties. Herds split up so frequently into component parties and one-male groups, and likewise show considerable scatter along cliffs at nightfall that on successive days one is often unsure whether a given herd is composed of the same animals. One well-known herd on Ambaras was, however, found travelling slowly westwards along the gorge for a period of 3 days covering about 5 miles leaving pockets of monkeys behind it. It travelled out of the study area but drifted back soon afterwards. Another herd at Addis Gey completed a round trek of about 6 miles in 3 days, 3 miles out in one direction and then back again. In general herds appear to drift up and down the gorge sides over a range of about 4 miles. This figure is probably relative to the Semyen gorge conditions reflecting distances of relatively unbroken cliff rather than a behavioural characteristic. Ranging is limited to areas near cliffs and must accord closely with the topography. Open country ranging such as that described for *Papio* by De Vore and Hall (1965) does not occur in the gelada.

Limitations on movement imposed by the availability of precipices may also account for the distribution of local gelada populations in Semyen. In a trek along a gorge near Ambaras few geladas were seen on slopes that were far from cliffs. On Geech mountain likewise herds appeared to centre on the bluff crags of Emietgogo and Kadardit, tamer slopes being less frequently visited. These crags thus formed the "core areas" for local populations ranging in their neighbourhood. These "demes" probably consist mainly of one-male groups loyal to the area. Nevertheless, the extent to which such groups may wander independently, together with the absence of any herd organization restricting entry and departure of groups, suggests that free interchange between neighbouring demes is frequent so long as barriers to movement (i.e. the absence of cliffs) do not prevent it. Contrasts in colour between local populations on different mountains certainly suggest that wandering on a larger scale is infrequent.

CONCLUSIONS AND COMPARATIVE DISCUSSION

The results of the 1965 expedition now permit a number of summarizing statements describing the manner of dispersion of individuals in gelada populations.

(1) The gelada occurs in herds whose size varies in different places and at different seasons. Herds are constantly dividing into smaller parties, the main social unit being a "one-male group" consisting of a large mature male, a group of females with their babies and infants and occasional attendant juveniles. These are the indivisible units of the population which form herds through congregation. Within the herds juveniles and infants separate from the one-male groups to form their own play groups and foraging parties but become distributed among the groups again as the herd fragments. Many sub-adult and adult males are not members of one-male groups. They collect into small units of their own—the all-male groups. All-male groups and one-male groups may scatter quite independently, and in some areas the population is dispersed entirely in this way and herds are not seen.

(2) Geladas never move far from cliffs and crags to which they run for shelter from weather and predators and on which they sleep. Typically geladas are found along the rims of precipitous gorges where such protective features are unlimited for considerable distances. All gelada movement and ranging is done with strict reference to topography and the position of the cliff line.

(3) A large gelada herd shows a marked structure particularly apparent on montane grasslands but still detectable around villages and threshing floors. The herd section nearest the cliff contains intermingled one-male groups, play parties of infants and small juveniles. Furthest from the cliff large males and well-grown juveniles are found. When moving a herd progresses in such a way as to maintain the predominantly female section nearest to the cliff edge. The movements take the form of forward pulsations usually initiated by males in the van. The rate of movement depends on the percentage of individuals sitting, grooming, feeding or walking forward at any one time. Fast marches of the whole herd were seen under poor feeding conditions.

(4) A day range probably rarely exceeds 4 miles. It occurs within a narrow belt of country not more than a mile deep from the gorge edge at any one time. The steep slopes of gorges down to about 2 500 m are normally part of a ranging area. The animals move out and up from the sleeping cliffs in the morning and back and down again in the afternoon. The return journey is never as long as the outward journey so herds move along the gorge edges on successive days. Sometimes the return

journey is not apparent, the animals simply descending directly onto cliff faces below them.

(5) On successive days a herd may move 5 or more miles along a gorge rim before beginning to retrace its advance. The distance over which a herd moves along a gorge is probably determined largely by the presence of good cliffs, any gap tending to prevent further movement.

(6) Likewise the congregation of the population into demes centred on particular areas with fine cliffs, and which thus provide core areas to local ranges, is probably determined primarily by ecological factors. The tendency for groups to wander separately and the absence of any mechanism for exclusion of groups from herds suggests considerable interchange between neighbouring demes when ecological factors allow a certain amount of movement. Often, however, isolated demes were discovered centred upon remote crag-sided mountains (ambas) and surrounded by country entirely unsuited to geladas. Colour contrasts in pelage were noted between such isolated populations.

The above points reveal two main factors determining the population dispersion of geladas: firstly the presence of cliffs or crags for security, secondly the availability of food. Dependence upon a cliff-line imposes (1) the linear nature of the range, (2) the division of the herd into two sections oriented with respect to cliffs, and (3) the splitting of the population into demes centred upon a stretch of cliff functioning as their core area. Under conditions of food abundance the one-male groups and all-male groups congregate into large herds. Food scarcity at the end of the dry season causes the following changes: (1) increased fragmentation of herds into small parties; (2) one-male groups and all-male groups wandering widely and independently from one another; (3) an increased rate of group travel; (4) reliance on food supplies away from villages and bare harvested land.

Kummer and Kurt (1963) and Kummer (to be published) have drawn attention to contrasts in social organization within the genus *Papio*. Their Ethiopian studies confirmed Zuckerman's (1932) work, mainly in the London Zoo, on the "harems" of *Papio hamadryas*. This species has a social organization based on a "one-male group" and very strictly disciplined—a female wandering more than 5 m from the male is chased and severely attacked. These groups rarely intermingle and yet, in the main study area in Harar province, only rarely separated from the sizeable herd. The groups centred activities on a limited number of sleeping sites but frequently changed their site every night. The herds occupying the area appeared to be divisible into several "troops" which, although corporately using the sleeping places, otherwise moved separately and sometimes showed aggression to one another.

The *hamadryas* system differs from that of the gelada in the following main ways: (1) gelada groups intermingle more in herds and although males have behavioural means of integrating females (Crook, in preparation) they do not physically assault them by using the *hamadryas* neck bite; (2) gelada groups may wander apart entirely independently and in some areas the whole population is largely dispersed in this way and no big herds are seen; (3) gelada herds do not appear to contain mutually exclusive troops, differentiation between herds seems to depend more on preferred ranges and the location of population "demes" around favoured cliff sites.

The recent work of Hall (1965) has revealed yet another type of "one-male group" among African terrestrial primates. *Erythrocebus patas* of the open grassland savannah was studied in Uganda and the populations found to be dispersed in large one-male groups mutually isolated from one another at all times by occupying largely separate ranges and showing mutual avoidance. The males play a special role as sentinels for the groups and direction of movement is largely determined by females. These remarkable monkeys furthermore scatter for the night into isolated trees; safety in the open grasslands at night is a matter of dispersion and crypticity since secure rock or tree refuges do not occur.

Each of these three species thus has a social system based in its own way on the "one-male group" and all contrast markedly with the better known multimale troop system common to *Papio cynocephalus* and species of *Macaca* (Table IV). The new discoveries effectively dispose of Kummer's and Kurt's (1963) concern over whether in *P. hamadryas* the one-male group might not be an ecological artifact. Certainly extended studies are required before a thorough picture is attained but enough is now known to reveal two basic grades of social life among terrestrial primates.

In a survey of primate social systems, Crook and Gartlan (1966) suggest that the *hamadryas–patas–gelada* type of social system is basically an adaptation to sparse feeding resources seasonally more limiting than *P. cynocephalus* and *Macaca* habitats. The one-male group in such conditions is considered the most efficient social unit for a sexually dimorphic population in which females are both smaller than males and more numerous. This is because a smaller proportion of available food goes to the individuals least concerned with infant nutrition and reproduction generally. In multimale units the large males must take a much greater proportion of the food. The large size

TABLE IV

Comparisons between African ground dwelling primates with multimale and one-male social units

	Papio cynocephalus	*Papio hamadryas*	*Erythrocebus patas*	*Theropithecus gelada*
Habitat	Mostly rich savannah habitats often on forest fringe or near gallery. Much habitat variation	Arid savannah	Savannah grasslands with few scattered trees	Montane grasslands near precipices. Also agricultural land
Food type and availability	Vegetable food, occasionally carnivore. Some seasonal scarcity	Vegetable food occasionally carnivore. Probably severe seasonal scarcity	Vegetable food. Probably only moderate seasonal scarcity	Vegetable food. Seasonal scarcity moderate on natural grassland. Very severe on agricultural land
Population dispersion	Multimale troops of constant composition. Max. 200. Mean 25–30. Isolated adult males but no all-male groups recorded	Herds of large size, mean 126, max. 750, near sleeping sites	One male groups, 6–31, mean 15. Occasional isolated all-male groups. No herds or congregation of groups	Large herds, mean 156 in Semyen. Max. 400 decreasing in size at times of evident food shortage when all-male and one-male groups scatter with little reference to one another

TABLE IV—*continued*

	Papio cynocephalus	*Papio hamadryas*	*Erythrocebus patas*	*Theropithecus gelada*
Social structure	Troops characterized by male hierarchies and female promiscuity. Males determine direction of movement. Aggressive	One-male groups strictly disciplined by aggressive males. Usually in herds.	One-male groups with male acting as watch dog often remote from group. Females may determine movement. Little aggression	One-male groups intermingle completely within herds but show spatial and temporal distinctness in movement. Males determine movement. Not very aggressive. Frequently separate from herd
Inter-group relations	Overlapping home ranges. Troops tolerate, avoid or show aggression apparently depending on local conditions	Groups usually distinct within the herd. Herds may comprise separate "troops".	Little overlap in home ranges of one-male groups	Complete mingling of groups in herds but behaviour mechanisms ensure group integrity
Sleeping sites	Cliffs, rock outcrops or tall trees. Same places often used on successive nights. Changes occur. All sleep together	Vertical rocks and cliffs. Frequent changing of site causes mixing of different one-male groups each night	Individuals scatter to sleep singly in trees in different areas on successive nights	Groups descend onto steep cliffs to sleep in huddles of several animals or singly. Congregate again above cliffs on following morning. Different cliffs used on successive nights

TABLE IV—*continued*

	Papio cynocephalus	*Papio hamadryas*	*Erythrocebus patas*	*Theropithecus gelada*
Means of protection from predators	Co-operative and individual defence by males. Troop has males peripheral to females and infants	Presumably defence by large males. Little recorded	Groups retreat by fast running on alarm from watchful male. Males alert behaviour especially adapted to open range without protective features	Males move furthest from cliffs during herd movements and provide a protective flank. Herds run to cliffs on least alarm. Males may be aggressive to predators near cliffs otherwise run to them after the females
Ecological features primarily determining nature of day ranging	Troops based on sleeping places and range from and back to them. May move from one site to another periodically	Positions of sleeping rocks determine the movements and congregation of one-male groups	No especial restriction in open grassland. Little dependence on water sources	Range is linear along gorge or escarpment edges. Gaps in cliff line cause natural breaks in both ranging and distribution
Sources	Hall and De Vore (1965) Hall (1964)	Kummer and Kurt (1963)	Hall (1965)	Crook (in preparation)

of the male in both *hamadryas* and *gelada* and the development of shoulder capes and canines enhancing the appearance of size and strength are considered the result of intense intra-sexual selection for females, the development of hair being economical in that extra exploitation of food is avoided (Jolly, 1963). In herds these impressive monkeys play protective roles but in isolated one-male groups, as Kummer (to be published) has pointed out, their defensive role must be less effective. This, however, would depend upon the predation pressures bearing on the groups. In the case of patas, in areas seemingly replete with dangers, the male has assumed the role of a passive watch-dog rather than an assertive guard. Probably for both *P. hamadryas** and *T. gelada* predation from carnivorous mammals is a much less significant risk than for either *P. cynocephalus* or *E. patas*.

Kummer (to be published) wondered whether the one-male groups of hamadryas could be an adaptation to restricted food supply. This could only be the case if the individual groups wandered separately over a wide area (thereby avoiding local over-exploitation by large herds); a condition not apparently frequent in this species. It may, however, occur in parts of Ethiopia with less food availability and a better supply of sleeping sites than in the area studied. Kummer's large hamadryas herds are probably imposed on the local population owing to the lack of frequent sleeping places in the habitat, animals simply crowding into those that remain; but the food supply obviously must have been sufficient locally to maintain the system. The data presented here on the gelada do much to overcome this difficulty. Sparse food supplies correlate with a scattering of one-male groups whereas conditions of abundance favour herd formation. It appears adaptive for geladas both to scatter and to congregate under the appropriate feeding conditions, and the toleration shown between gelada groups is not a function of a scarcity of sleeping sites for these are amply available. The one-male groups of the patas are likewise probably an adaptation to food supply; the contrasting ranging behaviour and nightly dispersal being special adaptations to open country without protective features. By contrast, the habitat of *P. cynocephalus* is certainly both richer in food and contains plenty of protective retreats. Heavier predation likewise probably exerts positive selection for a multimale assembly with corporate male defence.

In conclusion it seems probable that the differing types of social organization discussed are essentially functions of habitat conditions differing with respect to three main variables: food availability,

* Heavy local predation may be a factor maintaining large herds of this species in some areas not limiting in other respects.

dispersion and seasonal shortage, predation pressure, and the availability and nature of secure places for sleeping sites. The greatest interest attaches to "comprehensive studies" (Washburn and Hamburg, 1965) of these forms in a range of contrasting habitats. These will determine the adaptability of each species and reveal in detail the faults of the present hypothesis.

References

Allee, W. C. (1931). "Animal Aggregations." University of Chicago Press.

Crook, J. H. and Gartlan, J. S. (1966). Evolution of primate societies. *Nature, Lond.* **210,** 1200–1203.

De Vore, I. and Hall, K. R. L. (1965). Baboon ecology. *In* "Primate Behavior" (I. De Vore, ed.), pp. 20–52. Holt, Rinehart and Winston, New York.

Hall, K. R. L. (1965). Social organisation of the old world monkeys and apes. *Symp. zool. Soc. Lond.* No. 14, 265–289.

Hall, K. R. L. (1966). Behaviour and ecology of the wild patas monkey, *Erythrocebus patas,* in Uganda. *J. Zool., Lond.* **148,** 15–87.

Hall, K. R. L. and De Vore, I. (1965). Baboon social behavior. *In* "Primate Behavior" (I. De Vore, ed.), pp. 53–110. Holt, Rinehart and Winston, New York.

Hall, K. R. L. and Gartlan, J. S. (1965). Ecology and behaviour of the Vervet monkey, *Cercopithecus aethiops,* Lolui Island, Lake Victoria. *Proc. zool. Soc. Lond.* **145,** 37–56.

Jolly, C. J. (1963). A suggested case of evolution by sexual selection in primates. *Man,* 222.

Kebede Tato (1964). Rainfall in Ethiopia. *Ethiopian Geogrl J.* **2** (2), 28–36.

Kummer, H. and Kurt, F. (1963). Social units of a free-living population of Hamadryas baboons. *Folia Primat.* **1,** 4–19.

Matthews, L. H. (1956). The sexual skin of the gelada baboon (*Theropithecus gelada*). *Trans. zool. Soc. Lond.* **28** (7), 543–550.

Rüppell, E. (1835). Neue Wirbelthiere zu den fauna von Abyssinien gehorig. "Saugethiere," pp. 5–8. Frankfurt.

Scott, H. (1955). Journey to the High Simien district, northern Ethiopia, 1952–53. *Webbia* **11,** 425–450.

Washburn, S. L. and De Vore, I. (1961). Social behavior of baboons and early man. *In* "Social Life of Early Man" (S. L. Washburn, ed.). Viking Fund Publications, New York.

Washburn, S. L. and Hamburg, D. A. (1965). The implications of Primate Research. *In* "Primate Behavior" (I. De Vore, ed.), pp. 607–622. Holt, Rinehart and Winston, New York.

Zuckerman, S. (1932). "The Social Life of Monkeys and Apes." Kegan Paul, London.

Symp. zool. Soc. Lond. (1966) No. 18, 259–265.

THE SPACE ORGANIZATION OF NUTRIA (*MYOCASTOR COYPUS*) POPULATIONS

LECH RYSZKOWSKI

Polska Akademia Nauk, Zaklad Ekologii, Warsaw, Poland

SYNOPSIS

A study of a nutria population, breeding in an enclosed marshy area of 192 ha, is reported. During the study (1956–60) the numbers varied between 445 and 2 000 specimens. Nutria possess home ranges, but these are freely overlapping and no territoriality is shown. Young animals remain in family groups but adults are solitary. The nests of several individuals are interspersed throughout a given area. When population density becomes high, the vegetation is damaged by the nutrias' habit of concentrating their feeding in particular places. Two different factors determining movement away from areas of too-high concentration are suggested. In one set of circumstances the level of aggressiveness between individuals becomes high and dispersal occurs before damage to the vegetation. In other circumstances high population densities are tolerated and deterioration of the vegetation ultimately forces emigration to occur.

RATIONALE, OBJECTIVES AND METHODS

Studies of population organization include both assessments of structure (density, distribution in space, age structure, etc.) and of interactions between animals. These may be direct (e.g. fighting, co-operation, parent off-spring contacts, etc.) or indirect (as when mediated by changes provoked in the environment).

Because they have diverse evolutionary backgrounds, different species of mammals are characterized by different types of population organization. The different types of population organizations will be expected in mammals according to whether individuals lead a solitary life or live in herds, are nomadic or sedentary, exhibit aggressive reactions to other members of the population or can tolerate them. In turn the habits of animals can be modified by the environmental conditions under which they live. Therefore, in order to form a picture of the space organization of nutria populations an answer to the following three questions should be obtained:

1. What is the territorial behaviour of nutria taking into account their type of population organization?
2. What are the environmental factors which promote closer contacts between animals?
3. In what way do the contacts between nutria influence their distribution?

The investigations to be reported were carried out in an enclosed marshy area of 192 ha, two-thirds of which was covered by sedge (*Carex*) and one-third by reeds. The area was intersected by a dense network of canals and included a lake of 25 ha.

During the four successive years 1956/57–1959/60 a population that varied between 445 (the initial number released in the spring of 1956) and about 2 000 specimens lived on this farm. During the first two years of breeding the animals were allowed to breed at will, during the next two years the entire population was removed into pens for winter, and then released on the whole area in spring.

Some supplementary data were obtained from nutria living on a fish pond (carp) farm of 5 ha covered by *Carex* sp., *Glyceria aquatica* and *Equisetum limosum*. The density of the population on this farm was about seven animals per ha.

The data were obtained as follows: (1) direct observations on the behaviour of nutria; (2) capture, mark and release methods. Five trapping stations were chosen with thirty-five to forty livetraps per station. The trapping period on each station lasted 10 days, traps being checked every morning and evening. Fourteen 10-day trapping series were carried out. To study the effect of removal of nutria from the population eight 10-day series of trappings were conducted in which the captured animals were taken away.

The lowest number of nutria caught during a 10-day period of trapping was seventy-six animals, the highest 158 animals. The following age classes were distinguished: (1) up to 1 month of age; (2) from 1 to 3 months of age; (3) medium aged, from 3 to 6 months, and (4) adults more than 6 months of age.

THE TERRITORIAL BEHAVIOUR OF THE NUTRIA

The analysis of seventy-nine cases where an individual reacted to the approach of another individual has shown that the average recognition distance is 1 m. Then observations were made of the distribution of nutria over the area covered by sedge, and the distances between adult animals were noted. During thirty-seven periods of observation it was learned that under field conditions 73% (of a total 582) of the individuals were dispersed more than 1 m apart, 8·8% were involved in pursuits but 18·2% approached within the recognition distance. The nutria which had come close to one another did not form stable groups but after some time dispersed again which shows that they only temporarily tolerate the presence of other animals and do not form close herd relationships.

To support the conclusion that adult and medium-aged nutria live a solitary life the following observations were made: oats were put on feeding posts (1 m^2 in area) and the number of feeding nutria was recorded. Only 9·5% of the adult and medium nutria tolerated close associations under such conditions (total number of nutria observed 147). The difference between the tolerance score from field conditions and from feeding posts is statistically significant ($P < 0{\cdot}05$). The same type of observations were made on the fish-pond farm. Close associations were tolerated by only 3·9% (total 458) of observed nutria. From these data the conclusion was drawn that a preferred food (oats) decreased the level of tolerance between nutria, and by that token it is inferred that they do not form herds.

Special experiments on the formation of groups of nutria were undertaken. Five artificial groups of adult nutria were formed in boxes. Any animal which started to fight was removed from the box and replaced with an animal which did not show aggressive behaviour. After 4 months the animals were released on the fish-pond, but the group organization was not maintained and animals dispersed.

The analysis of the trapping records show that at all trapping stations the distribution of catches of adult females and males is random. These distributions were computed for the first capture of an animal in a given trap, recaptures of the same animal in the same trap were omitted. The statistical analysis of the distribution of animals in space was made with reference to a Poisson distribution where variance (s^2) is equal to the mean (m). To check the discrepancy of the empirical data from theory the standard errors were computed in the manner described by Greig-Smith (1957) and then the t test was used.

Due to the fact that the distribution of catches of adult nutria was random it was concluded that adult nutria do not defend territories (territory in the sense defined by Burt, 1943). If there were territorial behaviour the catches of nutria should show a uniform distribution. The catches of medium-aged nutria showed in one case a clumped distribution and in twelve cases a random distribution.

In order to ascertain whether or not medium and adult nutria restrict their movements to a particular area that they regularly frequent, an analysis of all captures (including recaptures of the same nutria in the same trap) was carried out. On four out of fourteen stations adult males showed a clumped distribution. Adult females on ten out of fourteen stations showed a clumped distribution and medium nutria on seven out of thirteen stations.

The conclusion was drawn that adult females showed more restriction of their movements to a particular area than males.

The next question to be investigated was how many nests a nutria has in its home range. Of sixty-nine adult nutria which were directly observed entering their shelter places at least twice, 39% had more than one shelter place. Shelter places separated from one another by more than 200 m characterized 18% of observed nutrias. The fact that the shelter places of different animals were interspersed in the area supports the conclusion that nutria home ranges overlap. But in spite of the interwoven pattern of nest distribution, animals did not enter the nests occupied by other nutria. If, by chance, such a situation occurred it usually caused a fight between the animals. All the data presented above concerned the medium and adult animals. Quite a different picture was obtained from observations of young nutrias.

Observations have shown that young nutria up to 3 months of age live in family groups. The percentage of single young nutria observed in the field was 38% (from a total of 117). Single adults and medium-aged nutria observed under the same conditions amounted to 73% of the observed sample.

The distribution of catches of young nutria always showed a clumped distribution.

A more detailed analysis of trap records revealed the decline of family bonds with the increasing age of the nutria (Table I).

TABLE I

The decline of family bonds with age

Age of nutria (months)	Percent of captures			Total no. of captures
	Single	With mother	With other animal of same age	
0–1	33·0	31·0	36·0	114
1–3	87·0	0·3	12·7	1 042
3–6	98·0	0·0	2·0	1 143
Over 6	100·0	0·0	0·0	3 142

On the basis of the above data one can characterize the type of nutria population organization as follows: they are animals which live a solitary life when adults, and they show an aggressive reaction to one another, or only temporarily tolerate the presence of other members of the population. The family forms an exception and strong family bonds exist between a mother and her young offspring. Nutria have overlapping home ranges within which only the nest is defended against other animals.

THE INFLUENCE OF ENVIRONMENTAL FACTORS ON THE DISTRIBUTION AND CONTACTS OF NUTRIA

It was found that the boundary between water and reeds is the most attractive habitat for nest building. The centre of reeds and the boundary between reeds and sedge are second in attractiveness. The boundary between sedge and water are less attractive and the least attractive habitat is the centre of the sedge (Hillbricht and Ryszkowski, 1961). This gradation of attractiveness is probably connected with the shelter offered by the conditions of habitat but not with the species of plant as such. The nutrias disperse very easily along the network of canals.

Observations on the activity of nutria in a water canal have shown that there is a high correlation between the number of swimming nutria in a given part of the canal and the number of pursuits between them ($r = 0{\cdot}81$). From these data the conclusion was drawn that when the configuration of the terrain produces more frequent contracts between animals the number of fights is increased.

The same holds true in the clearings of vegetation made by nutria. Nutria have the habit of cutting the vegetation on the spot where they are feeding. Such spots attract other animals to feed in the same place. This in turn increases the chance of animals meeting and stimulates fights between them.

THE INFLUENCE OF POPULATION PHENOMENA ON THE DISTRIBUTION OF NUTRIA

The influence of the relationships between animals on their distribution can be divided into two groups: (1) indirect ones through changes made in the habitat, and (2) direct influences springing from the contacts between them.

With regard to the changes made by nutria in plant cover, according to the work of Hillbricht and Ryszkowski (1961) they were as follows: on clearings made by nutria the growth of nitrophilus species of plants, caused by overfertilizing, can be observed. In addition the majority of persistant plants are resistant to treading. The number of poisonous plant species increased from one to six in parallel with the intensity with which clearings were used. Where plants that are poisonous for nutria were most numerous they covered 50–60% of the cleared area.

The conclusion may be drawn that the intensive feeding activity of the nutria decreases the nutritive value of the plant cover and by that token stimulates the dispersion of nutria to new habitats.

In order to study the direct influences of contacts between nutria on their distribution an analysis of nutria dispersion into an area from which resident animals had been removed was carried out (Ryszkowski, 1962). The results of this work can be summarized as follows.

1. When animals are removed from an area, their place is taken largely by specimens with the greatest tendency to migrate (adult males).
2. When trapped animals are again released in the place of capture, migration through the area is lower than when they are removed.
3. From these two phenomena one can draw the conclusion that the animals occupying a given area control the migration rate of new animals into this area.

CONCLUSIONS

The impression of the space organization of the nutria population under investigation that emerges from these investigations has the following main features that are worth underlining. The nutrias have overlapping home ranges with an interwoven pattern of nests. They defend nests against other members of the population and show aggressive reactions on meeting. The changes made by nutria in plant cover cause a decrease in its nutritive value. This degradation is encouraged by their habit of feeding in a spot where plants have been cut off and so promoting over-use of the area. If their feeding activity is evenly spread out over the whole area the plants will get the chance to recover and there will be no change in species composition of the vegetation providing the density of nutria is not kept too high artificially. Because of their aggressive behaviour when meeting they probably control, to a certain degree, the rate of immigration into the areas in which they are resident. It is pertinent to mention that when about 400 nutria lived in the closed area of 5 ha for 3 months the tolerance to the presence of other individuals within the recognition distance increased twice in comparison with field conditions. This indicates that their behaviour can change under conditions of overcrowding. Whether this happens under field conditions is not known to me. But the possibility of behaviour change exists and we can conjecture on two possible developments when a population builds up to a large size.

In one case, when the animals' level of aggressiveness is high, some of them will start to migrate to new areas as a result of too-frequent aggressive contacts. But this could happen before destruction of the plant cover.

In the second possibility it can be postulated that a decrease in aggressiveness occurs and the animals start to migrate to new areas following destruction of the plant cover.

One can think of other causes of nutria dispersion beside the two described above but I have no data to check them.

References

Burt, W. H. (1943). Territoriality and home range concepts as applied to mammals. *J. Mammal.* **24**, 346–352.

Greig-Smith, P. (1957). "Quantitative Plant Ecology." Butterworth, London.

Hillbricht, A. and Ryszkowski, L. (1961). Investigation of the utilization and destruction of its habitat by a population of coypu, *Myocastor coypus* Molina, bred in semi-captivity. *Ekol. Pol.* A, **9** (25), 505–524.

Ryszkowski, L. (1962). Differences in trapping frequency of coypu. *Bull. Acad. pol. Sci. Cl. II Sér. Sci. biol.* **10** (3), 91–94.

AUTHOR INDEX

Numbers in italics refer to pages in the References at the end of each article.

TAXONOMIC INDEX

Only Latin names cited in the text are indexed below.

SUBJECT INDEX